THE MACMILLAN ANTHOLOGY 1

Edited by

JOHN METCALF AND LEON ROOKE

Macmillan of Canada
A Division of Canada Publishing Corporation
Toronto, Ontario, Canada

Canadian Cataloguing in Publication Data

Main entry under title:

The Macmillan anthology 1

ISBN 0-7715-9385-6

1. Canadian literature (English) — 20th century.* I. Metcalf, John, date. II. Rooke, Leon.

PS8233.M24 1988   C810'.8'0054   C88–093399–2
PR9194.4.M24 1988

Design: *Craig Allen/The Richmond Studio*

Macmillan of Canada
A Division of Canada Publishing Corporation
Toronto, Ontario, Canada

Printed in Canada

CONTENTS

ACKNOWLEDGEMENTS

"A Maritime Story" by Norman Levine first appeared in *Encounter*.

"Preacher's Geese" by Holley Rubinsky first appeared in *The Malahat Review*.

"Brutes' Cave" by Terry Jordan first appeared in a different form in *Exile*.

"The Porter" by Marlene Cookshaw first appeared in *The Malahat Review*.

"Bones" by Keath Fraser first appeared in *The Malahat Review*.

"Argentina My Voice" by Keath Fraser first appeared in *Descant*.

"Damages" by Keath Fraser first appeared in *Prism International*.

"A Simple Story" by Diane Schoemperlen first appeared in *The Fiddlehead*.

"Late Summer Dinners" by David Donnell first appeared in *The Malahat Review*.

"A Visit to the Zoo," "Elephants," "Shanti-deva," "Terrible Storm on Lake Erie," and **"Blue Irises"** by David McFadden first appeared in *The Malahat Review*.

"Railing Through Europe" by Derk Wynand first appeared in *The Fiddlehead*.

"Earthquake" by Derk Wynand first appeared in *The Malahat Review*.

"The Chosen Husband" and **"Leaving the Party"** by Mavis Gallant first appeared in *The New Yorker*.

INTRODUCTION

THE MACMILLAN ANTHOLOGY is to be an annual event. We propose to represent every year the best new work of our established writers and to welcome the work of talented newcomers. We are open to fiction, plays, poetry, essays, extracts from works-in-progress, profiles, essays, and memoirs.

We propose to publish every year new portraits of the writers we have chosen to feature; we are proud to present in this first volume new portraits of Sinclair Ross, John Newlove, Keath Fraser, Diane Schoemperlen, John Metcalf, Leon Rooke, and Mavis Gallant by one of Canada's greatest photographers, Sam Tata.

THE MACMILLAN ANTHOLOGY aims not only to herald the new but also to capture and celebrate our literary past; we are delighted in this first volume to welcome a memoir from Sinclair Ross, a piece of writing that breaks a long silence. We are also delighted to publish what John Mills describes as "a Rigmarole," an involved memoir of the literary life and an affectionate tribute to his old friend and rival Irving Layton.

THE MACMILLAN ANTHOLOGY will also offer, in an essay called "The Year in Review," a thoughtful consideration of each year's literary books; this first volume surveys the significant books of 1987.

The editors welcome comments and suggestions — and may even print some.

John Metcalf
Leon Rooke
1987

A MARITIME STORY

BY NORMAN LEVINE

When I think of Max Bleenden I see him driving a long red car in Fredericton, dressed in grey flannels, a navy blue blazer or (if it was warm) a light purple shirt, and smoking a Gauloise. He looks solid. Broad shoulders, a strong neck, a wide face. His dark wavy hair is brushed back and receding. There is a slightly crooked smile. He wears glasses. The eyes are brown. In public he has the air of a celebrity. People look pleased when they say, "Hello, Dr. Bleenden." I can hear him come up the worn steps of the George hotel, knock on the grey-painted door of my rented rooms. When I open the door he speaks in a rough low voice that has something of Europe in it.

"Can you lend me five dollars? I forgot to go to the bank. I have the gardener coming this morning. And I need to buy some tea and eggs. It's a tradition. I always make breakfast for the gardener."

I would give him the money then make some coffee while he looked around at the way I was living in this hotel with the second-hand furniture, the worn linoleum.

"I envy you," he said. "You live such a simple life. Mine is complicated."

Later, leaving Fredericton, he was driving me to the airport. We were silent. Suddenly he said, "You're going away . . . that's awful . . . I won't have anyone to talk to. There's no one down here."

Norman Levine was born in 1923. He is the author of such distinguished story collections as *One Way Ticket, I Don't Want to Know Anyone Too Well, Thin Ice*, and *Champagne Barn*. He is currently completing a story collection to be entitled *Something Happened Here*.

I came to the Maritimes in 1965 because of Max Bleenden.

He had written to me in England. He said he liked my short stories. Would I like to come to Fredericton and be resident writer. And because we needed the money I said yes. I owed rent for two years. Had a lawyer's letter threatening action from the landlady's son. The landlady was a nice old lady who apologized for this. It only came out when she was sick. Her son happened to see what I owed.

I left wife and children behind — I had no intention of settling in the Maritimes — and flew over at the end of August.

Max Bleenden was to meet me in the lobby of the Beaverbrook Hotel. As he came in he looked around expectantly. But as soon as he saw me he looked disappointed.

"I didn't think you would be so short."

Max was several inches shorter. He drove me to his house — a solid greystone facing the river with a gravel drive, grass on either side, and a heavy front wooden door. Behind the house were tall trees and large gardens of fruit, vegetables, and flowers. Inside, the rooms were high, painted white, and lightly furnished with antique wooden furniture and blue carpets. On the walls were abstract oil paintings, and a photograph of a serious young girl. There were irises, roses, gladioli, in different colours, in glass vases and earthenware pots. There was a glass bowl full of fruit.

His wife came in. She was a bit taller than Max. Thin and shy with red hair. When she smiled she looked like a pretty Tallulah Bankhead. She hardly spoke. If I spoke to her, she smiled back. We sat in the comfortable chairs, in one of the front rooms, looking out at the river, and had tea.

A large elderly woman in grey walked in with sandwiches on a tray. As she went out Max said:

"She is here to look after my mother. My mother's name is Nettie. I want you to meet her."

He led me up the stairs, past three rooms, to a bare white room where a small elderly woman sat in a high-backed chair. Her hands were clutching the arm-rests. Her feet were not touching the ground. She was dressed in a purple blouse, a black skirt. Around her neck a light silk lemon scarf was tied loosely. Her grey hair was cut short and permed and I could see the pink scalp between curls. She sat by a window and beside a fish tank that had three small fish swimming in it. Max introduced me.

"Who are you?" his mother said in a flat voice.

"I'm Max's friend."

"Do you live here?"

"Yes."

She looked out of the window at the road, the river, the far shore, the sky.

"I write to Max every week," she said. "Did you know I'm going to Canada?"

She left us again. Went back to the window.

She had an interesting but worn-out face. She must have been pretty for the structure was still there with the prominent cheekbones, the small mouth with the noticeable front teeth as if a smile was never far away.

"I hate this house," she said. "It goes quiet. I don't know where everyone is."

She looked at the tank.

"They are trying to fob me off with fish. I don't want fish. I want people."

She looked at me.

"Suddenly it's quiet," she said. "They don't explain things. I don't know where they are. I don't know when they are coming back. They don't ask me if I want to go. They just go away. . . ."

"Did you know I'm going to Canada? To the Maritimes. I have a son in the Maritimes."

Max began to walk impatiently up and down. She followed his movements. When he stopped near her she said:

"How long am I going to stay here?"

"How long would you like to stay, Mother?" Max said. "For ever?"

"That's not very long," she said.

As I was leaving, Max said he and his wife were driving to Boston tomorrow for a short holiday before the academic year started. Would I like to come?

When we got to Boston all Max wanted to see were films. We saw six films in three days. He also wanted to go to a striptease. We went into a dark place where a young girl with long legs performed on a small stage, in the centre of the room, while the customers stood around and watched. A cigarette girl, not young, came by. Max picked up a small cigar, from her tray, and took out a coin from his pocket.

"Can I put a quarter in your box?" he asked with a grin.

"Don't be an ass-hole," the cigarette girl said. "You can't get into my box for a quarter."

She couldn't have known that she was talking to the Dean of a university.

On the drive back from Boston, with his wife asleep, Max told me about himself. He was born in Hamburg. "Both my parents spoke Yiddish. I also spoke Yiddish. But I have long forgotten it." His father was a publisher. They had a comfortable life. When he was thirteen — it was 1933 — his mother brought him to London. They didn't see his father again. He went to an English grammar school, then London University. They had little money. His mother did a variety of jobs, whatever she could get. It was while he was at university that his poems began to appear in the little magazines. His reviews in the weeklies. And talks on the BBC. That's when I first heard of him. But we never met. Although I used to go to the same Soho clubs, the same pubs: the French, Joe Lyons, the Mandrake. Max said he played the piano, for a while, at the Colony. And we talked about Muriel Belcher and Francis Bacon. After the War ("My father was a conscientious objector . . . his father was a conscientious objector . . . so I was a conscientious objector. I was sent to work on the land. I was digging ditches. And all I wanted to do was fly a Spitfire") he came to Canada to lecture at a small college in Nova Scotia where he met his wife, the daughter of a General. She inherited money. They moved to Fredericton. "After I married, the writing stopped. The instinct for it had gone. And I haven't written anything since. But I can tell the real thing when I see it. And *boychick*," he slapped my knee, "you have it."

But despite this friendliness I was uncomfortable with Max.

In the first week of term he asked me to meet his creative writing class. There were about twenty students, mostly girls. "Here is our resident writer," Max began. "He writes short stories. They are mostly stories about being hard-up. But look the way he is dressed. He is wearing an expensive English suit, expensive English shoes, an expensive shirt and tie."

I didn't know where to look.

(The thin light-grey suit I bought in a discount house in Truro, Cornwall, for £9. It was made in Bulgaria. My shoes, also cheap, I bought in Exeter. They were made in Romania.)

I also disliked the way he took it for granted that I would just fall in with his plans. He never asked. He just said, "Let's go — ," or, "I'll pick you up for a football game at — ."

My reaction to this was immediate.

When I was supposed to be at the President's reception to introduce new members I was in the Riverside Room of the Beaverbrook Hotel drinking a beer and reading a thriller.

Next morning he came to my office, three doors away from his. A hurt expression on his face.

"Why weren't you at the President's reception?"

"When was it?"

"Yesterday. I made a speech telling all about you. People clapped. We waited for you to step forward. Nothing happened."

I turned down all invitations.

Max would walk briskly into my office and say: "I just had a phone call from the Rotarians. They have a monthly meeting. The food is very good. They would like you to be their next speaker — "

"I'm busy," I said. "Working."

I wasn't working. I was moving. From the Beaverbrook, that he put me in, to the George which was less than half the price. I was also getting to know Fredericton. The long residential streets with the front lawns and the large wooden houses with verandahs and trees. The short business streets, by the river, with the small stores and Chinese restaurants. But it didn't take long to walk through it. And I had a feeling of isolation, of being cut off.

One morning I walked to the supermarket by the river to get some groceries. When I came out a mild man in glasses, dressed like a farmer, came up to me.

"Have you got education?"

I didn't know what to say.

"Have you got education?"

I thought this was a new way of asking for money.

"Yes," I said hesitantly.

"What is eight at fifty dollars each?"

"Four hundred dollars."

"Four hundred," he said loudly. And repeated it as if he didn't believe it. He walked away delighted.

Another day I went to the Legislative building. I was listening to a debate on fishing from the public gallery when an usher came up to me and whispered:

"Sir, you can't sit like that."

I had my legs crossed.

"Why not?"

"The members below — they can see."

"I'm wearing trousers."

"It's a rule sir . . . because of the ladies. They'd come here . . . sit like you . . . and from below, with some, you could see the time of day."

On Armistice Day I went to the cenotaph. A service of remembrance was going on. Names of local people killed in the Second World War were being read over a loudspeaker. The voice said:

Graham Budd, Royal Canadian Air Force.
Robert Pichette, Royal Canadian Corps of Signals.
Jim Smith, Royal Canadian Air Force.

Brought to you by Frank's Fast Foods. . . .

Tommy Symons, Royal Canadian Navy.
Fred Towers, Royal Canadian Engineers.

Brought to you by Dominion Supermarket. . . .

I wasn't sleeping well. At first light I'd walk to the river to see the trees in their autumn colours, the solitary white house on the far shore, reflected in the water. After breakfast, I'd go out again, buy a paper. Then to the Post Office to see if there were any letters from my wife. I wrote three times, sometimes more, a week (as she did) telling her I missed her. That I disliked being here. And couldn't wait to get back. Meanwhile I was going to earn as much money as I could.

With this in mind I walked to the newspaper building in the Square. And was shown into the owner's empty office. The owner walked in. Small stubby brown shoes with thick heels and thick soles and rounded tops. A black eye-patch over his right eye. He was about five foot ten. He had a small moustache, thin dark hair, and spoke in a clipped English voice. He was referred to as the Brigadier. And told me he was a friend of Beaverbrook, knew the Duke and Duchess of Windsor and, for my benefit, he talked about Arnold Bennett. He said that when Arnold Bennett reviewed a book in the *Evening Standard* the book would sell out. He would give me a page, in his monthly magazine for the Maritimes, and he expected me to do the same as Arnold Bennett.

But the books I wanted were published in London. And often they didn't want to send review copies to a Maritime monthly they hadn't heard of. The Brigadier was furious. I saw him pick up the phone, in a rage, and shout to the London publisher demanding a copy. Sometimes it worked.

I did articles on an anthology of short stories, a novel by Graham Greene, books on Hemingway, Babel, Chekhov, and an anthology of the Second World War. I also had some of my stories reprinted. From this I earned an extra five hundred dollars a month.

It was by doing this work that I met the journalists who worked for the Brigadier. They were young Englishmen, from English public schools, that the Brigadier brought over. Their calling cards said *Gentlemen of the Farm*. They lived in a run-down rented farm across the river. In the city they wore suits, ties, clean shirts. I expected a rolled umbrella, a bowler hat. And when they played cricket or soccer, against the university or the Army Camp, their sports clothes were immaculate. But on the farm — they only had chickens — they wore worn-out shabby clothes. They went around unshaven, uncombed. The rooms had disorder and chicken shit. The kitchen looked as if no one had washed-up for months or put the garbage out. . . .

When I went for my early evening drink to the Beaverbrook, I would join these neatly dressed journalists and listen as they joked, discussed life and the world situation.

With them, sometimes, was Marcel, a French Canadian from Moncton. He was in computers. He drove a green MG. He was convinced that I was getting the wrong impression of the Maritimes by mixing too much with intellectuals and people with money. So he took me to various beer parlours. Then, to the outskirts, off the highway, and on to a dirt road, to a string of unpainted wooden shacks spaced far apart. Smoke came from a tin chimney. No one was outside.

Marcel then drove to an Indian reservation. The same signs of poverty and hopelessness. As if everyone inside was lying fully-dressed on a bed, not sleeping, in the middle of the afternoon.

"I don't read books," Marcel said on the drive back, "but I'll read one of yours. If I like it — I'll buy it."

Max came to the George.

"Have you been avoiding me? It's over two weeks since I've seen you."

"I haven't," I said.

"Come for a ride."

Then he said: "Let's go back to my place for a drink. I'm depressed."

When we got out of the car instead of going into the house he went around it. We cast long shadows on the grass. He led me to the trees. And, among them, to a wooden hut. He unlocked the door.

Inside it was spartan. A plain wooden table. An ordinary wooden chair. Used books on planks of wood held up by bricks. An open fireplace with sawn wood stacked beside it. There were picture-postcards stuck on the walls of paintings by Rembrandt, Monet, Pissarro, Chagall, Bonnard. A small sink, a single tap, an electric kettle. Empty jars of instant coffee, packs of Gauloises and matches. A bottle of Rémy Martin was by a small radio. A used upright piano by a wall. Beside another, a couch was made up as a bed.

"I feel at home here," Max said. "The house . . . that's my wife's place. This is mine." He indicated the books, the faded poster of *The Threepenny Opera* on a wall, the faded magazines.

I looked at the books. I knew them. They were English books of the late 1940s and 1950s. He showed me magazines with his poems, his reviews.

"That was my time," Max said. "Who knows what I would have done had I stayed in Europe. But I'm here. And, *boychick*, most of the time I like it."

He showed me letters he had from T. S. Eliot, Picasso. And, from another folder, he brought out obituaries that he had cut from *The Times*. They were of writers, painters, editors of little magazines, who were known just after the war and who died young. They were people I also knew.

"That's why we get on," Max said. "We have the same references."

The only sign of luxury was a large window looking out to the trees and gardens. "I come here when I can," Max said. "In the morning the dew is on the grass . . . the birds have started . . . the flowers are at their best . . . I read, I smoke, I have a drink. I listen to the BBC overseas service for the news . . . I play the piano . . . I day-dream. It's my bolt-hole. Then I go to work."

He poured Rémy Martin into the cracked cups. He sat on the couch. I on the wooden chair. He lit up a Gauloise.

"I read the same books again and again," Max said. "Now that I don't write — I copy out things that I like." He opened a thick notebook, turned some pages, and read aloud.

" 'The heart — it's worth less than people think. It's quite accommodating, it accepts anything. It's not particular. But the body — that's different — it has a cultivated taste — it knows what it wants.'

"You know who said that?"

"No."

"Colette." He turned more pages. Read out: "to exist is enough." Then turned to the last page of the notebook, showed it to me. The only thing on it was: "The final unimportance of human life."

"Who said that?"

"I don't know," Max said. "I didn't. But when I read it — I don't feel so bad."

He put out a Gauloise, lit another.

"I'll miss Fredericton — "

"When are you leaving?"

"When I'm 65, I'll retire to England. Somewhere in the country. Not too far from London."

"And your wife?"

"She won't want to come. But when the time comes she'll go. As you see, my wife and I don't talk much. Not now. We keep certain thoughts to ourselves."

We finished the brandy in the cups. He locked the door. We were walking to the house when his wife came quickly towards us.

"Nettie's escaped."

"When?"

"I don't know. I went into her room. And she wasn't there."

"I'll use the car," Max said. "You," he said to his wife, "look in the restaurants, the library, the stores."

"I'll look for her," I said.

"Fine. Do the side-streets and by the river."

"What was she wearing?"

"A pink sweater," his wife said, "grey skirt and slippers."

I walked and looked for over an hour and a half. No sign of Nettie. I phoned up Max, from a call-box, wondering if she was still alive.

"The police have her," he said calmly. "I'm going just now to the station to pick her up. She was trying to get on a bus. She had no money. She told them she was going to Canada."

"Has this happened before?"

"Yes," he said.

Two weeks later it was a different Max who came to the George. He had come back from a three-day conference in Calgary. And he talked non-stop about women. "It's all in the angle of penetration. . . . If they have large bums . . . it's better to use a pillow. I picked up a professor at the hotel bar . . . about 35 or 36 . . . a medievalist. . . . I asked her to spend the night with me. She said she would if I promised I wouldn't do anything."

"What happened?"

He looked surprised. "Nothing happened. I gave her my word."

That night he picked me up for the annual party of

his creative writing class. The parents, he said, were away. "We'll enjoy ourselves." There were drinks, music, food. Max was the first one to start dancing. Then spent the rest of the evening, in a dark corner, with the girl who was giving the party. When he drove me back to the George he was like an adolescent. "Now you see why I have these creative writing classes."

"Better wipe the lipstick off before you go in the house."

Next morning he walked into my office. He was excited.

"I needed a new secretary," he said. "They sent me one. But I'll have to let her go. I couldn't work with her."

"Why not?"

"Too sexy. Come, I'll show you."

He led me down the corridor to the main office. And introduced me to this young tall girl who was smiling. She looked like girls I saw in the street. Blonde short hair, healthy, outdoor type, in a tight sweater and a tight skirt.

"Turn around," Max said.

And she did, as if she was a fashion model, still smiling.

"How could I work standing close to her?"

"She probably needs the job," I said.

"She'll go back to the typing pool. Alone with her . . . I wouldn't trust myself."

I liked Max better when the macho side of him was absent. One afternoon he picked me up and drove by the river into the country for about an hour. "I make this trip about once every six or seven weeks," he said. "My wife goes more often. We have a daughter. She lives by herself, a solitary. She's a lovely girl, 24, you'll see."

We went down a dirt track. There was a wooden shack with asbestos on the outside and on the roof. In a clearing, a small vegetable garden and some flowers. A brown dog came out and a black and ginger kitten. The dog barked. A voice said,

"What is it, Fred?"

Then Max's daughter came out of the shack. She was tall and slim and she looked like one of those Pre-Raphaelite paintings. She ran over and kissed Max.

"Hello, Dad."

He introduced me. She looked a bit shy. She spoke

softly. She brought us inside . . . made some coffee.

There were different herbs . . . books to do with the psyche . . . Buddhism . . . happiness . . . there were plants growing in small pots . . . lots of paperback books . . . and postcards put up . . .

I went out to leave them alone.

We stayed about an hour.

Max didn't talk much on the drive back. "Every time I come back from seeing her I feel sad. And there is nothing I can do."

Before driving to the airport, I went with Max to see Nettie in her room. I told her I was leaving. But she took no notice. Max had bought her a colour television for her 70th birthday. She was watching a train going across the country from the Atlantic to the Pacific. It was a travelogue showing the different provinces in the autumn.

When it was over Nettie was silent.

Then she said to Max:

"Why did you keep that country all to yourself?"

I returned to England, to my wife and kids, paid off the debts. Had a three-week holiday with the family in London. And there was enough money left for the next nine months. I began to write.

All the time I was in Fredericton, I thought I hated it. But bits and pieces began to appear in my next novel and in several short stories.

Max and I wrote regularly. He always included small details that I suspect he thought I might be able to use.

> ". . . on a freezing night our mayor was pushed out of a moving car on the main street at three in the morning. He was pushed out by a lady who wasn't his wife. He was in the nude. . . . They tried to burn the George down twice since you left . . . both times the fire-engines arrived too soon. . . . The Brigadier died while on holiday in the Bahamas. . . . The Gentlemen of the Farm gave a farewell party . . . they are leaving for British Columbia. Sometime after midnight we went out of the farmhouse and there was a large wooden cross burning fiercely. Someone said: Ku Klux Klan. Someone else said: This is New Brunswick. . . ."

At Christmas he sent £5 to each of our daughters.

The following summer he and his wife came to see us. They were travelling through the South-West in a rented car. In St. Ives they stayed in the best hotel, the Tregenna Castle. Max took us there for a meal. As we entered, and saw the glass chandeliers, he said,

"Ribbentrop was promised this hotel for his residence by Hitler after he conquered England."

Next day it rained. They stayed with us in the house. Max played ping-pong with the children. Then records. *Hair* was in fashion. Max played it over and over. He twisted to the music, he sang the songs, he liked the naughty words ("Mummy, Mummy, what is fellatio?"). He tried to get my wife to dance on the table.

That is how I remembered him on that cool September morning when I heard that he and his wife were killed when their car went off the highway.

Later that day I wrote his obituary for *The Times*.

I came again to Fredericton, eighteen years later, this summer, to give a lecture. I stayed at the Beaverbrook. After a good breakfast, by a window facing the river, I went for a walk. I walked along the main street and to the side-street where the George was. It was burned out . . . gutted. Planks of charred wood were hanging precariously. And where I had my rooms I could see blue sky.

Wherever I walked I kept remembering Max. And things that happened. But for some reason I couldn't find my way to the university. I asked a woman on the opposite side of the street. She said she was going part of the way. She told me she came from Ontario, from Hamilton. And couldn't wait to get back. They had another year here — until their only daughter finished school.

"This is failure city," she said.

I walked up the slope, by the trees and the grass of the university. They named a new building after him — Max Bleenden Hall — a girls' residence. And on the quarter-hour the clock, above its entrance, has a delicate chime.

BRUTES' CAVE

BY TERRY JORDAN

Terry Jordan was born in 1953. Last year he worked as a carpenter in the Arctic and spent two months at the Leighton Colony at Banff. His stories have appeared in *Exile* and *Canadian Fiction Magazine*.

B y day, my father mined guano out of the bat caves of southern New Mexico. By night he'd tell stories of the old country, of castles and idiot princes, of flawless white horses pulling aged queens through mountain villages on giant-wheeled beds. Often he'd carve small human figures out of our firewood as he talked, or he'd sing songs of his childhood, softly playing the violin. With those same fine-boned fingers, for six days out of seven, he'd load a wagon with bat droppings to be hauled out of the subterranean depths to the desert above.

Our house was filled with the rock fossils he'd brought home and a hundred skeletons of baby bats, picked clean by guano beetles within minutes of losing their hold and falling from their mother's side to the floor beneath them. He would come home with yet another set of small bones in his pocket and describe to us the sight of the bats sleeping, glistening with winter dew, sometimes frost, hundreds of thousands of tiny jewels in the mine's half light and how, as they trembled, the moisture that had condensed on their fur fell like a light spring rain on the miners below.

At times I'd walk down after school to meet my father and, when he'd finished work, we'd sit together outside the largest cave and wait for the light to fade. He'd slowly roll a cigarette and smoke it, whispering to me about his day as I sat listening for the bats to waken. The noise of their wings would begin as the far-off rumbling of thunder, seeming to get closer as it got louder, and I'd look to the sky for dark clouds and always be surprised when there were none. Then the sound of their squeaking would rise above everything else, gaining volume, getting more frenzied, and just as I'd feel the push of warm, damp air against my face they'd explode from the cave mouth in a giant spiral and it would be dark for a moment before they fluttered away in all directions to feed.

Each time I watched, my father's hand would be on my shoulder calming my excitement and fear. To stop my shaking he would speak in a slow and even voice as though I were not afraid. He'd talk about the bats and make zipping noises between his teeth to describe the sound of their wings as they plummeted from the sky each morning, to the caves and their sleep. I would imagine them falling like stones, their bellies heavy with insects, banking at the last possible moment, inches above the desert ground, to their roosts in the cave below. As we walked home, I would be safe beside him, speechless with the wonder of it all.

One afternoon the miners were blasting an access tunnel to a new cave when my father and a few others, shovelling a large valley out of the guano to the cave bottom, looked up after one of the explosions as hundreds of years of powdered bat shit, fifty feet deep, shifted and slid down on top of them before most had a chance to draw a breath. Two survived by running and clawing their way close enough to the surface and having luck enough to be found in the panic that followed. One man died from the blade of a shovel as his fellow workers dug furiously to rescue him.

My father was buried for nearly ten minutes, surviving only because he'd fallen in a sitting position. He'd pushed his back against the slide as it moved over him, trapping just enough air in the hollow of his chest and stomach to scream into, defenceless as the beetles feasted on the exposed skin of his face and neck. His arms were pinned in front of him, his head bowed and held motionless by the slide's crushing weight. He continued to shriek, horrified by the pain and his helplessness, until the insects were biting inside his mouth and he had to crack their bodies between his teeth and spit them out before he sealed his lips against them and passed out.

At home, from then on, he slept in the living room with the lights on.

During the day he spent a lot of time outside. Often he'd stop suddenly and for no apparent reason stand as though rooted to the ground, his eyes vacant, his head snapping sideways from the spasms that jolted his body. Sometimes if the sky was perfectly clear he would stand in our front yard with his head tipped back, his mouth wide open to the heavens like some nestling waiting to be fed. If one small cloud appeared in the open sky above him he'd snap his mouth shut and the twitching would instantly start again.

He was ever wiping his mouth and eyes with both hands.

"Bones covered the valley as far as we could see," he said to me yesterday. "The birds were long gone but they had done their job well. A white desert it was and we found the brutes' cave but we did not go in."

The dried-up alkaline sloughs we are passing through in this truck look like snow patches in the spring. Nothing moves but the sun, adding subtle colors to the salt flats as it sets, but we are not watching any more. My father beneath his blanket is trembling, he is making squeaking noises and looking at me, and we do not know where we are going.

THE PORTER

By Marlene Cookshaw

"So there I was at midnight."
The feet of the women upstairs cross and recross the floor. In and out the window on the near side of my bedroom wall the cat pursues mice and dreams. Each time I surface from sleep, the streetlight persuades me I lie in yet another of the houses I have lived in: it surprises me how many have a window at the foot of the bed. My mother's voice as clear as if she sat again on the Hudson's Bay blanket.

Between the window of this Vancouver basement room and the streetlight the heavy-headed peonies swing shadows on the blind. So much movement. "Like trying to sleep," my mother says, "in Grand Central Station." She went once to New York, with two friends: one of the three things she promised herself to accomplish before she married. She also saved a thousand dollars, but she never did own a fur coat. I'd like to think that was not a failure but a reconsideration.

On the train trip east across the prairies, at a watering stop, she stepped out for a breath of air — the ploughed fields in the dark like marten skins — and the train left without her.

"So there I was at midnight!" she laughs. The only light as far as she could see was the one above her head that marked the siding. Undecided what to do, she turned to follow the train. Her friends would alarm the

Marlene Cookshaw was born in 1953. She lives in Victoria and is editorial assistant to Constance Rooke on *The Malahat Review*. Her first book of poems was entitled *Personal Luggage*. She has just completed a second collection called *Cuba*.

porter; no doubt someone would come for her.

She walked east, she set off for New York. She had a year to go before the marriage date, a lot to think of. It was May 1947, the peonies not yet in bloom. My mother was thirty-two. Nine years since she'd taken the plane ride, her first, through the Rocky Mountains to Vancouver, the cold peaks higher than the wingtips on both sides of the two-seater craft.

The railway ties would blacken the hem of her gown before she'd crossed Saskatchewan. She'd worn the dress as bridesmaid at her girlfriend's wedding. Altered, slit down the front for a peignoir, bound with satin, it was the first garment in her trousseau.

The sky on that flight was a fathomless silky blue, a rent in the white corridor through which the pilot steered. At the Calgary Stampede a gypsy had told her she would marry a man whose name began with S — "My friends call me Nell," she told the pilot — and give birth to three daughters. The snow-draped cliffs like sheer curtains she would hang in their bedroom windows.

We liked to imagine, the three of us, that she walked all the way to New York, clambering over the Laurentian Shield, raising her gown to wade through Lake Ontario.

On the night of the dance at which she met my father, the band played a song about a lost love, a lady dressed in blue. My mother remembers neither the incident nor the lyrics, but I know all the words; while lying here awake, I can still recall them in her voice. I must have been young when she sang it, must have slept still in the gigantic white crib my father built, with drawers underneath for linens. He danced the exaggerated steps in my bedroom in his socks.

> We waltzed in a world of blue
> How can my heart forget?

Mother sang from the doorway, and my father danced, his arms swinging in time to the lantern that approached her out of the dark.

CUTWORK

BY MARLENE COOKSHAW

I like home, its dusty quiet, sun through the dripping fruit trees. I like the man I live with: we share apples, don't smile much, we sometimes drink vodka in the morning; the bed is unusually high, with cast-iron head and foot boards and an eiderdown the colour of milky tea.

Under the blankets used to be a flannel sheet, under the bed the tiger, who had a reach only fractionally shorter than my longest leap at bedtime. This was after the season of falling out of bed, which I did without waking, sometimes several times in a night.

I think this is why we outline the edges of things, why Rouault, with a thick rope of black paint, held back his colourful pauvres from god knows what horrible muddy intermingling.

And maybe you never went to Vacation Bible School, but I'm sure someone showed you how to outline with your fingertip the edges of figures to keep them attached to the felt storyboard. The poor isolable figures of Rachel, of sheep, the expanse of green felt that signified fourteen years in a foreign land.

The division between yourself and the world as thin as skin, fallible as glass. On the sidewalk in front of St. Andrew's Presbyterian Church a man touches a woman's back. They touch. The earth steadies.

I forgot to say I wear glasses. Have you noticed how, when you run, the world bounces on your nose as though it were an image painted on the lens?

In a cubbyhole beneath the basement stairs my father

stored turpentine and paint left over from the upstairs rooms. Various colours dribbled from the rims, but the labels all said Eggshell. A finish as fragile as that. My mother folded her half of the newspaper and slipped it beneath the teapot. Cuba, I heard her say, again, and the Cold War. I emptied the paint cans into the floor drain, the colours melting into one another like a map of the world in relief. I swept the cubbyhole and stocked the shelves with canned food from the pantry, spare light bulbs, my bedside radio.

How much water would five people need?

Saturday my sisters and I walked with Mother to the park. She sat under a tree, and we played hopscotch on the concrete steps that led into the lake, where the polar bear enclosure of the old zoo used to be. When we came home, the beans and Campbell's soup were back in the pantry; we had rice pudding with our tea. No newspaper in sight.

I write when my life slips out of joint, when home is threatened, but the older I get, the larger home becomes, and I fear I won't be able to keep it all together. My father tries to help. He comes to me in dreams and says, Put your head next to mine so the bones behind the ear connect.

His pulse ticks like a crystalless watch, and the world flies apart.

There is, of course, no tiger. But something has clawed in the hardwood floor beside the bed a breach I haven't always the ability to clear. The white cotton sheet, the creamy eiderdown, the iron headboard painted glossy brown. I cannot, some mornings, get beyond this.

But the world will not leave you alone. Even with the curtains drawn you can hear sparrows rattling the empty feeder. The bricks of St. Andrew's Presbyterian Church could crumble at any moment. The sheep could fall from the storyboard. The polar bears walk into the lake. Sparrows crystallize and shatter.

And skin will never be enough to contain us.

LORNA CROZIER

❧ DOMESTIC SCENE 1

I mop the floors, admire again the grain,
the beautiful simplicity of wood.
The cat we named Nowlan after the poet
who just died, cries for his tin of beef.
You stuff the salmon with wild rice
and watercress, its flesh pink
as Nowlan's mouth, his perfect tongue.
How lucky we are to have found each other,
our fine grey cat, a fresh Atlantic salmon.
Tomorrow we may get drunk and fight
or buy two tickets to Madrid.
But tonight the light in our kitchen
is as good as you'll find anywhere.
The plates glow with possibilities
and the cat licks himself completely clean.

Lorna Crozier, who has previously published under the name Uher, was born in 1948 in Swift Current, Saskatchewan. She has worked as a teacher of English in high schools, as a guidance counsellor, as a reviewer and host for CBC radio, and as a writer-in-residence variously. At present she lives with Patrick Lane in Saskatoon, where they both teach at the University of Saskatchewan. Margaret Laurence was moved to describe her as "a poet to be grateful for." Her books include *Inside Is the Sky* (Thistledown Press, 1976); *Crow's Black Joy* (NeWest Press, 1979); *Humans and Other Beasts* (Turnstone Press, 1981); *The Weather* (Coteau Books, 1983); and *The Garden Going On Without Us* (McClelland and Stewart, 1985, reprinted 1986 and 1987).

❧ WHITE CAT BLUES

The white cat with sapphire eyes
can't be colour blind
must see the world
                        as blue.
Blue horses, blue light spilling
from the window, blue willows,
blue women
carrying bowls of bluish cream.

              How beautiful I feel
all blue — shoulders, feet and hair,
the brilliant air,
blue wind
                 touching everything.

Tonight desire
                the distance
between the moon and the white cat
sleeping under the apple tree
                 (the apples cold and blue)
will be the precise colour
of the cat's dreams of rain.

❧ *CAT, FRENCH CLASS, GROCERY LIST, ETC.*

The cat rolling on the rug, the poem
begins here, how beautiful his body,
his grey, striped fur. I want to stop
the mind's wandering, the hum of the furnace,
the conjugation of *être* for my French class
tomorrow, the *passé composé*, the *conditionnel*,
the grocery list in the pocket of my jeans,
milk and lemons (your handwriting) *fresh parsley
if you can find it*, grey cat on the rug,
only himself and his body's knowing,
our bodies too, how to stay in them,
the mind in the fingers, the smell of you
on my mouth, *l'article indéfini*, a cat.
Berger's question: What does it mean
when an animal looks at you? That moment
of recognition, that seeing; in Florence
seeing Michelangelo's *David* the first time,
how different from the photographs, not
still but only a pause in the movement,
the arm about to rise, the leg follow through,
marble veins warm to the imagined touch,
the blue of your inner thigh, here and here
where I place my finger, conjugation of desire,
je suis, *tu es*, *une* and one, I can't say
un, my tongue twists on the vowel, a poem
starts here, cat rolling on the rug,
parsley for the sweet potatoes, *serais*,
seras, the poem tongue twister,
paws in the air

🌿 SEASONS

I wish there were a season for mating
like with grouse or salmon (the Atlantic
kind that survives, adding ring after ring
to its scales).
                    One time of year
you wanted it,
drumming or defying gravity,
and for the rest
you just went about your day.
A grouse folded in feathers,
a salmon moving its fine bones downstream.

Or being human, to fall asleep
late in the afternoon in a double bed,
naked or not, the body
busy with its own life, giving up
on love and beauty, words
like *hand, shoulder, inner thigh*,
meaning simply what they say.

LORNA CROZIER

❧ THE OLDEST SONG

The hens in the dusty twilight of the chicken coop
sing in strange low voices, not the squawking
we think we know, for that is all they do
when we are near. Weird sisters these, all white
the dance they do while the woman sleeps.
Her own small egg, perhaps her last, travels
the dark to its inland sea. Heads swaying from
side to side, the hens all lift one foot, pause,
before they set it down as if it were the first
time they touched the ground, here only
for one night, so white, they could have fallen
from the moon, her pale blunt wings. The woman
sinks into feathers, into her own dark
dreams. That part of her that walks in sleep
and won't remember in the sun's first light
wonders at the voices her body moves towards,
the hens singing their oldest song
while strings of moonstones
grow warm inside them.

❧ SO THIS IS LOVE

So this is love, a kind of sad dance
and who's leading? I lie in bed
without you, your side not slept in
and I don't care. It's over one more time
just like it's raining once again,
a cat dies, you get another. Call it
the same name, remember the generalities,
not the specifics of their small deaths.

It makes me smile how we said this
is different, we've never loved before,
not really *loved*, you know. So here I am
again, trying to work up some kind of anger,
trying to find a word that fits what I
no longer feel.

The cat we got two days ago lies on your pillow,
purrs like he's been there all his life.
Perhaps he has, it's hard to tell the difference.
The rain feels like yesterday's, the long silences,
the same old tired dance.

❧ CHILDHOOD LANDSCAPES

LORNA CROZIER

On the merry-go-round at twilight
the children you don't see in the day
are spinning. Holding the bars, they run in circles,
jump on the boards and turn and turn.
If you could see their faces you'd know
you'd seen them before
on the posters in the supermarket,
on the back of milk cartons at the breakfast table.
They've been sitting in the dark a long time.
You don't know what to do with them
when they show up in your neighbourhood,
you don't want to admit they're there.
In the middle of the playground
where you sit in the afternoons, a book
in your lap, your eyes on your daughters,
your small sons, at twilight the quiet ones are
twirling. Even the dark that moves
from the trees, the back alleys, the empty lots
between the houses where your children sleep,
cannot hurt them anymore.

❧ TURNING INTO FLESH

Hidden by trees, not deliberately,
just wanting to be alone, I watch a man
not far below me drive a stoneboat
to a hollow in the earth, heave something heavy,
something the size of a full-grown pig,
over the edge. Whatever it is gleams
like an animal without any skin.
He leaves without seeing me and I wonder why
I feel such relief. There's nothing to fear.
It's mid-morning. I can hear a tractor
in the neighbouring field, a magpie,
wind in the dry grass. Part of me
wants to walk down that hill, look
over the edge, see what's there.
Part of me stays in shadow,
watches the magpie fall from the branches,
disturb the swarm of flies that lifts
the shape of whatever it is into the air.

❧ *FRAGMENTS FOR A LONG DECEMBER*

*

In this month of long nights
everything moves inside
                              or moves away;
the shortest day
will be grey and bitter cold
though the snow gives us
                              a kind of light
when the moon hides
and the lights go out
in the neighbourhood.

*

Sparrows churrr on the fence,
feathers fluffed like dusters.
The cat paces
              his teeth chattering.
When we let him out, the birds
turn to snow. He looks at us
through the window as though
we have betrayed him
                              dropped him
with a stone in a burlap sack
into the cold
              the empty day.

*

In the supermarket it is still
summer. Butter lettuce. Avocados.
Golden apples with skins of wax.
Oranges we used to call Japs
but now are Mandarins.
The trick as a child
to remove the peel in one piece.
                    Jap Oranges. A name

that makes us feel ashamed
though when I see them in my head
that's the word that's there.

*

Three weeks before Christmas
two writers kill themselves.
          First a woman, then a man.
With him it is what he left
that matters: two kids
                    a pregnant wife.
With her it is the act itself
that won't let go.

Always when we saw her dance
she wore ballet slippers.
We smiled at that.
          Now we wonder
if she slipped her narrow feet
into satin, knotted long pink ribbons
before she tied that other knot,
          her toes perfectly *au point*
spinning small tight circles
above the porcelain tub.

*

Walking to the 7-Eleven at night
for milk and bread. No one else about.
The snow crunches under my boots
like small bones. In the streetlights
the sky is crystal. Each snowflake
lighting on my skin,
                    disappears,
sinks through. Tonight as I walk
I am full of stars.

*

We buy a blue spruce, flat
as two hands pressed together.
When it thaws, unfolds its branches

in the dry heat of the house,
the needles fall. I think of
the pregnant woman, her children,
their Christmas tree, the delicate
heirlooms of glass. They break
so easily in her hands.
I remember as a child
the angel hair that went on last,
how beautiful it was,
how it cut my fingers.
Sometimes its long white strands
wore spots of blood.

*

Last year too little money
to fly anywhere, too cold to drive.
We stayed here, shared our turkey dinner
with Luis from Nicaragua, Oscar from El Salvador.
Only seventeen, Oscar drank Pepsi, practised English:
how do you say, how do you say . . . ?
A teacher in his country, here
Luis shovelled snow. His job would end soon.
Oscar had two more months of English classes.
All night he said, *I speak only*
present tense.

*

I wrap presents,
                seal them
with bell and blossom stickers.
How I would like to put love inside,
a blessing, a bit of angel hair,
the real thing.
                A satin ribbon,
the knots pressed out. An orange
whose peel comes off whole.
No broken bits of anything,
no lost pieces.

*

Under the feeder
              bird tracks,
a beautiful cuneiform,
blue shadows on snow.
Perhaps sparrows traced the first letters,
our ancestors finding meaning
in the delicate tracks, frail
shapes linked to the things
they saw:
              birds, animals,
              death in winter.

Perhaps the message sparrows leave
makes sense of things,
giving us
              a broken song
to make it through
this long December,
three more months of cold.

* * *

# MALE THRUST

*"I can take no pleasure from serious reading . . . that lacks
a strong male thrust."*
— **Anthony Burgess**

This poem bends its knees
and moves its groin.
It does the Dirty Dog
at parties. It pushes
against cloth, against
the page. It pokes
between the lines.
It breathes deeply,
closes its one eye
and wets its lips.
It writes lewd words
in the margins.
Wherever you are reading —
on the bus, at home
in your favourite chair,
in the library —
it flips open its coat
and flashes.
It backs the librarian
against the wall,
it comes
all over the stacks,
over *A Clockwork Orange*,
over *The Naked and the Dead*,
over *A Golden Treasury of Verse*,
over *Sexus, Nexus and Plexus*.
This poem won't stop.
Even when you close the book
you can hear it
making obscene sounds,
smacking its lips,
completely in love
with itself.

BONES

By Keath Fraser

elling myself things in the dark because the light's rationed. And at home I worry after a storm if I have to reset an electric clock. Anyway, we're all grateful about landing. The Belgian said an Ilyushin doesn't land, it gropes for earth like a shipwrecked sailor. This place really is something else. In the morning for sure I want a bath.

In the wake of war and French colonial cooking, Bartlett's omelette tasted of shell, his butter refused to spread, the milk substitute clotted in his coffee. Nothing dissolved.

After breakfast a soldier led away the terse Swiss advisor and this left their party at five, not counting the pretty guide who welcomed each of them with a handshake into the black limousine.

"Good morning, Dr. Bartlett."

Her holster rode high like a Mountie's under the right breast of her uniform. Asian, her breasts tripped demurely in bondage of their own.

"Just Bartlett, Miss. We all set?"

If you asked her to disco Bartlett bet she'd find out what it was and come back ready to shoot you for the frivolous invitation.

Something voyeuristic about his own profession made him feel slightly exposed here, like standing at a London Drugs' scanner with the name and price of his last purchase frozen above in bright green light —

Keath Fraser was born in Vancouver in 1944. He has travelled widely in Europe and Asia and lived for some years in England, where he studied at the University of London. He taught English for five years at the University of Calgary but now lives in Vancouver and devotes himself to writing. He is not to be believed when he says, "My constituency of readers will fit comfortably in the back seat of a Honda Civic." Oberon published *Taking Cover* in 1982 and General published *Foreign Affairs* in 1985 — both collections of stories and novellas. He is currently working on a novel and a new story collection.

Sheik Condom — while the cashier takes her time wiping down the last litre of Ivory Snow, spilled and unwanted by other shoppers, with a bottle of Windex and a rag.

He still thought of the world in terms of home.

Along littered arteries of the capital no other traffic flowed and the passengers sat peering into deserted streets. Grass had taken over: grew in potholes, out of sidewalks, along curbs. Cars had lain down in the middle of roads and rusted through. Locks and shutters of shops bore the spreading rust of more than one monsoonal season. Their limo's unexpected appearance startled a tattered trespasser into hiding down a sidestreet. The Malaysian grunted. In response to the Romanian advisor, the pretty guide assured her the citizens would be permitted to return to their city soon. Rockets or angry elephants appeared to have gnawed away at entire buildings.

"Mortar eggs," explained the guide in an alien locution.

The Romanian looked fifty and sensitive over a bad moult of dandruff or else psoriasis she kept ruffling from her blazer onto Bartlett's bare arms. He tried coughing to blow it off.

His arms had a flush of winter tan. A golden beach, bar girls, the fragrant frangipani nights. Agreeing to come here, cutting short his stay in Pattaya — Bartlett now wondered if his elevator went all the way to the top.

Walls around suburban mansions mouldered under lichen, not a stray dog could be seen. No one's woof or word broke the serenity until far out on the decaying highway a roadblock suddenly loomed. "Trouble?" asked the Belgian. Soldiers stood around a cordoned-off patch of the cratered road. An armoured truck was the first vehicle they had encountered since jeeps at the airport.

Mr. Strajik, the lanky Swede, spoke to the Malaysian first, who stepped out of the car with the Swedish official clapping his shoulder and returning his black suitcase. This Malaysian advisor they left behind in gesticulating conference with an officer.

Two decades ago their limousine was fit for a prince. Today it bumped and swayed with the grinding of age and a will to be liked. Bartlett put it down to shot shocks. He enjoyed the wily movement of this lover past her prime, a fine perversity. The air conditioner rattled on loyally, stubbornly, trying to be cool. For January the sun was getting hot.

The Belgian, who spoke excellent English, was telling everyone about his infant daughter. "I like the way my wife can plunk her in front of an old Shirley Temple movie and be certain sooner or later the little actress will belt forth a song that nips crankiness in the whaa!" Like Mr. Strajik he was a man used to addressing himself to the spaces between people. He knew about travelling.

The village on stilts they came to next looked lifeless and its rice fields parched. Dusty bicycles stood abandoned, not a hen clucked.

"I will see you later, please?" chirped the Romanian, opening her door reluctantly.

"Right," said Bartlett, unfolding his arms. He smiled warmly. "Break a leg."

"No, never," she replied, misunderstanding.

After introducing her to several peasants, emaciated and fervent, who emerged from a shed to shake her hand, Mr. Strajik climbed back into his jump seat. He gave the woman his thumbs-up sign but she was busy nodding attentively at her welcomers.

A secondary route of even worse surface led through scrubby jungle and in time to a bombed-out bridge. At the riverbank was a little camp of huts and an old woman turning a pig on a spit. It was the Belgian's turn. Mr. Strajik introduced him to a grim-looking soldier carrying large scrolls under either arm and a weariness that gave him a stoop. The Belgian walked him down to the river as he might a child whose walking stride was not his own. He listened carefully, thoughtfully, as the guide translated a summary of the project to hand — or something just as brief.

Alone now with his host and the pretty guide, Bartlett watched Mr. Strajik spread his elongated limbs out on an empty seat as the driver turned the limousine around. Over the decades the leather seats had cracked into dried-up tributaries with the wear and rub of privileged backs.

"Dananga and I were going to drop you in the countryside," said Mr. Strajik in his Swedish lilt. "Maybe, you know, to break in slowly?" Bartlett, curious about his role, knew nothing. "But she insists priority is in the capital. So we are returning you to the city."

"Okay by me," said Bartlett. He relaxed, getting used to this escort service, wondering if Dananga was as unassailable as she appeared.

They re-entered the capital, moving with black purposefulness to its dead heart, where the driver turned down a boulevard of large shade trees and stopped before a grand house — it looked to Bartlett like a reclaimed embassy.

The guide and Mr. Strajik led him up steps and through a lavish vestibule into a ballroom of spectacular sunlight pouring in through open French doors.

Mr. Strajik paused.

"This is where you come in," he said.

Bartlett's eyes adjusted to the ballroom's unnatural brightness and saw one, then three million bones.

Fathoms of bones: hip, thigh, breast, collar, shin, jaw, rib, you name it. The piles seemed indiscriminate.

"Me?" said Bartlett. "What is this place?"

"Your advice," said the Swede.

"The Grief House," said the guide.

"Where victims," said Mr. Strajik, "of the government were debased and buried."

"N'est-ce pas?" asked Dananga.

She introduced a civilian she called the curator, a short man with intense eyes in a moon face. She spoke French to him, moving her hands like budgies in distress. He might have been Bartlett's age, in his early thirties.

"He hopes you will show his workers all about skeletons," said Mr. Strajik.

"How to rebuild them," suggested Dananga.

"Where to begin," said Mr. Strajik.

They were constructing, it turned out, a bone repository.

Bartlett was floored. There were thousands; thousands of shattered skeletons, it looked, hundreds of thousands of bones.

"Listen," said Bartlett. "I'm a chiropractor, okay?"

Mr. Strajik studied his hot face closely. "Yes, exactly." To Bartlett he seemed to be saying, in a very concerned way, "You don't play ball I'll close down your bingo hall."

Workers with wheelbarrows were circling in through the French doors with more and more bones. Their soiled booty already covered the dance floor. Women with rags were wiping earth from these bones in a slow, dispirited way. Flies buzzed them, buzzed the remains. The gardens outside had been heaved up by relentless digging and implacable fatigue.

"Imagine," said the Swede, "if these neighbours" — he nodded in Dananga's direction — "had not made their invasion and driven out the thugs. . . ."

But Bartlett was having trouble imagining what he was looking at.

The pretty invader said to him, "The survivors of the Grief House wish to commemorate the holocaust."

Mr. Strajik, wiping a hand through his thinning hair, glanced at his watch. "Our Swiss banker at the exchequer will be wondering, yes?" He touched Bartlett's arm, politely. "You will excuse me, Dr. Day. I must see if he has all the records he requires? Thank you."

"Hey," piped Bartlett. "What am I *doing* here? What am I *supposed* to be doing?"

Dananga pointed. "Follow, please."

She threaded a little path among the bones to a huge dining table around which the curator had gathered half a dozen assistants. "Please," she smiled, touching the table. "A lesson."

There were bones all over the once-gleaming surface. Who'd eaten here? Who'd danced?

"Listen," said Bartlett. "I manipulate backs."

"Politics," Dananga prodded him, a little curtly, "is only medicine, I think, on the big scale?"

In Bangkok, when Mr. Strajik had introduced himself at the International Congress of Alternate Healing, he'd said nothing of bones. "It was the way you handled yourself, yes? I felt I should come and talk to you."

Bartlett had beamed.

Mr. Strajik was "with the International Committee of the Red Cross," though reluctant to mention that particular organization "at this congress," he said, his gaunt face smiling slyly. Over dinner he'd asked Bartlett to delay his flight home in order to assist him with "something of a nightmare." Nightmare? Invited him to a needy country, all expenses paid, a small delegation.

"What country?" asked Bartlett, painting his *gai yang* with a sharp Thai sauce. He was all pumped up with the success of his lecture. "Sir?"

"It's a secret," replied Mr. Strajik.

Bartlett chuckled. "A secret?"

"Singapore. That's the first stop."

"That's south a ways."

"There we will meet up with the others at Raffles and wait for the Aeroflot flight."

"That's Russian," said Bartlett. When he swallowed, the chicken caught fire.

His new acquaintance said, "Unfortunately, no one else is allowed to fly there."

Bartlett drank off a glass of water. "I'm no politico, okay?"

"You won't get us into trouble then."

"Trouble's a possibility?"

"You're a man taken by history — I could tell that listening to you. This is a chance to bear witness." He leaned across the table "Dislocation?" He was reminding Bartlett of his speech to the congress. "Doesn't dislocation *require* adjustment?"

Unimpressed, Bartlett had quoted Strajik's compliment in his diary that night. Then added, giving in to the revolving little cassette in a fit of enthusiasm, *Hey I should consider it. I should just take off.* He could cut short his scheduled holiday in Pattycakes — however you pronounced it.

Dananga translated the moon-faced curator's question into English.

"He wishes, Doctor, that you show how to know bones and what bones to lay out to tell the awful stories of this mass grave."

"Hey, listen," said Bartlett.

"On the floor," she said. "In the fields."

"I'm sorry. What?"

"You will please show these workers how to cope." She spoke smartly. "The driver will return for you in due time."

With this she retreated across the bony reach of femur and clavicle, radius and tibia and sternum, phalange, humerus, metacarpal, fibula. Rafts of bones. Bones by the ton.

Bartlett gazed at the table where someone had placed a skull in the middle as though to confirm that every skeleton required one. He wondered if bone assemblage qualified for foreign aid in Ottawa. The shovels seemed to have set asunder every bone they aspired to raise.

After a while he said to the curator, "Listen." He was trying to sound sensible. "I don't see any vertebrae here. Get me some vertebrae. All I see is ribs."

But the museum workers only stared at Bartlett Day.

"I don't believe this," he said. Turning, he heard a loud snap and discovered, looking down, his Wallabee mashing a shoulder blade.

"Hey, listen," he exclaimed. "Where's Dananga?"

Their pretty translator appeared to have vanished in Mr. Strajik's jump seat.

Perhaps it was his bluff way of complaining only about the workers and not also the grave that made Bartlett's news more shocking to his fellow advisors. His seeming lack of anxiety when he told his story impressed them. They set down their forks, their reserve and self-importance.

Comparing notes over dinner in their empty hotel, they were lamenting the bridges down, mines planted, farms in ruin, currency worthless and — after Bartlett spoke — the bones interred.

A time of interregnum, pleaded Mr. Strajik. They must all please contribute what they could to national reconstruction. There were villages and towns to visit. To dally was immoral.

Mr. Strajik was a guy with both oars in the water.

Of course they now realized what country he had brought them to, descending by turbo-prop over pagodas and temples, ushered by an alien guide into an empty city. The rumours were confirmed. The tragic little nation was still out of bounds to international correspondents — its fate only suspected — and Bartlett refrained from mentioning the country in his diary in case their hosts, the invaders, should resent his blabbing and confiscate the recorder.

Instead he mumbled quiety, *The driven snow of history.* . . . The water had come back on, he was lying in a dark tepid bath trying to soak away slime from his hands and body. In Bangkok, like a beggar, the humidity had at least stayed outside.

" 'Co-ordination is the principle of harmonious action of all parts of an organism, in fulfilling their offices and purposes. . . .' "

Announcing this mothball text for his Bangkok speech, he had patted his plastic skeleton on her backside, moving right into a joke by pretending his voice was hers, complaining about her spine.

"True," he'd told his audience. "Maybe you haven't heard about bipeds like ourselves, whose vertebrae were supposed to be flat, but whose brains tempted them to stand up on two legs instead of four. Right, so today our joints suffer. Our pelvic floors aren't what they used to be. Neither is anything else. Arteries bulge, sinuses clog. We get rickets and the runs, fallen arches and flat feet. That kind of stress isn't natural, it saps our energy. All because our brains told Mother Nature to buzz off."

He was warming up the conference to his profession although pedigree was not a trait particularly valued among alternate healers. There were holists from Cairo, nutritionists from Buenos Aires, hypnotists from Marseilles and Perth, psychic surgeons and herbalists from Shanghai — God, body therapists from Bombay, biofeedback practitioners from Singapore and Cologne, naturopaths and faith healers out of Dacca, Kuala Lumpur and Atlantic City, all kinds of Indonesian and Burmese reflexologists, plus rolfers from Melbourne and a trichologist from Rhodes. Every country had its specialists. In one thing alone were they all united. They resented the worldwide clique of the drug and medical profession, with its germ-centred theory of disease.

"Know what I mean?" Bartlett asked them from the podium. The conference room was large and panelled in expensive-looking tropical wood along the top of which ran, in a hidden runnel, diffuse golden light. "Whenever it's a matter of deep pain I work hand in hand with Mother Nature. That's why I'm a chiropractor and not some vivisecting doctor. Out to restore the natural balance." He looked at his audience. "Like you. One of you comes into my office, say. I ask you when was the last time you had a spinal examination? You could have a dislocated spine and not know it. Razor back, for instance. A deviation of the thoracic vertebrae, some sort of structural disturbance, short leg, for example, or spasms in the shoulder girdle. You should make a date with me if you've been doing any improper lifting. Any bumps, jars. You might've slipped a disc, I'd tell you, and be wondering what the pain in your backside is. Know what I mean?"

Ever practical he rattled Bea his skeleton out of her sleep. "Sometimes I just grab hold wherever I can. Right off the bat, by whatever hold I know. Bilateral transverse, the million-dollar roll, the shunt. If we had time, I could show you a full nelson, a knee chest drop, even a lower sacral thrust."

Bartlett raised an eyebrow and it got a laugh.

"In case anybody's sceptical, ask the Workers' Compensation Boards. I'm paid to get loggers and longshoremen back on the job. Ask the old ladies who come in, the athletes, the shoppers, I'm hand in glove with the whole population. Pop singers, cartoonists, boxers. Ask them."

Leaving home seemed to have loosened his instinctive rein on fabrication there. Reality was just different when you travelled; what your nose detected in the air determined what you could get away with. Entering other people's houses you tested the air as a matter of course. You never did this entering your own house. It seemed the same with countries.

Entering the ornate ballroom next morning Bartlett met a man cautiously plastering the wall with unsmiling photographs of men, women, sometimes children, posed before the same black curtain. Prisoners who had been processed and tortured in the Grief House — whose bones, said Dananga, Bartlett already knew. He stared at this luxation of time, breathing shallowly.

At the table the curator and his assistants awaited them mutely for the lugubrious lesson to commence.

In order not to feel queasy Bartlett decided he would have to move, act and be aggressive. Hollow in his eardrums he could detect the deep, repetitive sound mares make with their teeth eating hay.

"Right," said Bartlett cheerfully. "Today we've got

wire. Yesterday we named bones. Today we'll dangle this composite rascal from the chandelier. We'll wire him together."

Dananga's translation puzzled his clients. Answering, the little curator sounded self-righteous.

"They think you are making light of the dead," explained Dananga, deadpan.

"Pardon? Oh the chandelier, it's just a place to start, you know, to hang the specimen?" Bartlett was eager to please. To straighten up their stooping postures, charm, get a bearing on his situation.

He had a situation on his hands no question.

Without a drill to thread an exact space between bones — ribs, for example — he set about wiring together yesterday's remains, lashing joint roughly to joint and sockets into place. Two and a half hours later he was ready, after tethering pelvis to torso, torso to eye orbits, to raise Franz to the chandelier and see if this makeshift method of knotting wire around bones could be used to suspend other approximations of skeletons in a similar manner. What did they want in this grief pit, boneracks on a thousand hooks? Stiff articulations for the sake of visitors? Bartlett asked his assistants to bear Franz — but on second thought he dropped his habit of naming every skeleton he met and referred simply to "the victim" — to bear the victim by table into the centre of the ballroom.

The curator walked on bones in his haste to clear a way wide enough through their tide.

Bartlett studied as it moved this work of his upon a bier.

"Listen," he finally muttered. "It's buckshee."

"Please?" inquired Dananga.

He ran one end of copper through the cavity of the absent nose, stepping onto the table daintily, for a plump man, to loop the rest through a crook in the chandelier. Warning the others back, he proceeded slowly to raise the victim off the table, skull followed by bones in more or less correct sequence like a toy train with dangling boxcars, until what tarsal and metatarsal bones they had managed to find left the table, and Bartlett stood there in a hangman's muffled pride, the wire cutting into his palms with the collective weight of who knew how many victims' bones.

"Look upon me," said the skeleton, protesting its hybrid composition. Bartlett pulled the wires.

Bartlett pulled the wires.

The curator and assistants applauded dutifully, as though saluting the winner of an Olympic contest whose flag they did not recognize.

In the midst of this ceremony misfortune struck. Somewhere in Bartlett's construction a knot slipped causing the victim to collapse with a ratatat on the table, leaving a few bones still hanging from the chandelier like fractured concrete at a demolition site. The squatting women with their rags glanced up at the racket.

"This is definitely dumb," said Bartlett, standing at attention on the table.

The wheelbarrow men too were watching the show. But the curator and his assistants chose to stare at their feet rather than embarrass a foreign expert.

"This really is definitely dumb!" repeated Bartlett with feeling. Throwing up his hands he released the final remains and the skull plunged to the table, gouging the mahogany. It thudded like a cigar box.

"Jesus," he exclaimed. "The idea stank in the first place." He felt preposterous. A tubby Canadian jumping off his platform, a quack.

Dananga commiserated but without much sympathy. She seemed to think his lack of persistence pretty childish.

Bartlett tramped up the curling rococo staircase to the second floor. From the balcony outside, a barren flagpole slanted toward the boulevard. Turning abruptly, he travelled through the vast colonial mansion, Dananga following him room to room, pointing out where inquisition and torture had gone on. "*Murder*," she stressed.

Trying to recall home he couldn't get through.

She indicated iron cots where corpses had lain abandoned by the retreating murderers as brute evidence of their genocide. Of their tragedy. Used for eliciting confessions, electric wires dangled from ceilings. Leg chains hung from springless bedsteads. She tried to shock him with shreds of fried flesh scored to the metal; strands of hair; blood and brown stuff staining mattresses. Mouldy clothes lay thrown into corners.

"Primary exhibits," warned Dananga. "Touch nothing. We leave everything."

Like any man in an awkward position, expected to deliver and unsure of the map, Bartlett could feel the shape of his jaw and set of his teeth. He detested the Grief House.

But she was on to something. He told her, "No. Mixing and matching isn't where it's at, you're right."

"Explain?"

He couldn't, not in so many words. But below in the ballroom he actually watched himself take the wirecutters to release his contorted victim from bondage. He was suddenly impatient. "Nix the skeletons. Piles are where it's at." Dananga did her best to translate. "Just piles and piles. Skulls. Let's quit being fancy."

He went at it bluntly, up to his elbows, pitching eagerly into bones. Bones that shed no clues of having danced inside bodies anywhere. He suggested to the curator that he order a halt to wheelbarrows dumping any more discoveries inside. The digging ceased.

Bartlett did not stop for lunch.

He was a willing pioneer.

Out of the crests and valleys he asked that all skulls be carried to the far wall. Here he co-ordinated their anchoring in rows, faces forward, one on top of another.

The humidity made everybody sweat like pigs. But the work's rhythm, the bending to salvage, the squatting to drop, felt good. The curator's intensity, instead of waxing in the turmoil, waned in phases. The mounting skulls spoke mutely without jawbones, in a chorus of death. Yet the clamouring silence dissolved none of their pain nor the house's grief. The walls wailed.

That night the bathwater spun slowly down his drain the colour of mud. The spools of Bartlett's diary were spinning too. *Bones*, he spoke decisively, *are the driven snow of history*.

At dinner he avoided the Romanian agronomist keen to quiz him on the museum's infrastructure.

"Their goals, yes? Are the same as I describe in villages without tools and fertilizer?"

She dusted the tablecloth with anxious hands and tucked her elbows into the nest of her hips.

In the morning he fell mesmerically to work again. He avoided breakfast. When the workers had collected and stacked four thousand skulls plus, when no more skulls remained above ground that were not piled to the ceiling opposite the wall of photographs — buttressed along the floor with a low wooden paling — Bartlett began to contemplate the tens, hundreds of thousands of other bones of which the human frame is composed in such a mass grave.

Outside, the heaved-up earth would have to be levelled and returned to gardens.

Singing birds.

Inside, plotting his release, he wandered back and forth across the dance floor. He was co-ordinating a plan.

Starting with the kitchen, and working his way through other rooms on this floor, the curator could fill these up past the embassy's windows with undulating seas of bone, into which — as in rooms of a carefully preserved heritage house back home, where visitors are prevented from entering by a braided cord — future visitors might peer. Bewildered, they could also look in from the gardens. The little man understood and nodded at the unreality of it all.

"He says you are a shrewd advisor," said Dananga.

That evening, avoiding the Belgian who wanted to play cards, Bartlett told Strajik his work was done. "Ask Dananga," he added.

Mr. Strajik bridled. Had Bartlett not promised him two weeks? The Belgian agreed. Bartlett's claim to have completed his aid would single him out for the disapproval of his peers. Even envy. "Work beyond imagination," said Mr. Strajik. "There is no end of reconstruction, I'm afraid." The spirit of the time would teach him patience.

There followed discussions of roads, villages and disarray. Foreign workers were expected soon to follow up Mr. Strajik's advance guard with resident agencies of international rescue. In the meanwhile, stressed the Swede, the cost of contribution was not a price you paid with ingenuity but the value you offered in time. The others agreed. They seemed used to thinking of themselves as interdependent citizens in a very compressed state of being.

At dawn, as if dreaming, Dr. Bartlett Day found a message at his door to pack up and prepare to travel deeper into bones. A Lada awaited him, driver and guide. He had been all ready to go home.

His progress north was slow. He ate dust as the sun rose in the sky bathing dispossessed nomads. It was no country for old men. People evidently requiring the chiropractor's expertise made his guide stop everywhere.

Villagers were blighted.

Starving, actually.

"Supposed to eat, yuh, yuh," said the decrepit guide, probably no more than forty, making eating noises with hand and mouth. His English relied on semaphore and could no more uncover idiom than a flag could shuck an oyster. In this country, it was enough.

People mopped the fields for blades of forgotten rice. Their forced labour had produced only years of sterile fields and ransacked souls. Bags of rice appeared and disappeared, bicycled in from a border, selling and reselling for profit. Nobody without means to barter could afford free Red Cross gifts.

These sterile fields turned out to be Bartlett's goal. Their excavation was leading to spontaneous catharsis all over the country. Liberation, if it had removed fear of murder, was also renewing the grief.

Each village uncovered its proof. The educated and disobedient, the suspected and despised: their bones were bleaching upon every one of Bartlett's arrivals. Wrist bones still bound with wire; skulls still blindfolded. Even better as graves than the rice fields were B-52 craters, saucers in the earth now overgrown with vegetation.

The simplicity of his advice made Bartlett's transmigration nimble. He took a stick; he drew in the dust. Long, two-shelved sheds open to the air. *Look*, he pointed, upper shelf for skulls, lower shelf for all these other bones. . . .

Every village offered a variation of the same story. Five thousand, eight thousand, ten and more thousand in bigger towns, struck on the head with iron bars, pokers, rifle butts — anything to save bullets said his guide — and buried by fellow villagers, after victims had dug their own graves.

And every night Bartlett the voyeur told this story to his diary. Record, tally, log of each pit's disclosure. It felt like a lie. He slept on dirt floors and ate infested rice. He was gnawed into lumps by mosquitoes. His quarters smelled. Dysentery touched him with the hand of hyperbole. Storing up memories deliberately for the first time in his life, he treated himself to new batteries and might have bartered dead ones for food.

News becomes news as it gets famous, he spoke sombrely into his machine. *I don't even recognize stuff I can't look at on a screen.*

These suddenly liberated people seemed to expect more of him than he could hope to deliver. They wanted hope for their lives, not advice about the dead. He was certainly hand in glove with the lot of them — or might have been had he any real relief to offer. They still felt enchained. They showed him trees where people had been tied and left for twisting hooks to extract their livers.

Back home, he recalled, his office was full of gadgets to keep suffering patients coming back. Technology soothed, so did tradition.

" 'Look well to the spine,' " he had told delegates at the Congress of Alternate Healing, quoting a potted Hippocrates, "'for many diseases have their origin in dislocations of the vertebral column.' "

He liked to tell the story of the human back, from ancient Egypt through the fall of the Roman Empire, the dark ages, the evolution of bonesetting in the Renaissance. This story of dislocation gave his profession a history.

By the time he got to the invention of chiropractic — and here he pressed home his facts — by a Canadian in 1895, who had to migrate south before he could overthrow the old ideas of taking care of bodies, Bartlett had quoted from ancient Chinese documents on tissue manipulation, cited examples of spinal adjustment by a number of cultures including the Inca, Toltec and Maya, plus the Sioux and Winnebago. Even today, he claimed, the Maori in New Zealand still walked across each other's backs to cure pain caused by nonaligned bones. Bone manipulation was a democratic phenomenon given international distinction by a Canadian.

He had suggested this rather proudly.

And concluded confidently, "Bones are character. Bones helped our forefathers get to my country. Bones helped them make sails, splice ropes, hook fish. I know their secrets by the bones they kept. In the old country they kept bones for shuttlecocks and chastity belts. In Canada they turned them into clappers and pastry crimpers. Bangles and snow goggles. Earplugs and dog whistles. Bones," he had boasted, "keep me in touch."

He had given his amanuensis another slap. Bea's slats shone as white as snow in the lights. Hubris made them both glow. He had hired an enterprising Thai to make a video of his address and planned to play it in the waiting room of his office at home. With Bea he had even waltzed a bit and got a hand.

In this Bangkok hotel on the river, plied once by trading schooners and seafaring novelists, he was asked to dance that evening by the striking, pearl-necklaced hypnotist from Marseilles named Dr. Legatt, and Bartlett told her he was going to Pattycakes — Pattaya — in the morning and she should come too.

"I feel," she replied, in very limber English, "your idea with me is the best thing since apple betty." His heart had skipped at this domestic little allusion that was confident of, indeed pleased with, itself as idiom. "But my husband and I leave tomorrow for Rome.

"Not," she added, hands on his chiropractor's shoulders, "that my husband would mind."

Reported Bartlett, later, *We could learn a lot from the French.* . . .

Now, on his last night in a fractured little country, he ended up in an abandoned luxury hotel, once a refuge for travellers from around the globe. Over the country's ancient ruins it had started to rain. The jungle smelled sour. Vast temple mountains, towers and courtyards, balustrades and moats, shrines and niches to ancestral kings of a dislocated future — a wonder of the world, claimed his guide, just beyond the window. Bartlett dutifully wondered.

He thought of home, the old house he lived in between apartment buildings, and imagined an empty city. The way a neighbour's rusted Pontiac no longer returned like a tired animal, tires scraping the curb, engine rumbling until kicked to charge it up for morning, then switched off, sounding like the last and unexpected breath of a buffalo.

In the morning a small plane would land at the unused airstrip and return him to the capital. He had no answer for the guide and driver who wanted to see the skyscrapers of Singapore.

Bones are the driven snow of history. Bones not stones were the real record, a nation's memory. The record of experience was bones.

And grief, he concluded.

Without it you were a quack.

Tuneless.

Bartlett got out of bed to close the shutters in the large, unelectrified suite. He felt his way back again in darkness.

The white dust of bones left out in the air would start falling years hence over this jungle, this country, this people. But no one would feel it, see it, know it. The dust would be falling over the ruins too. He heard the little spools of his diary dissolving in silence.

It'll never sink in anywhere, he added, killing the mike.

Against the wooden shutters the rain fell harder.

ARGENTINA MY VOICE

BY KEATH FRASER

Connivance, finally, had us listening to her sisters as if she *had* sisters, except this is how she wanted it, from the day she arrived bossing them around like a ventriloquist. Talk, talk. Sometimes she inveigled Merrilee into retorting, sure, but never Phoebe.

The hot May her mother died my cousin came to live, and missing home she moped and slept and cried. Her new mom, my old one, rolled dough for her and baked it light. Time collapsed like a lung as she huffed in the heat for breath. Long hair stuck to her cheeks, you found strands in the porridge. Her skin in the tub rubbed through the door, you heard it, skin and tears. Hair there too, our house was full of hair. Under her arms it grew as fine as corn silk, and as red. Scrubbed and limp she reclined on the veranda with nothing to do but grieve. Pollen fell from the anthers, comic books curled in the sun, our senses had the feel of blonde, bulging withers. On tropical evenings we watched the sprinklers — and aboard a wooden ship, look, floated out to view them.

"That's water for fodder, isn't it? You'd mourn your corn if it wasn't, I'm sure. Wouldn't you?" Rhyming, she spoke brazenly. "My tears are over Rover, so are my teeth." I looked at Daddy. My cousin looked at me. She meant the sugar lacing Mom's pies. "How can I sing with rotted teeth? Don't *you* think I should sing-a-ding-ding?" I thought she should check her marbles. "Well," she said. "I might." Her name was Argentina. That summer, at sixteen, she outlived first one, then both her imaginary sisters.

Daddy did some singing himself, a weekend western singer whose band was also our hired help. Mom said he hired help on purpose from ranks of unemployed musicians. Quinn and Ivar and Tulley preferred dance halls to fields. So did Daddy. On Saturday night he put on a white satin bowling jacket with a string tie and pineapple toggle, wore cowboy boots and a lemon shirt. The rest of the week he practised in the cornfields with the high tenor voice of Slim Whitman and sang Slim's big hit, "That Silver-Haired Daddy of Mine." I listened through the stalks. After intermission, after lunch, he always tried Slim's first hit, "The Indian Love Call." It never worked for Daddy, he couldn't yodel. He practised yodelling, had been practising since puberty: first Judy Canova, then Wilf Carter, at last Slim Whitman. By the time Slim came along my father was a silver-haired daddy himself.

He sang at dances to help ends meet, forced his talent and growled at his farm. In a plain between mountains and river he grew silage for dairies and sweet corn for tins. Because he hated Perumbur, and to soothe his strained cords, he gargled baking soda to lift his soul.

Talk about a character.

My cousin couldn't have shucked ears for apathy. She just bathed and sulked and let in flies. In bed Phoebe, her youngest sister, made love to a Coke bottle. She was the laziest sister, looked dead, like spat-out gum bleached into highways. Languishing on the veranda every evening, she wasn't happy. This imaginary Phoebe, her pores, smelled like corn leaves up your nose, prickly and suffocating.

Argentina spoke out at the falling darkness, maybe as a way of forgetting where she was and why. "It's a daisy being lazy," she said, lying late on the veranda looking wide-eyed and distracted. "If I had a horse, of course . . ." No, there was no telling where she would canter. Her eyes strayed to my hoed-out hands. "You're a worker," she said, "I'm a shirker." I said I thought rhyming was for kids. Mocking me she said, "You're learnin', Sterlin'," as if a name were hers to trifle with. You also became Irving, Sheldon, Euple, for her swerving, well done, scruples.

She had the rhythm and eye to attract an uncle. Giles was Daddy's stage name, and his real one, he'd never changed it. For Saturday dances he blackened his hair with shoe polish and was picked up looking as young as his sidemen. They all drank and came back late dancing in their headlights. Humming in her room, Argentina slipped downstairs to greet Giles with a smile and the aspirin tablets to stop his headache Sunday. She handed him a glass of water. Mom slept soundly till the imaginary Merrilee died. Fat Merrilee died suspecting evil.

You could tell by the way Merrilee sat at meals Argentina was poisoning her. Sat with her fat back sideways, sat that way on the veranda too. Disturbed was not the word for this weight squatting on her soul. In the hallway upstairs she finally opened up and called her sister disgusting. The older girl replied that Merrilee was done for. "You fat bat. Your belly's jelly and you think dink!" They quarrelled loudly, Argentina doing both their voices, the ventriloquist hounding herself as well. Merrilee's skin blotched like red dots in a comic and tears blistered upon her cheeks. Nothing could have saved her from the choking weather, the mugginess. She balled out her eyes.

"I'm a fan," said Argentina, "of your old man." She'd have said anything for the chance to sing with his band. She smiled to hide her teeth. Yodelled in the tub, paraded herself with ears curled around the chatter of Daddy's sidemen in the fields, asking questions about tassels and suckers but mainly lyrics. I listened. Daddy listened. "Giles smiles," she claimed, on her.

"The way to succour grief," said Daddy, "is take it dancing." Grief wore a cowboy hat and kisscurls stiffened with vaseline, and she and he sang duets. According to Daddy she was as slick on stage as dolphin skin. His band's business picked up — church basements, community halls, parties anywhere after bingo. Phone calls trickled in from up and down the valley. "A girl singer's the novelty a band needs," he said.

Maybe Mom knew what Merrilee knew, something was making Mom's mustache grow, the heat maybe. Tackiness kept us all awake the Sunday morning Argentina came home in the moonlight laughing, to whip the cat with corn tassels. At breakfast she said gin punch, funny, made your head go crunch. She couldn't eat her porridge. Eating porridge year round was a bad family trait, but eating it in summer was like putting on longjohns. She said it was no wonder Phoebe turned to Coke; no wonder she was rotting. Merrilee ate porridge with the despair of a fat person. Her blubbering became June's voice of grief. It sounded worse than May's, since it seemed no longer to be accusing Argentina of betraying a dead mother — just a live one.

Ivar, the banjo player, foresaw Merrilee's departure when he retold the story of Tulley's tremors on steel guitar. "Diagnosed whatchumacallit up here," he said, tapping himself quietly between the eyes. He too was conniving. Argentina mimicked him with the painted fingernail she was shaking dry. "So he give it up," said Ivar.

Merrilee's giving up was easier and painless. I found her in the closed garage with dried tears on her cheeks — I can see her still, a comic in her fist. She's sitting in the back seat, waiting. Our Packard is out of gas and the fumes all leaked away.

To humour the girl Mom laughed, then she wailed, remembering her own sister's funeral in Perumbur's little church. She doubled her baking to soothe her grief. She dribbled in the shortening. "The genes that give out," she said, flexing the fingers of an unstable family skeleton. She missed the flatter, plainer prairies of her girlhood.

To make matters worse Phoebe could not, or would not, eat anything. Would not lay one hand on cutlery and passed hunger by. Merrilee's death had bequeathed dresses that hung on her like grain sacks. She wore a new one every afternoon for a week, then nothing. Refused to climb out of bed, lay stretched out on a worn cotton sheet, biting her lips coral.

Argentina braided Merrilee's dead, cutoff hair calling it a grieve-weave. She pinned it to her own piled-up bun. Her own hair went up and down like hope. Mourning became her, and she cultivated the tempered airs of sorrow. She gazed off the porch like Our Lady of the Sea.

You could have drowned in corn. In the heat the fields seemed wet enough to fish in. The kitchen too, we could have used a punkah. Mom baked pies and cakes and jam rolls. But not for Phoebe. That sister lived for Coke and the pleasure of exercising the bottle's lip, its thicker glass. Mom's steadfast worry caused Argentina to warn us her sister had never eaten beans. Beans, said Mom, is what she needs. In case she had worms.

Conniving. Conniving.

Before Phoebe died I had fat dreams, fattening her up with Old Dutch sprinkled on cookies to bleach her insides. Yet who could have been chaster than a fourteen-year-old making love to eel-soft glass? After Merrilee's death she closed the door and to see her you watched through the wall. What a dear sweet cousin, what a bonerack. In her wide double bed she hardly moved and her scalp shed hair worse than the cat. In corners you found bales of it. Mom never noticed, she kept house like a trollop.

By the time husks started fattening, Phoebe had lost consciousness. Ivar studied me like he thought I'd stolen her food. "Didn't you even try to talk to her?" he asked. Embarrassed, I plugged the hole in my wall with Spearmint and hoed harder in the world outside. "Who named these girls?" Ivar asked my cousin. "They're stupid names." But Argentina didn't care. She took her sister up a glass of whole milk, Merlin Vitamin Pills, a piece of fresh raspberry pie. One afternoon she found Phoebe as spent as a used match. From the veranda she called, "*Mom comme!* . . ." It sounded like a railroad junction. "*Mom-comme! Mom-comme! Mom-comme!* . . ." her voice losing music to nonsense and, at last, hysteria. We came. The thing was, with Mom in the kitchen, Argentina had run right by her.

The doctor fretted over Argentina but Phoebe never woke up. Grieve? For Argentina, Phoebe's death now made a chain of death. She made us feel the niblet factory was like a beach we were cultivating sand for, it seemed that pointless. Nobody mentioned creamed corn to her, nobody joked about popcorn. Mom even stopped baking. The band made its way through the sweet corn singing mournfully. Daddy kept shaking his head till Argentina lost her voice.

"Shock," said Mom.

Three deaths for Argentina, three arrows in her heart. It amounted to a curse.

A disease. The doctor, returning, called it aphonia.

"Sympathetic aphonia," he told us. Daddy figured it was not that she couldn't talk, but wouldn't. He approved of bedrest ordered by the doctor and resigned himself to singing solo. But he got bored reaching for notes higher than he could scale. It threatened the band.

"This cursed family," said Mom, lingering aimlessly in sweet rows of depression.

Poor woman, lubricating her adopted daughter with molasses and pills and love, handing Daddy his Cow Brand in a glass of water, clucking Ivar to attention when his eyes roamed south to hair in this girl's palms.

As the corn gained weight my cousin, just like Phoebe, started losing it. Her grieve-weave in Merrilee's memory fell apart in her hands. With her own hair she wove pony tails, horse tails, gawky manes. She was like the ugly sister with hair that never pleased her. But it never fell out, she didn't lose her hair as she did her voice. Her singing now no more than a larynx scratching linoleum, she spent days in bed fiddling with brush and mirror.

I watched her gargle the heat. I opened her window and closed it and opened it, bringing her molasses and smacking flies with a rubber glove. Once I pulled the glove over my head like a toque. She stared, then smiled. She showed me my image in her mirror: the red glove's empty fingers waggled like a rooster's comb.

Said I, "I'm a rooster booster."

This tickled her, and for a moment she forgot herself. Said I, "Combs roam. My comb, your comb. Look in the mirror, dear." This nonsense, copied from her, spilled out. "I've got masses of molasses, right?" She hated molasses and her smile disappeared. I began appearing with ice cream. "To help you dream," said I.

She licked the spoon. She was still a child, had temples with the hollows of a child's and her round shoulders stuck out naked from a little girl's nightie. Rhyming, I fanned the heat off with a pillow case, a jester in my cousin's court. She had not spoken since she lost her voice.

In August the band fell apart. Nothing to do with Argentina, it was Tulley, he and Daddy quarrelling that month over Daddy's share of the take. All Daddy did, said Tulley, was sing four or five songs then leave the others to play the dance. Daddy came home on his own complaining of tonsillitis. After Tulley quit, Quinn, who hated the cornfields anyway, said it was crazy to try to play dances without a lead guitar, and he quit too. The lazy way he brushed his drumskins had made him a perfect country drummer, and Daddy went begging. He could not go on without a drummer and a lead guitar. Just Ivar was left, and what could you do with a banjo picker? Still, Daddy was careful around Ivar, needing him for when the harvest started and, if he ever got one going again, a band. Ivar tapped the vellum and plonked tunes with finger picks on five wire strings. "Pingatore," he said, "daddied this little instrument." He knew everything about things and very little of bodies. Ivar dressed the way a squirrel dozes spread-legged and stomach-down on a branch, with no thought of style. "But I play good," he said. We sat on the porch at breaks. Daddy, white hair in his ears, had stopped singing in the fields. Mom said there was no way *he* had lost his voice, just his self-esteem.

One late night in August I heard a noise upstairs, then nothing. I had come down for a glass of milk. I let out the cat, locked the screen, washed out my glass. The air was still and sticky. Taking a cookie I put out the light and moved up the stairs. Outside Argentina's room I stopped to listen. I tried her keyhole, saw blackness, listened some more. Just the usual sounds of dreams scratching for a voice. Also some groaning in the gloaming, I later thought, chewing my cookie.

Gloaming, coming across it two days later in the dictionary, I found on the same page as Gloppen. I remember Gloppen because nothing I could think of rhymed with it. Just the word I needed that night when I walked into her bedroom.

When I walked in I gloppened Daddy. Startled him.

"*What? What do you want!*" he hissed. Gloppened too, I dropped my cookie on the carpet. He rushed at me in the dim light cast from the stairwell. "*Have you let out the cat!*" he hissed. Before I could think he hit my head a knock that scared me. "*I've been talking!*" he fumed, disappearing down the stairs.

Turning on Argentina's lamp I saw the rucked-up bed, smelt the shoe polish. Awake, tears in her eyes, she was licking the tip of her nose.

I wanted to ask if my father had bitten her.

Instead I cleared the hair off her face and whispered, "Rest."

"Chest," she said.

I wondered if she was hurt, pained into utterance. I put my ear to her breast as to a conch shell. Listened for the rise and fall of a tide, our river, some reason for her voice. Her heart seemed clocked to give nothing away but its regularity. Chest, I thought. Rest.

Gently I placed my fingers on her to acknowledge the word. Ashamed, I turned away to look for my cookie.

Down in the kitchen Daddy had gone out and let in moths. I kicked out the cat and locked the screen. Stood before the open refrigerator in the stifling night. Instead of ice cream I found seven dill pickles in a cold jar, so I took these to the table and ate six. The seventh I kept for rubbing on the lump where Daddy'd socked me. Imaginary Merrilee must have known everything. You could still hear her boohooing. I felt sorry for Mom. I felt sorry for Argentina. No word could I think of to rhyme with Argentina — not Indonesia, no Guatemala. Home was not where my heart was at all. Around us, cooling down, the old house released the sun, shivered on its wooden raft, expired and fell asleep. The pickles were sour.

Next morning Mom said if her niece had said a word she would like to know what it was, thank you.

"Suitcase," I said.

"Suitcase?" She put her cup down slowly. "Is she thinking of leaving us? Did she find her voice after three weeks just so she can leave?" She turned to Daddy who was stirring his eyes in his porridge. He looked like he'd slept in the barn. "She's only a kid. She's an *only* kid. We can't let her run off!" Her face was less alarmed than I expected. "She's in no condition to travel. Where could she go?"

Daddy ate his porridge not saying anything.

"I'll have a word with her," said Mom. She served Daddy his toast and wiped her hands on the tea towel. When Ivar arrived, toothpick in mouth, Daddy vanished into the fields. Ivar stood there letting wire laces slowly, imperceptibly, tear out the eyes of his boots. "Whatchumacallit," he said. "Try some." He meant bran, the elixir of health, Ivar's health, the All Bran he called Little Logs. "They work for me every time," he said, delighted at the mystery.

Mom came back down. "She can't talk. I don't know what you're telling lies for. I didn't see any suitcase." She went to the cupboard. "Here. Take her up these molasses. And try her on porridge and cream. If we don't look out, she'll follow Agnes." Mom looked like she might follow

Agnes herself. Her eyes drooped over large dark bags as she slumped down with her tea.

Ivar told her she should start in baking again, that he wanted to see her wrist wiggling the cookie-cutter some more. He didn't mention her last cookies were stale. He shuffled on the linoleum and went out the door.

When I went in to Argentina she was sitting up with hair all over her head. A blue-bottle, the beggar, was buzzing it. She pushed away the tray.

"Tired?"

She looked at me. A little huskily answered, "Mired."

I tried again. "Horse."

"Force," she whispered.

"Glide."

She came back, "Lied."

This was therapy like ping-pong, ping-sing I thought, one-note conversations batted back and forth over logic's net. You lost a point for half rhyming the ball, or not trying at all. If I was tired from hoeing, I took in the dictionary.

"Gloaming."

"Roaming," she answered.

"Doleful."

"Hoe full."

Some days were worse and she struggled in despair. At night I kept an ear tuned for Daddy prowling like the cat. I listened outside her door. I listened outside his own door for a set of snores from him and Mom. Giles and Rhoda. Nothing except the soda Rhoda fed Daddy's tonsils rhymed with my mother's name.

By late August the corn had grown near the sky, the river had dropped to its lowest level in half a century, and Daddy had taken to the sheds to prepare his machinery. He meant to punish me. He kept me hoeing till my hands swelled and the blisters popped. Even the ocean, miles west of Perumbur, the thought of setting out across it Kon-Tiki fashion, had begun to make more sense than being used as a joeboy.

Looking up Joeboy I found Joskin.

"Saucepin," she said.

Saucepan.

Mom herself must have wondered at what she heard. I told her I was getting somewhere and not to despair. She would have needed a bright imagination where I was concerned to think of concupiscence — an unrhymable word I was saving up. Her ear at the keyhole, a lobe I loved, would have been more startled than her eye.

PAWKY	LUPINE
YOUNKER	TROPE
ROCKY	SUPINE
CONQUER	DOPE

My cousin and I shared the dictionary and served up unrhymable words like Gloppen to win a point. She had no memory of sentences, they left no impression when I spoke them. Words by themselves made her listen.

Phoebe.

Merrilee.

Lonely words, stupid names. Characters without voices.

By late summer I had begun to feel words as substances. In the past, heat and voices were humidity you suffered through, excused one another in the middle of, or drowned in hating. A bad family trait. Now when you spoke them in our baking heat, words moved on the tongue lighter than pastry.

That year Indian summer was as hot as real summer. Copper days, golden corn: dent, sweet and a hybrid flint corn of Daddy's confection used for fritters and popping. When the cobs glistened, when the dimple in each grain showed the soft starch dried out, when a dark dot appeared at the cob's tip, two hundred acres were ready for harvest. Daddy told Mom he had had no luck hiring help in town. Ivar drove the Finning that pulled the thresher that cut the stalks, blowing the whole works as silage into a trailing wagon. Daddy harvested the sweet corn with more refined machinery.

No songs that year, just work. Loading and unloading wagons, weighing corn by the bushel, by the ton, telephoning wholesalers and arguing with dairymen. Perumbur dairies depended all winter on our corn rotting sweetly in their silos. School for me was out till the harvest was in.

From Ivar I learned corn had more uses than his

tractor. Husks for dolls, stalks for paper and wallboard, cobs for charcoal and solvents and pipes, grain for dextrose and booze. All these were the wider uses he said Daddy never bothered with. Daddy only sold corn for silage and canning. His concession to Lacey's cinema hardly counted when you figured out the price of popcorn and what they paid him. But he liked the Odeon because its manager showed Gene Autry singing as he unwound fencewire. Daddy must have counted on singing again himself, if only in his fields, when I wasn't around to remind him of what I knew.

Argentina agreed to come down at last and sit on the veranda. It was sweltering that evening and she had on a dress. I sat in the rocker beside her, moving like a fan, talking softly. Her interest in therapy had worn off as the heatwave kept on. To each of my words she seemed content to offer only half a rhyme. "Bosky," I might read. Her reply, "Lusty." If you pronounced Polyonymy with a careful and tricky serve, she batted it away with Dummy.

"Fetter?"

"Brine."

Mom had no idea what we were talking about. She sat off a ways in a wicker chair listening to notes Ivar was picking on his banjo. She could not understand how, if her niece could say separate words, she could not speak in sentences.

The next evening I tried the hardest word I knew. "Argentina."

The others sat waiting too.

She gave no answer. Just sat there watching the mountains receive the copper sun.

In the morning she was dressed and down to breakfast. She had brushed her hair till it shone. Taking her chair she asked for waffles, done on the griddle till they crusted please. A sentence delivered in lumpy phrases that held the texture of her voice without resonance, or rhyme. The sound of it stuck to our ribs. Its request caused Mom to give thanks to the saints, walk to her stove and begin baking again. Waffle batter.

Deceived, I decided my cousin's aphonia, like her rhyming before that, her ventriloquism and hyperbole, had only been ways to get noticed. Now she no longer spoke in rhyme. She spoke crisply of her sisters' virtues, mellowness and assent, and refused to finish high school. She borrowed Daddy's guitar. Determined to become a singer, she dressed up in cowboy boots and sequins. She put on weight, where it counted she claimed, and yo-delled in the bath. She dreamt of capped teeth. Unwilling to chip her nail polish, she turned down housework and chores with the cheek of a princess. The perfume she wore set the cat purring on her shoulder.

The way Mom found out about her niece and Giles was the same way I had, more or less. Except it happened one afternoon, after harvest, when Mom was shopping and I was in school. She'd come home early and found them together in bed. She never said what they were doing, never even said where she'd found them. But her face had turned as white as flour. The staff of life, wheat of the world, she survived a vanished mustache and cheek-bones fallen to a lower place.

She quit baking and cried in the corn like Ruth.

Argentina packed her suitcase and was gone by the time I got home. On the sheets of my parents' bed I sniffed Lily of the Valley. Daddy claimed he didn't understand anything that was happening and swallowed a chaser of Cow Brand. He growled to deflect the vast front blowing in upon us and just gaped at the thunder. It rained regu-larly after that for years. In the spring my cousin wrote to me once from the home of other relations. She had forgot-ten some lyrics in our sideboard drawer. Truly Yours she signed off, but I never believed it, I never found her songs.

In time, as they came out, my father learned "Cold Empty Arms" and "At the End of Nowhere," off Slim Whitman records, and sometimes talked, not of rebuild-ing the band, but of retiring under bougainvillea. Florida was where his hero Slim was born, had worked in ship-yards and joined his first band. Ivar joined a band called The Rhythm Sons, up the valley where I saw him once at a dance. My mother, like her sister before her, ruptured an aneurism and went to an early grave.

On the radio I would listen to a talent program for new country and western artists, but Argentina wasn't the name of any girls introduced. Their songs weren't "The Indian Love Call" or any others you remembered. Starvation, war. Alien voices creeping into popular songs, and it may be she found consort in this newer music we normally, habitually, tuned out.

DAMAGES

BY KEATH FRASER

I am going to confess something libellous. Can you sue yourself for libel? Am I liable to myself if I reveal this lamentable thing? The reason I hesitate is I wonder if it's worth my while confessing or would I be better off keeping quiet. I guess I like the contact. Like lots of women when I talk I risk losing a settlement against myself. It's not fair. By telling the truth I'm punished for indiscretion. I know the best defence against libel is to prove it's true. You see what a position this leaves me in. I could lie and say blackberry thorns really hurt me in the pleasure of filling my pail. But they don't.

The stars know this. They risk libel every night they turn on in the hills. The stars are foolish and who notices, who suffers? We do. Their watchers do, we suffer for them. We read libel in their glitter. We make a to-do about the showboaty stars and it gives them pleasure. Not till morning can we trace our scars, their scars, with our fingers. The skin declines to lie.

Take just one star. Look at the things she has had to face. Bobby Darin. A gun, her father came after Bobby with a gun, so that was the end of a potentially huge romance. Bobby married Sandra Dee. Bobby died. Then her brother was murdered. Her two, three marriages fizzled out. She miscarried. One husband beat her. She had typhoid fever and bled from the ears. A perfectionist about singing she just made her pain worse. Lost her voice, attempted suicide, became psychotic. It got gross. She travelled in and out of clinics like a laundry van. A court found her incompetent to look after her own affairs. Twice. By the way, it was the mob in New York City who shot her brother — in the driveway of his New Jersey home. He was a racketeer.

These facts are part of our public record. I think it would be wrong to repeat them at all if magazines hadn't reported them, newspapers, if she hadn't told us herself. It's all true. Kicking a policeman, the lithium treatments, problems in her fourth marriage. Everything. I have watched her growing darker, I must admit, watched with more than wonder.

Take, for example, when a knife-armed stranger broke in and raped her in a Howard Johnson motor lodge, I too experienced a loss of self-esteem, failed to recover my usual good nature, and little by little lost my pitch till I *whrrrred* like a pheasant with strep throat. I couldn't have sung to save my supper.

"Something eating you?" asked Mr. Delmore, not looking up. "That . . . uh, tenant still troubling you?"

Nerves in need of the sun I told him, since it was December by then.

"Feed a fever," he suggested. "Starve a cold."

After the lawsuit she tried comebacks. She lip-synched on the Dick Clark show, I watched her on TV, and she flew home from L.A. feeling like a fraud. She who had sung for the Queen, sung in Carnegie Hall, been chosen Female Entertainer of the Century at Expo 67. She made herself go back to finish an engagement at the Westbury nightclub where she was singing the night of her rape. But nothing soared. She couldn't repeat the past. She was already passing into myth.

You felt it was all going to come out: barricading herself inside her house, inside her bedroom, where her wretched change of voice seemed to echo the men who'd violated her. A father who pushed her, husbands who left her, the stranger who raped her and was never caught. She herself blamed it on air-conditioning. On the effect of air-conditioned rooms on her throat, after surgery to narrow her nose and the operations afterwards to fix up the first surgery's leftover scar tissue. It's hard to say. You admire vanity.

But who can write off the gagging fruit of evil?

Listen. *All* her hits came before the rape, before the marriages, before she found out her brother, who was rubbed out for squealing, was a crook.

Right to the end, just like a friend,
I tried to warn you somehow . . .

I don't know who wrote that one — my father once said it was an old song, a real poco andante. He'd sniff his Dutch-Reform-sniff at the Hit Parade, at how it sparked, then doused its stars. He was right. The stars flared, went shooting, died out. Frankie Avalon, Neil Sedaka — her father tolerated those two though he hated Bobby Darin, who went on to become a bigger star than either of them. Frankie befriended her, Neil wrote her songs. Such songs, even one song could have made her a star. Isn't it your memory of a song that stays constant when the flame that inspired the words is gone?

I could show you the river where Bernice Hailey and I were sitting in her father's Mercury when Tony Bellis sang a song on the radio that should have become a bigger hit and never did, not really, "Robbing the Cradle." Or where I was when Ricky Nelson gave me the answer, "Uh huh," in a falling third to every question asked of me for a week, from his big hit "Poor Little Fool." I was at Mrs. Kabush's kicking the slats out of used lettuce boxes for her stove — not a thing in neighbourly conscience I could dodge, stocking her kindling.

"I'm in your hands, dearie!" she would scream. "I'd freeze and starve both without you!"

I just bet I thought.

"Hold on, dearie, I'll turn up the radio!"

The old have ways of wheedling life from the young. What is dignity?

When I reported the record settlement for negligence against Howard Johnson, in the millions, to Mr. Delmore, he only stared out the window at passing traffic and said lawyers were so many farts in a closet. I think he said ten. He should know, he wrote the book on fustiness. Darkness. Not that litigation has ever threatened Mr. Delmore, he's too wary. I help Mr. Delmore to manage Stay-A-While outside Lacey. We're the last resort for travellers who, because of indifference or bad timing, are unable to reach the coast before nightfall. They come out of the Interior, over passes, down the Canyon, before making their mistake. Our highway isn't the Trans-Canada but a secondary route veering away at Hope. "Typical," mutters Mr. Delmore. He's been trying to sell out for years. Power lines buzz overhead and remind him of electric chairs.

He's an aging man with gas-station sideburns and a need of blunt pencils. He'd rather go to jail than mark anything, a cheque or crossword puzzles, with a pen. The nearness of an eraser encourages in him the conceit of retraction and the second chance. Around me he prefers to listen than comment, so I prattle, and dust lightly. He has no love for people who wear him down and all of us do. His face at the counter resembles the slumped side of an old boot, propped up at the chin with the heel of his hand.

When I say "manage" I mean changing sheets, vacuuming carpets, Cometing sinks. The things a wife'd get stuck doing for free to help her husband in any one-man operation of ten units. Mr. Delmore has that many peeling cabins around a weedy driveway and seldom more than four occupied per night. Nobody stays longer than a night. The Datsun trucks and Suzuki motorcycles all pull out by eight, eight-thirty, in the morning. Good riddance to the grumps. By noon yours faithfully is on her way home.

Except once. Just once in twelve years have I had to enforce noon checkout and I was not a success. This was when I first started. I was new and hating the job, my morale was rock-bottom. A young man with dirty yellow hair who hadn't bothered to close his blinds was still in bed, on top of it, in underpants. He groaned when I knocked on his door to explain who I was and what time the clock said. I heard nothing till he fumbled open the door, just enough to reveal a moley face and skinny chest. I looked away. He wasn't telling me anything, he muttered, if he was to tell me he thought he might drop dead from wild oats. He didn't look sarcastic so much as hung over.

I had to knock again, this time sharply with a broom handle. I walked to the window and rapped there too. He slowly guillotined my view with a downward pull of the blinds. So I walked over to the office and reported him to Mr. Delmore. Mr. Delmore looked at me, said it was nothing to get upset about, and pencilled in No. 9 for another day.

"What if he ups and leaves without paying?" I said. "Look, Mr. Delmore. I haven't been here long but I know a smart ass when I hear one. He'll just out and away on those parked wheels."

Mr. Delmore raised his chin to window level. "Got his Gibson."

Casually he pulled out some baggage from under the counter and unzipped a canvas bag to show me the smart ass's guitar. A shiny, expensive instrument.

"He give it in for safekeeping."

"Who's he afraid's going to burgle it? Other guests?"

Next morning I discovered the blinds still down and the same motorcycle on its kickstand. The licence said Saskatchewan or Manitoba. I knew how to wake the lazy ones by rattling my key in their locks to remind them it was time. This time I pushed forward and ran into the night chain. Into the unresponsive gloom, wondering if I ought to shout through the crack, saying I was the cleaning lady. I tried.

The only rough part of the little episode was Mr. Delmore, finally, who had to come and lean in with a hacksaw across the chain. The minstrel in underpants offered no more resistance. We prodded him, God knows we tried to get a rise out of him. . . .

As it happened he *had* dropped dead, and of course I felt shock as well as grief. I really did. What he died of Mr. Delmore didn't bother to phone the RCMP back to find out, after the ambulance took away the body. The heart, he guessed, gummed up with drugs. To the police he neglected to mention the guitar when they took away the motorcycle. Mr. Delmore is like that. Guests can do what they like to mess up, even exit their rooms in body bags, so long as they pay in advance and I'm around to clean up.

That afternoon I think he came near to firing me when I refused to enter No. 9 and he had to scour it himself. But he kept his tongue. If he found a syringe he kept that too. He was liable for nothing as long as no evidence of neglect surfaced to threaten him. Negligence of the heart didn't count. Such hopes as once beat in the dead boy's breast didn't concern Mr. Delmore. And he was safe from reporters. Our guest would become no star. Had not in all likelihood, coming west, even managed to see salt water for the first time in his life.

In the Carthage shopping mall that Christmas I listened to a choir carolling "O Holy Night" around the ears of K-Mart customers. It reminded me how run down and depressed I felt. My spirit was taking a beating, my lungs felt padlocked, my priorities had been misplaced somewhere along the way. Where? How very pissy the future looked. At twenty-eight that year I was still living on a dairy farm with my parents. You didn't need a little bird to tell you when you had a crisis on your hands. In the presence of a cat, barn swallows can drive you bughouse.

Tonight, looking back, I'm thinking of stars who peter out too. Who can't see themselves till too late to stop the damage, the libel of dying larger than life. I bruise easily in August, but I see farther. I see how we have three ages: young, not young, old. I see that the abiding age is the middle one. We are not young most of our lives. An evil age because we learn what decay is and face it sometimes with bad grace. I did. I understood history then without understanding the stars. The stars who flail longest against any intrusion of this knowledge and fade badly.

Aren't I a peach at hindsight? I could run a clinic for guests at Stay-A-While. As a matter of principle, I've stayed far too long myself since those days when Mr. Delmore's sideburns were still brown and boys carried guitars.

I was sure about the sun then. I believed in it, yes. But spring failed to renew me and made Christmas seem by no means the lowest I was going to sink. Whiny, I moped a lot. Mr. Delmore was dying to tell me to take a powder.

At home I behaved like a schoolgirl with no responsibilities to the parents who'd wheedled her into staying. I was to come into their farm — but who wanted a farm? I went silent. Noises gave me a headache. I couldn't pee without clenching over water. For someone who liked to talk, I was so far off the beam I was in danger of flying smack into silence. I made up my mind to fly south.

Club Med in Guaymas, Mexico, on the Sea of Cortez, is an Indian pueblo village above a lagoon with the dry Bacochibampo mountains behind. When I saw the violet hills and cactus desert I thought of the Interior with the same Mediterranean climate that attracts stars to southern California, along with reptiles and greasewood. I might as well have been in California, if you counted the swimming pools, tennis courts, and restaurants.

I'm not athletic but was willing to make an effort. I played volleyball, bocce ball, ping-pong. I horsebacked into the desert, rafted on the Yaqui River, tried deep-sea fishing and caught a sunburn. I visited the quaint town of Santa Rosalia, ate too much, above all *talked* to anybody who would listen. I was determined to reacquire cheerfulness. Finally, in the evenings, I snuggled up to the fire listening to singsongs. I love songs. I love the way a singer trusts a song, the way she trusts a stamp not to poison her when she licks it. I listened closely those nights. Stretched thin, my throat wasn't up to flight.

Those were my two weeks on the surface. Black and white, cut and dried. No great fissures. My two weeks underneath are another story if this trip south isn't to sound distorted, even a lie. They say the greater the truth the greater the libel — the worse the libel they mean. I want to be brief.

I was talking so much, to anybody who'd listen, because of what happened after landing and busing in to the club. This I was trying to put out of mind. All Club Med bungalows are based on double occupancy, so if you go alone you end up, unless a single man tumbles for you in the plane or airport bus, sharing your room with another woman. The odd thing is I ended up in a double room of my own.

The other girl assigned to this room opened the door, looked at me, coughed, and backed out again with her luggage. I thought she had the wrong room — what she wanted me to think, in her straw Stetson. I was hanging up my dresses. Then it happened again, a second girl looked in, hesitated, vanished. Maybe her lip gloss needed freshening. Who were they looking for, Linda Ronstadt? Who was I, Linda Leper? Downstairs the G.O., a camp counsellor for adults, a French boy with lean tanned cheeks, introduced me to a third girl, from Wyoming. "No," said the girl. You see she was expecting a friend to show up any minute now. You like a lie when it's well turned.

I went back up and pretended nothing was the matter. Pretended I was going to have a very nice time. Made up my mind to it. Pretended I was not an unattractive young woman. I kept busy, as I mentioned. Kept talking.

I talked to people in a breezy way and refused just because it was popular to shy off a kissy face. I took lessons in scuba diving to be included in a group: that group, any group. People were polite and this hurt. At meals no one shunned me, but no one lingered.

My room on the second floor was right below an identical room on the third, with a moonlit view of the Bacochibampo, where I'd hear two men at night, and sometimes a man and a girl, depending on who was changing rooms and shacked up with whom. Atmospheric conditions in a Club Med are randy, there's no other word for the weather. Swapping has lots of singles on the hop all night.

On the last night I woke up with a body pressing down on mine and smelled cocktails on its breath. It recognized its mistake right away and apologized. This calmed me down. It was nothing to get upset about, *he* wasn't going to get upset, he acted lazy and reluctant to leave. He knew he was an intruder, I knew he was an intruder, we both knew where we were. In that climate you learn to guard your privacy with a little less dignity.

"I think you have the wrong room," I said, turning at the same moment he chose to slip his hand down the side of my bare leg, under the blanket. In the moonlight I recognized the body as belonging to a bank employee from Seattle, a not unpleasant young man I'd made a point of talking to on a trail ride to the waterfall. Arthur Perry. Peterson, maybe.

"Holy smoke," he said, suddenly embarrassed.

His fingers twitched and he looked away, down toward his fingers. In all the moments of my life none has seemed more glacial, more eternal, than that moment. He didn't know what to say in a place that didn't cater much to talking, having to talk, your way out of anything. Like the girls backing out of my room he couldn't think of anything to say. Small talk, anything, might have cheered me up.

Just listen to what he concocted, in this ticklish situation, listen to what this strong silent type said very carefully to me, who was more or less a stranger.

"*So help me . . .*" he began, whispering with real passion. I thought for a moment he was just trying to make the best of a bad situation.

". . . So help me Christ, I could give it to you ten different ways to breakfast . . . do you understand? . . . and have you screaming from every orifice like Tonto in a teepee."

Whispering, he was coming on to me like life depended on his performance. He definitely sounded menacing.

"Savvy, sugar? I'm saying I could eat your ratatouille like you've never had it eaten before. How would you like right now . . . to give me a dish of ratatouille and for me to wolf it?"

He was moving the tips of his fingers over my burnt leg, rubbing them under the covers. He was staring down to where his fingers were misusing my leg.

"Tell me," he whispered, "how you'd like to feel the mouth of hunger so bad it gives you spasms for a week. Tell me how you couldn't stand supper from any other teeth. Who wants fast food, hey, when her gravy train is pulling into the station for pork loin buffet? Tapioca pudding? Christ, I've got teeth so sweet for you they're singing in my gums. Listen . . ."

He couldn't stop talking like this, turning himself on I figured, getting cruder and cruder like he was making up a libretto for buddies at a stag. Some of his other lyrics I remember are, "You can wait for it like a mare in heat, sugar, but try kicking me and I'll have you broken into saddle so quick it'll fry your curlers." And, "I don't take prisoners. When the sun comes up you'll find yourself either eaten alive or looping the stars. Or both." And, "So help me Christ, I'm going to stuff you backwards like a Thanksgiving turkey. . . . Brown juice is going to run out of you so fast I'll need the gift of tongues to lap it up . . . and spit it over you till you get down on your knees and thank me to do it some more."

I may not have this last lyric right, it doesn't have much of a beat. It was pretty disgusting. Circling, he kept on like this for four or five minutes, whispering, waiting, watching his own grazing, invisible fingers. I wondered about his obsession. I mean talking like that, hard and voguish, he'd begun to give himself away. His whispering sounded passionate but the words sounded hollow. He sounded like he was lying. If anything, too big for his boots, he didn't believe his own threats. I was concerned but not terrified, the way I would've been with a total stranger. I was tense but not rigid. The point is I was not screaming.

He stopped then. Talking, he hadn't so much as

removed the blanket with his hand, but had kept rubbing his fingers in menacing little moons on the skin of my thigh. I could tell he was up against me in an uncomfortable position. But that wasn't his problem.

His problem was, anger had gradually got the better of him. Silent, quiet anger. He'd stopped whispering. In the end he was angry to the point of violence. You could have set fire to the silence.

"God," he said at last. In a normal voice, glancing up at my face, he said, "You haven't heard one word I've said. Not a word, have you?"

His anger gave way to pity. He removed his hand and sat up.

"Yes," I whispered. "I have, Art."

"No you haven't," he repeated, irritated at this licence. "You haven't heard one single syllable. I pity you," he said. "I feel sorry for you, you know that?"

Maybe he was trying to cover up his own tactics, his own violent language, his own embarrassment. His own failure, for all I knew, to think up any more sexy threats. He stood up soberly in T-shirt and bathing suit, then flapped in thongs to my door — his thongs hadn't even fallen off — opened it and went out.

I thought about reporting him to our Gentils Organisateurs. I thought over his dirty talking, what he'd meant by it, just talking like that. And the disgust, the pity in his venom. I felt sorry for him, for how foolish he was going to feel at breakfast for talking to me that way.

I don't exactly recall the hour that morning I thought I might have it wrong. *Him* wrong. No knife at the throat, no gag in the mouth, had stopped me from calling out. Worse, if I was being honest, I hadn't even felt insulted. This man was testing me, he was putting me on trial, and I just lay there . . . *listening*!

I confess I cried after that, for a long time. The moon moved on. I cried for ages and ran my fingers over myself for a long time afterwards.

People at breakfast were nicer than normal because I didn't try to talk to them, and at our last breakfast it made them feel guilty. I must have looked like death warmed over. It was like they knew at last what I knew they knew. That they were young and full of the future, or so they thought, and I was not. I went out of my way not to glance at Arthur's table, not to notice it, not to acknowledge its existence. I felt raw.

On my return Mr. Delmore didn't look up, but he had about him a generally sympathetic air. Maybe he missed me, laundering for the transient, unplugging their toilets.

"Sounds like your cold's got worse. Wintertime in Mexico too?" Only he pronounced it the Spanish way, Mayheeko.

I didn't want him to think I liked working at Stay-A-While any better than when I'd started, but couldn't think of anything smart to say, when he said, "Here. Take it."

He was holding out to me the canvas bag with the Gibson.

"Take it," he said.

With his pencil he returned to a real estate flyer, the heel of his hand covering back up his wealed chin.

I still sometimes take out this guitar and think of the dead boy and wonder if he'd known suffering, and how well he'd played the blues. *"Who's sad and blue . . ."* strum, pause, *"Who's crying too . . ."* The boohoo strains of a blue guitar. You can never learn the bridges too well.

Like tonight, I sit here in the window on the second floor, strumming, looking out at the fields. Mountains surround the meadows and from up here I can see the river where the brambles grow. A mist this morning was lifting off the mown hay and my father, old and rheumatic, was calling in the herd. Bawling like a little sheik. It's a large Holstein herd. He came out from Holland to help drain the polder when this river overflowed its banks in the forties. He thought with his lore of flood plains he wouldn't need to stay in Perumbur past spring to contain the damage. But tempted by offers of cheap land he stayed on to do the Dutch thing and build a dairy herd. He built this house. We followed him, my mother and I, an infant.

The lamentable thing is I'm now thirty-nine and still living with my parents. There was a time I would have lied about this. A time when I believed in the right to be free of oppression, that I had a right to be happy.

No more.

Listen, dearie! I can hear myself calling to the young a generation from now. . . . But no one uses kindling these days. It's the young who blame their parents for the nar-

rowness of age, including their own. The not young with-
draw their accusations and settle down to compromise.
We insist on paying rent in spite of objections they don't
need it, no, they don't need it, please.

Notice how the tempo of my strings picks up to
mock revolutionary fervour? The other day in a glossy
magazine from New York I saw pictures of Beirut guerril-
las modelling the latest fashions in uniforms. These boys,
these men, in murderous pose — checked scarves over
heads, bullet belts over shoulders. Asses over teakettles. I
could have screamed! The myth of the young is their belief
in the right to be free of oppression. What right is this?
Who gives it?

Fashion's who. That tyrant of our age. The guerrilla
as top dog, character of history, supreme individual. Listen, Mr. Fatigues, in your oversized boots.

What about me?

I often want to love and can't succeed in loving. I
seek my own defeat without finding it, and am forced to
remain free.

Like Elvis. Fattened on junk food and drugs, he fell
off his toilet in the en suite bathroom of a mansion where
his heart, with no more room, lay enlarged and surrounded with fat. Bloated, beatless, his body needed fourteen mourners to carry its casket. Today it lives on in
T-shirts and mugs. Is this dignity?

It's the stars who go to parties wearing the glass
facsimiles of diamonds in safes at home. The false stones
make those real stones look bigger than life. It's the same
with the stars. To be bigger than life they leave their real
selves at home. It makes them illusions like stars in the
sky, glittering, long after dying into holes. Their light takes
so long to reach us, so long to matter, sometimes we forget
we're looking at history! Glitter has become its opposite: a
dwarf, blackness, vapour: time run out of gas. It's only
distance that makes them appear to throb with life, poor
things, unable to face death, condemned to be young.

This morning when I phoned Mr. Delmore to excuse
myself from work he just grunted. Leery of being horsed
around, he'd have to mop up, scour, sweep on his own.
But he won't. He'll leave the dirty rooms for me as though
I'd never missed a day. In real estate, as Mr. Delmore
knows from long experience of trying to sell out, the three

important things are location, location, location. In the case of libel I sometimes think they must be detail, detail, detail. Tomorrow all the rooms will be dirty and I'll be hard-pressed to launder so many sheets. If you knew that sometimes I leave the unsoiled ones, stretch them tight over mattresses to look unused, would it shock you? The next guests never notice.

In spring the dike along the river protects us in these lowlands, an earthen wall of grass with a small road running on top, a trail, really, for the cattle. It stretches miles and looks natural. The river comes out of the lake. The delta comes before the sea. Where the river runs into the sea we learn, slowly, to read the sand dollar as a microchip of evolution — fossils implanted in its shell like scars in our own. Skin. Soul, it's the same. When your soul meets history you become liable for the damages. And they say you cannot libel the dead.

Some nights like tonight I accompany myself back to life, fret marks in my fingers, the memory of this song my deepest, no, wildest pleasure.

Sam Tata

JUST WIND AND HORSES
A Memoir 〜

BY SINCLAIR ROSS

This is a memoir about my mother — a woman as difficult to describe as she was to live with. You never understood her; there were too many contradictions. She was vulnerable, and often winced, but it was seldom she didn't spring back, resilient, head up and chin out, ready for more. Plain and shapeless and sensitive to her appearance, she never tried by so much as a discreet touch of lipstick to improve it — just an occasional dab of talcum powder "to take the shine off my nose." (But she had enough to say about the shameless ones who fixed their faces as if ready for the street.) Out working as a housekeeper she would say, in spitfire moments of defiance and exasperation, "I may have to cook and clean for you but I'm better born," and always got away with it, was never told to pack it up and take her blue blood with her. Of course, she was an efficient housekeeper, a good cook, and they may have just shrugged and said let her enjoy herself.

She often talked — enjoying herself — about her father, a Unitarian minister in Edinburgh who traced himself back to Simon Fraser, the first Lord Lovat and the last man to be beheaded in the Tower of London. "Oh, yes! There was a tree — a family tree — that showed everything. I belong to a race of cattle-lifting Highlanders — thieves and rascals, every last one of them. Old Simon was one of the worst. The story goes that he had his way with a young woman of noble birth, but when her father and brothers came wanting to hang him she said no, he was a man after all, not a dirty old goat as she

Sinclair Ross, known to his family and friends as "Jimmy," was born on a homestead in northern Saskatchewan in 1908. He spent most of his career working for the Royal Bank of Canada. On his retirement he moved to Greece and later to Spain; at present he lives in Vancouver. His most famous book, *As For Me and My House,* was published in 1941. In 1951 he published *The Well.* In 1970 *Whir of Gold* was published by McClelland and Stewart and in 1974 *Sawbones Memorial.* A selection of his previously published stories, *The Lamp at Noon and Other Stories,* was published in 1968 in McClelland and Stewart's New Canadian Library series.

had called him — she had got only what was coming to her. 'But make him marry me,' she said, 'and we'll work it out together.' And they did, and she proved herself a loyal and devoted wife.''

Once in orbit she loved it. Her ruddy Scottish face would glow, her eyes shine, then dim as if she could hear a distant skirl of pipes or the grieving of a pibroch. "A real old blackguard, but in his own way he proved loyal and devoted too. Loyal at least to Bonnie Prince Charlie — that's why, of course, he lost his head. . . . An enormous man — fat, round-shouldered. There's another story that when it was time to get him up to the block, the stairs, or ladder, or whatever it was, broke under his weight — twice! And Hogarth did a drawing, in fact, that shows him sitting on three chairs." Then with an approving pat to her own ampling thighs, "So I come by this honestly."

Talking about her family helped keep her in good humour. "You say your father came to Edinburgh — from Inverness. He was supposed to attend the University of Edinburgh — Right? — but instead he married somebody and got cut off without a penny. . . ."

"Not somebody — a bonnie Edinburgh lassie called Jessie Patterson, my mother, your grandmother. . . ."

"Well, if his mother cut him off without a penny what did they live on? He'd have trouble picking up a job."

"The Pattersons, I suppose. They were fairly well off. In trade, but respectable — if you know what I mean. He made rope. . . . And remember, his mother could cut him off only until he was twenty-one and not completely even then."

"If I know what you mean. Which I don't."

"She was his guardian, but under the law there was a part she couldn't touch no matter what he did. So there was always something. And he brought some money with him, I think a hundred pounds."

"He'd be sore though — is that why he turned Unitarian? Scotland after all is John Knox country."

"You don't turn because you're sore about something. Changing your religion is a matter of conviction. We Unitarians are serious thinkers. We reject the doctrine of the Trinity as unintelligible. . . . It was in America — under the influence of Theodore Parker — that he turned."

"And what was he doing in America? What took him there?''

"He went I suppose because he wanted to see it. And he

may have heard it was the land of opportunity. He was lecturing in theology in some college."

"Theology! Smart boy!"

"He was very smart, although that's not the word he would have used. Mother used to tell us what a fine mind he had. Everything a challenge — that kind of mind. Greek, Latin — he was even starting to study Hebrew. In fact, he found something wrong in Deuteronomy. The day he collapsed in the pulpit the church was packed. People were just beginning to hear about him, just starting to listen. — And young, scarcely more than a boy. He hadn't yet turned thirty-one."

"And he was always buying books?"

"Always buying books. I remember Mother telling us she'd be at her wits' end sometimes for stockings and jam and he'd come smuggling in another under his coat — a bargain he'd picked up in a shop somewhere — looking for all the world like a wee laddie trying to hide a sweetie he knows he shouldn't have. . . ."

"Fifteen hundred pounds — that was what they sold for? Sounds like a fair amount of money — but I suppose even in those days it wasn't a fortune. Anyway she married again — Right? Tom Holmes, a comfortably off old bachelor, and he brought you all to Canada?"

"Except Johnny. He had to stay in Edinburgh for his schooling. Something to do with being the eldest son — looked after by the church — I never quite understood."

"Johnny, he's the one who interfered — "

"It was Mother. She wrote him I was making a fool of myself over a lumberjack who could scarcely sign his name. Johnny was always her favourite. Now she started treating him like the head of the family even from away out here in Prince Albert. Write Kate and try to straighten her out — that must have been the gist of it. Feeling important, I suppose, he fired off a letter I didn't like — he always had brains and knew it — and I fired back a few home truths, if you know what I mean, that didn't go over very well either. . . . So there we were. You might say I made my bed while he went on making a career."

Years later: After marrying Pete Ross the lumberjack, she is now separated from him, and out working as a housekeeper on a farm. I am there, ten or eleven — and she comes across his picture in an old London paper. "My God it's Johnny!" I can still hear her voice as it burst out, then the sound of sobbing. In the thirty-odd years we were together I seldom saw her give way to tears, but that day her apron was drenched with them. Then, with decision, "I can at least let him know, just let him know . . . I won't beg, just let him know. . . ." A sudden hardening — "But he'll *think* I'm begging and I'll be damned if I'll give him the satisfaction of smirking to himself in the mirror that Kate after all didn't have the spunk to stand up to me. She came round. . . . Remember, Jimmy, you must never beg, never put your hand out. There's nothing like independence."

The paper she had seen was in a bundle sent out to her by an old Scotswoman she had met in a store and "blathered with a bit," on one of her rare trips to town. (Nine miles there, nine miles back again — horse and buggy: she found it easier to shop through Eaton's catalogue.) She telephoned the store to thank her but they said her friend had gone back to Scotland. It seemed to depress her; she stood at the window a minute looking across the bleak, windswept yard cluttered with wagons and machinery, then said, "I'd like to go too, but it's better here for you. Canada's all right — in a way. It's just some of the people they let in. There's so much they'll never understand. And try telling them!"

What had she seen in the paper? His picture with a caption reading, roughly, Sir John Foster Fraser presiding as Chief of the Scottish Clans Association at a banquet in honour of Sir Harry Lauder, Scottish comedian.

There's a lot I don't know, a lot I listened to with half an ear. She used to go on and on, over and over, and I used to be so bored. Now, trying to put it into sentences, I bridge the gaps as plausibly as I can.

He was a journalist. Popular — and for his time, I think, well regarded.

When still a young man he was selected for a cycling-round-the-world trip, so his sponsors, the paper, and, presumably, the bicycle manufacturers, must have spotted promise, at least promise, away back even then. (This is in part surmise.) A photographer was with him. They started out from one side of a London church, St. Pancras, and wound up on the other. For the departure there was not much fanfare. For the return, three years later, considerably more — thousands waiting in the rain to cheer the intrepid young traveller. In the meantime the paper had been running pictures and articles, and a book entitled *Round the World on a Wheel* appeared. A small gamble on the part of the sponsors; a little quick-on-the-uptake enterprise on his. So that's how it's done! Noted! His name is mentioned somewhere, perhaps in somebody's column, and he sees to it — money well spent — that it is mentioned again. . . .

Success story — his lecture fee goes up to fifty guineas!

"But who'd pay fifty guineas to hear him lecture on life in China or Russia or wherever it was he'd been?"

"Nobody paid fifty guineas to hear him lecture. That was his fee — for lecturing at a certain time and in a certain place. For someone who thinks he knows so much you can be awfully thick in the head."

"All right — half a guinea then or two shillings — you know what I mean — but isn't it true that the British in those days weren't interested in what they called the lesser breeds?"

"Oh, yes, they at least wanted to know what the lesser breeds were up to."

"You read that the British Empire was called an exclusive club."

"Not half exclusive enough . . . but travel itself just the same is good for you. It's broadening. Mother used to say her three years in the States left her thankful that she was what she was."

"And that's what you call broadening?"

"I'd take a trip around the world myself if I had the feet for it. You'd never see me for dust. Maybe I wouldn't come back much more broadminded, but the stories I'd have — my fee would be fifty guineas too."

It was the fee of fifty guineas that impressed her, the sound of it — the words and their overtones. "Ambitious," she would say, shaking her head as if distressed by such a ruthless streak in the family, but with a gleam in her eye. "And trust our Johnny — once he had his mind made up about what he wanted he let nothing stand in his way, absolutely nothing."

The fifty-guinea fee was only a milestone. Farther along in his career were more important things — that he had interviewed Dollfuss and Mussolini, for instance, had taken an active part in politics, been knighted at Buckingham Palace; but they were incidentals, jottings written in response to the letter she had finally got around to writing, to fill her in on what had been happening during the years they had been out of touch. The cheque enclosed in his letter — that was what interested her. Twenty-five pounds — in those days a hundred and twenty-five dollars. For her birthday, in April — he had remembered. Certainly not overdoing it, cautious perhaps, but following it up with another twenty-five pounds at Christmas. And the two cheques set the pattern. Not many years and we were counting on them as part of our income and budgeting accordingly. Roughly they took care of the rent. . . . And then there was a letter that Jimmy was saving his pennies for a trip to New York — he wanted to hear some good music. She let me in on it with a conspiratorial wink, had something urgent to do when I protested. A cheque for fifty pounds came made out to me with a note hoping I enjoyed myself. But she was furious, and for an hour or two there was a tremendous slamming of doors and kettles. It was not exactly that she grudged me the fifty pounds, but it was her brother's money and she, therefore, was the one who should control and bestow it. . . . A few months later it was another trip — home to Scotland this time. She had been thinking and dreaming about it for years — now perhaps was the time, while she could still get around and see a little. Two months there and another travelling — it would be at least one Saskatchewan winter she would escape. She planned to go direct to Edinburgh, take a room in a quiet, inexpensive hotel, and poke around at her leisure. She only hoped he would be able to spare a few days. The cheque that came in reply was generous and the message peremptory. Let him know ship and date and he would meet her at Southampton. She would spend Christmas and at least January at their place in Buckinghamshire — Edinburgh later. . . . She was frightened — "I haven't the right clothes — Yes, but I don't know what to buy. . . . And how to behave with people like that — it's easy for you to talk, you don't understand."

But at last she rose to it and had a wonderful time. Perhaps not quite as wonderful as she described it, not quite so many titled bigwigs who had never even heard of Saskatchewan and were fascinated when she got started on the early days. . . . "Everybody was listening — Constance had to interrupt. I was terribly ashamed to think I'd gone rattling on like that but they said no, it was lovely — only just at Christmas — so many things to do . . . perhaps another time." And yet at least to a certain extent a picture she brought back confirmed her success. A New Year's Eve Ball in London in which she appears at the head table, vivid but unperturbed in the glare of the flashes. Looking genial and pleased with herself, completely at ease, as if she had just finished a stint on the early days and was ready for another as soon as Constance gave her the nod.

When they visited us a few years later in Winnipeg — up for a long weekend from Minneapolis — she was still rattling on.

More early days . . . no reason they can't be used again. Johnny and his stories about being rotten-egged in China and fording rivers with his bicycle on his back, the daring young adventurer. Well, I'm no adventurer but I can tell a few too and I know my territory. . . . Sixty below zero, horses bleeding at the nose — how once she had to help a neighbour woman when her baby came three months ahead of time, ploughing through the drifts five miles to get there. "It was the first time I'd ever done anything like that and we got along fine, a tiny baby girl — they called her Catherine after me. . . ." And the three- and four-day trips her husband used to make to Lac La Ronge with oats for the missionary school. "Fifty miles of ice, nothing to break the wind, running beside the sleigh most of the time to keep his feet from freezing — and when he got home sometimes it would take half an hour to get the icicles out of his moustache. Poor Pete, he was the best man that ever lived until the runaway. . . . While he was away I naturally had to look after the stable. Sometimes there'd be a blizzard and so I wouldn't be blown away I used to tie a rope round my middle, I had cut it just the right length, and one day I fell and lay thinking my last hour had come but there was a lull, just in the nick of time, and so I'm still alive after all. . . . And a horse called Lady that Jimmy used to ride to school — a little sorrel with a white blaze — not so little either . . . if there was no one to give him a hoist into the saddle he had to have a fence or wagon. She was always taking the bit in her teeth and nearly killing him, and then, no shame at all, she'd come nuzzling for sugar — oh, yes, it used to drive me crazy, but he was a good rider and used to sit up so nice and straight — it was before he started getting the Foster Fraser shoulders. There's nothing worse than slouching in the saddle!" (For all the world as if she were the last word in riding-school deportment.)

Rattle, rattle — still in Winnipeg — "You chose well, John. She's a remarkable woman, always so poised and self-possessed — makes me feel a terrible old frump. I'm sorry I haven't a wee drappie of something for her — I can see she misses it. It's all right, she's still talking" — Constance was telephoning their hotel in Minneapolis about an appointment she had made with their hair-dressing salon. It was for the wrong day, could they change it? — "but just between ourselves, well, the wee drappies are having their way with her. It's the first thing you notice. I mean, it would be a shame to let it get the better of her."

"It isn't easy to get the better of Constance," he said curtly. "I suggest you don't try."

Later that afternoon I was alone with him for a few minutes and he spoke of London. "It's not a good time for making plans — there's a war on the way, probably a long one — but supposing things settle down and I arrange something . . ." He had seen two of my early stories and was encouraging; I knew he was serious. "I mean, what would we do with your mother?"

"She would probably shuttle, alternating Early Days with London-Edinburgh Nights."

He looked uncomfortable, as if he thought I was accusing him. "Our lives have been so far apart," he said, "there's nothing, it seems, that I understand about her, I don't know from moment to moment what to expect." I nearly answered that most of the time I didn't know what to expect either, but there was another interruption, and he was gone in the morning, and I never saw him again.

They've all gone. I am the survivor. What I write now is an old man's conversation with himself — questions and answers, the sifting of memories, guesses and surmises.

The stories about her . . . There have been stories that she broke up her home, such as it was, a homestead in northern Saskatchewan, and walked out after my father was in a runaway accident; other stories that she tried hard to keep home and family together until his behaviour, increasingly irrational and abusive, made separation seem the best solution. What happened? A thunderstorm; the horses bolted. He was still in the democrat and lost his balance at the sudden lurch as the horses reared — was pitched out on his head. That's one version. Another, he was already on the ground and tried to hold the horses by their bridles. What really happened? This irrational and abusive behaviour that made him difficult if not impossible to live with — was it released or caused by the knock on the head? The doctors didn't know. They experimented with electric currents through his body and later, with the aid of a chair, tugging and jerking, forced him to walk, his face twisted so you knew every step was torture. I was there, but my memories, spanning before and after, are confused, sometimes contradictory. The nearest hospital was in Prince Albert, twenty-five miles, and getting him there meant the lumber wagon over bad roads. I remember him stretched out on the kitchen floor while a houseful of neighbours waited for the doctor from Shellbrook — twelve miles, no cars, no telephones — to decide whether they should risk moving him into a bed. Paralysed, and yet I remember him saying, or think I remember, "Don't look so scared, Jimmy, I'm all right." Then there's a black box with coloured wires and a funny feeling in my hand I didn't like. A shock, they said and laughed — they were letting me try it. Then they put the wire back in his hand and turned the button as far as it would go and he didn't feel even a tingle. She yelled at him sometimes, and sometimes he had a poker in his hand. And then we went away. The two of us — she kept me with her. Maybe six months, maybe less. Where we went she was always telling me not to touch things. "Remember, they're not ours." After a while we came back and stayed maybe six months. There was a lot more yelling and shaking the poker, and we went away again. And came back again, this time for just a few weeks. Then went away again and never came back. . . . So she didn't exactly walk out on him. She kept coming back to try again.

Maybe she tried the wrong way. I still see her one day they were fighting. They were always fighting but this day it was worse. He was standing behind her with a butcher knife at her throat. That's what I thought. I screamed and started pulling at his leg to make him stop and my brother came and took me outside. He said I had it wrong. My father was trying to take the knife away from her. She was only pretending and my father knew she was only pretending; still, with somebody like that you can never be sure. You know she won't and yet you're scared she will. So you don't take chances.

In my novella *Sawbones Memorial* a farm woman called Ida Robinson is described by old Doc Sawbones as follows:

> A lot of women had it just as hard, some of them far harder, but she stood out because she had standards, her own laws. She didn't just survive, she came through with her head up, telling a joke on herself, ready for more. When she had to — busy times — she'd put on a pair of old overalls and a smock and go slopping around the stables, feeding pigs, milking cows, but she never slopped inside. Always dressed. It might be an old dress, patched and faded, but it was always clean — and always hung like a dress should hang. And she was always clean herself, always had her hair combed. You're looking at me and wondering what kind of woman wouldn't wash herself and comb her hair. Well, there were plenty. . . . on a long trip I would take care to have cheese and crackers with me. They'd ask me to sit in with them for a meal and I'd say my stomach was

cutting up. Ida though, I was always glad of a chance to have a meal with her (and Nat). Sometimes I'd even go a few miles out of my way. Always a good meal — she had a knack — even when it was only homesteaders' standard fare — salt pork and potatoes. And it was a chance to slip a dollar under the plate . . . but that gives the wrong impression because it wasn't just to help them that I went — I liked going, I enjoyed myself. She talked a lot and it was good talk — she could always see the funny side, always had a new one about the neighbors. . . . There was always a cloth on the table and a butter knife for the butter. You didn't dip with your own at her table.

Maybe when I wrote that I knew in a vague, half-minded way that I was lifting my description of Ida Robinson from life, maybe not. In any case what old Sawbones says has a ring of truth and authenticity, and the authenticity raises questions: were the neighbours right when they gossiped that Mrs. Pete was extravagant, that the Rosses were living beyond their means?

In the context of time and place — sixty or seventy years ago — a raw, struggling community, its head not far above the minimum for survival — it would seem the neighbours were right.

Our house, for instance — memories of the time I spent at home during my early years, up to seven, say, are blurred and shifting — now I'm there, now I'm not there — but the house is clear and steady. A big house, not a two- or three-room log shack. Two big rooms downstairs besides an enormous lean-to kitchen where we spent a lot of time except when it was too cold — at that I sometimes had breakfast there wearing two sweaters and a toque — and she would say, "You're an explorer going to the North Pole and your toast and cocoa's really frozen fish, so show what good stuff you are and eat up everything, heads and tails too." It was where the Happy Thought kitchen range was with the wood-box behind it and a bed for the dog, and two big wooden barrels — sometimes the top of the water was frozen stiff before we went to bed as well as in the morning. Oh, yes, cupboards galore, one on wheels that was always starting up on its own and being pushed back again where it belonged. And the trapdoor in the middle of the floor that had to be kept closed because when you opened it a ladder went down to the cellar. I was supposed to keep away from it when it was open — only one day I tried to follow my father and fell head first right into a crock of blueberries. My hair was long and nearly white then, but when he brought me up it was nearly purple. I wasn't hurt, just shaken up a bit. She was shaken up too but in a few minutes had settled down and was even starting to think it funny. And afterwards when there were visitors my father would tell them about it and tease her, insisting that she used the berries for pies . . . all that just to give you some idea how big the kitchen was. Now, back inside . . .

Two more big rooms downstairs and four bedrooms up-stairs including a spare room, strictly for visitors, with starched embroidered pillow shams, lace curtains, and braided mats. Not strictly, because once, when I had whooping-cough, they let me stay there a few days — a special favour. Only what difference does the bedroom make when all you can do is try not to be sick and hang on tight to keep the bed from floating up to the ceiling? There was a picture, though, I used to lie and look at. A girl in a nice gilt frame playing an organ, and she said, that's right, St. Cecilia at the organ. And the angels flying round her head, I asked, are they tom angels? What on earth has got into you — let me feel your forehead. . . . Because you said that with cats, the way to tell was it a tom or a tabby, the toms had big heads. Laugh, laugh — she loved a laugh, especially when it was at Jimmy's expense. For years she kept it up and it wasn't very funny. . . .

Anyway, downstairs again to the big room she called the dining-room where we ate when there was company and my father was warned to use his napkin and not bring out his red bandanna, and try to keep your moustache out of things. There was the sideboard, of course, where the best dishes and knives and forks were kept and in the bottom drawer a table cloth — damask, she called it — you could see the white shiny roses. It was never used — too big. Sometimes she would spread it out to let visitors see how big it was and shake her head and say, "I can't bring myself to cut it. I'd be willing to sell it but who in Wild Rose . . ." It was where the flowers were, pots and pots of geraniums, red, white, scarlet — her conservatory she used to call it — wandering Jew hanging to the floor and ivy climbing to the ceiling. I know, they didn't cost money, at least not much, so in a way they shouldn't be mentioned here — they had nothing to do with was she extravagant or not. But still they were important to her, they said something about her, and when it's a question of deciding what kind of woman she was they ought to be left in. A woman who likes flowers is not the same as a woman who doesn't like flowers, no matter how many other things are the same, so let her stay and enjoy her conservatory. She worked for it, digging, watering, fighting with my father for a stand with four shelves painted green and the corners planed smooth — she got it, too! Now, what else? There was a big stove with a lot of nickel on it, a sewing-machine, a desk where she kept envelopes and writing-paper — "For the last time, will you stay away from there! You've got busy fingers and I don't want you spilling the ink." That's about everything, except the red-plush curtains over the archway into the parlour — very grand — she always said wine, not red — and then into the parlour itself where there were all sorts of things. A big blue hanging lamp they never lit — it was too much trouble to get up and down; two wicker chairs with velvet seats — Never, never sit on them, the velvet's nearly worn away already; . . . doilies, doilies everywhere . . . three or four small bookcases . . . I remember some of the titles: *The Heart of Midlothian*, *David Copperfield*, *Pickwick Papers*, *Swiss Family Robinson*, *The White Company*. I don't remember them of course in the bookcases — I left the old homestead house for the last time when I was no more than seven or seven and a half — but my mother, anticipating bookless farmhouses when she went to a new place as housekeeper, always took a supply of reading-matter with her, including books that she thought I should read later on and that she herself might some time want to reread. *Books?* Traipsing around the country with *books?* No problem. She never travelled light. Besides the bulging suitcases we carried there were always at least three big trunks in the baggage coach. Wedding presents as well as books — a big sparkling cut-glass bowl for instance that went everywhere she did, even after it was badly cracked. She couldn't bring herself to throw it out. "The Millers gave it to us, Fred and Eva — you don't remember them." And a Sheffield-plate coffee-pot and cream pitcher that had belonged to her mother. The metal was soft and worn, and one day polishing the pitcher she put her finger through it, after which both pot and pitcher were left to take on at their own pace the darkening patina of storied heirlooms. What happened to them eventually is another story. And now back to rejoin the tour of the house just as it is finishing in the parlour.

We are admiring the organ, or harmonium as she used to call it. It is small, but if the wind is right you can hear it half a mile away. You get it going with your feet. You pump. She used to play hymns by ear, or for a change old Scottish songs, "Annie Laurie" or maybe "Robin Adair," and sometimes, all her sense of Unitarian dignity and decorum gone with the blizzard, she would put her head back and belt out something about rolling the old chariot along — three times — and the rough time we'd give the devil if he got in the way — three times — and for a triumphant finish, "And we'll all hang on behind!"

It sounds as if the Rosses for all their difficulties did have good times living in their big mortgaged house — at least good days, even fun days, but no! there was always the tension, always a feeling of something impending, a storm gathering, and it took only a word or a glance to touch off a quarrel. And the quarrel was always about money and my mother's extravangance. For it seems we had things — not just the organ — which many of our neighbours didn't have. Our clothes for instance — we had our everyday ones and others a little better for Sundays — and there were some who just huddled up when there was a cold spell in a couple of quilts or blankets till it was warmer. Extra things to eat, too. At Christmas, mince pies and Christmas cake and short-bread, a plum duff boiled in a cloth and round as a ball. Nuts and candies, not many, they had to last till New Year's, and she doled them out. And earlier in the fall a barrel of apples from Ontario — one a day while they lasted: sometimes she and my father wouldn't take theirs, sometimes they'd share one — he could split it without a knife, cracking it on his knee — I suppose because he came from Ontario. Sometimes they would start to go soft — we kept watching regularly — and then for a few days we'd eat apples like crazy.

Yes, it all took money, and we were getting deeper in debt every year. Quarrelling, they blamed and accused each other, cursing, pounding on the table. "So what if you bleach flour bags and use them for underwear — do you think you're the only one? You're a homesteader's wife. There's no money for anybody to throw away." "There's always money for tobacco though — the pipe's never out of your mouth." "The cheapest you can buy, maybe ten cents a day." "Go ahead and say it. Heaven knows it won't be the first time. I drink tea by the gallon and I like it strong. . . . You'd think you'd be ashamed! What kind of man are you! If you'd take hold and do something — or get somebody to help you — you don't know how to farm — you just keep piling up more debts." "Sure I keep piling up more debts, paying for your goddamned fancy curtains!"

She and I quarrelled often too. She was often critical and unfair. Of my attempts to write, she said bluntly I was wasting my time.

After she had read half a dozen of my early Saskatchewan stories her verdict was, "Just wind and horses." Which I rather liked, except that for a while the dismissive tone rankled a bit. One day when some of her friends dropped in she said, "He's been writing another masterpiece," and thrust a *Queen's Quarterly* at them, only to jerk it away again with a toss aside before they could even glance at it. This was her way of saying he doesn't amount to much but he does get into print — her Scottish anything-but-show-it way of saying she was proud of me. Of course, if I had sold the same story to a magazine that paid three dollars a line instead of three dollars a page she would have been infinitely prouder.

But sometimes when her friends were there she would say in an undertone that carefully excluded me and at the same time made sure I heard, "He's getting terrible to live with. Such a glum look, the weight of the world on his shoulders. And never a word out of him unless he's got something to say."

Yes, as I said in the beginning she was a difficult woman, as difficult to describe as to live with. Domineering, unreasonable, with a sharp and sometimes reckless tongue, foolish in her way of drawing the long bow, outrageous in her way of telling all-out whoppers with a straight face, insultingly taking for granted you were too stupid to see through her — but I cut short my list remembering that, redemptively, she worked. And remembering, I suddenly see her working — over *there*, right over *there* —

Up to her eyes in extra harvest hands . . . harried and irritable, face flushed and sagging with near-desperation weariness, untidy wisps of hair whipped across her forehead . . . killing and plucking chickens along with churning and scrubbing and cleaning just as usual — feet and ankles swollen twice their normal size . . . swearing at the dog to get the cows out of the garden — the half-acre vegetable garden that was her responsibility, spring to freeze-up — onions and peas, beets and carrots, a few bachelor's buttons and nasturtiums squeezed in, no time to look at them or smell them . . . the same as the two-acre potato patch — planting, hoeing, digging — people ate a lot of potatoes in those days — her responsibility too . . . Yelling at me if I had finished my chores to get on with my homework, never mind what's going on in the stable or what the hired men are saying . . . afraid I'd be Pete Ross all over again, determined never to let it happen.

Still difficult, more difficult than ever. For years I have been looking for a word or phrase that will describe her, serve as a kind of summing up, an epitaph; at last I realize I have been wasting time. For there is as much chance of revealing her in the flash of a word or two as there would be of revealing a Newfoundland, say, its qualities of courage, loyalty, and endurance, in a snapshot of a gambolling, blunder-footed pup. What can you do, after all, with such a woman except listen carefully, listen again, and finally give her the benefit of the doubt? Why not then give her straight off a blanket benefit of the doubt that will take care of the times I sulked or blazed instead of listening? I think so — and mixing my metaphors but knowing what I mean, which I trust the reader will know too, I wish her good listeners who accept it all as gospel.

PREACHER'S GEESE

BY HOLLEY RUBINSKY

Holley Ballard Rubinsky was born in 1943. She divides her time between Toronto, where she sits on the editorial board of *Descant*; Banff, where she is on the faculty of the writing program; and Kaslo, B.C. Her fiction has appeared in numerous periodicals.

Today, though, if she were taking the child home for lunch she would feed her real food, homemade chicken soup with eighteen-per-cent cream stirred into it and juicy bits of white meat and on the side a crusty Parker House roll warmed up from last night's batch, oozing with butter; real food, not those margarine sandwiches and soft little skimpy bruised apples and chemical cellophane-wrapped cakes her mother gives her. If she were taking the child home today, she would pull her out of the classroom on some excuse — she could get away with it, she's a special reading teacher — and buckle her safely, oh we would want that child to be safe, safe, into the car and drive carefully all the way back to civilization, quasi-civilization anyway, and then the child would see, with her own eyes, why she should learn to read, what her future could be if she could read and learn: a nice house could be hers, a dishwasher, real silver on the table, sets of fine china for every occasion. People don't have to live six to a single-wide trailer, people don't have to, for one thing, make babies all the time like her mother, she would see that there are other things in life. And other things besides pigs, which is kind of cute, the way the child, so delicate herself, wispy blonde hair, pale sprinkling of freckles like cinnamon across the bridge of her nose, loves her pigs and wants, with an endearing naivety, to be a pig farmer when she grows up. Although Preacher says she can't, because girls can't be pig farmers, which is enough, Lenore thinks, spinning the black Toyota into the school grounds, to make her side with the child. Oh, yes, girls can. This morning, though, Elsbeth Jane stomps into the room, dragging her dirty Cabbage Patch look-alike doll by one foot, and slams the door.

Inside Lenore's dress, underneath the feather-weight, so-called, girdle, her belly moves, and the move-ment is like a flutter of new life in her womb. She thinks it's the morning's laxatives going to work, but then it knots and descends and Lenore realizes her period, erratic beast these days, is starting.

Oh, it's not Lenore's first wrangled parent visit at all that has the child so upset, it's her pigs. One of her six weaner pigs is being sent away to live on a farm in Van-couver or so they tell her. He has a hernia, they tell her, and has to have an operation and that's why Preacher this very day is taking him away in a truck. She has kissed him goodbye on his pukey wet snout, he was the smallest, the runt, she says, and she's worried because she has heard of Vancouver, it's the city of sin Preacher says, so why would they take her dear little pig there?

Vancouver to Lenore is heaven compared to this stinky coastal backwater Jack insisted they move to. "He'll be happy there, I was," she says, and then, heaven forbid, tears are rolling down her cheeks, what a mess she is today.

Lenore doesn't know all the rules in this school dis-trict, but she vaguely thinks it's against the law to take a child in your car without parental consent, for one thing, or without it being designated as a school trip, but who knows? Everything is different here, maybe nobody up here cares what you do or how you live, they are all so damned depressed, their poverty, their unemployment, their general backwardness, even their damned sky which is grey all the time and dribbling, rain like pee, no city lights to break up the monotony, no plays to make one laugh, no reason to dress up even, no reason period. Jack likes it; as the town's only dentist he can be a big man, already president of the Chamber of Commerce, a force to contend with, he calls himself, chuffing a bit of a self-conscious laugh, but meaning it, she knows him. "You'll get used to it, old buddy," he says, leaving the crusts of his raisin bread on the plate, busily stuffing his briefcase with reminders and brochures, patting her shoulder on his way out. Old buddy, indeed.

The excitement of having the child in the car makes Lenore's brain blank the short distance between the school and the white single-wide trailer mounted atop concrete blocks where Elsbeth Jane lives, the trailer set at an odd, random-seeming angle, on the edge of a swampy field. The smell of sulphur sea is in the air, awful, it's brackish, the land, you couldn't grow anything on it. Even approaching you can spot the junk around the trailer, machinery scavenged from the mill, logs strewn about, the children must use them for play, a rusted, wheelless bicycle propped against the propane tank strapped to one end of the trailer, no tarp, of course, over the little stack of firewood that has been cut. In back of the trailer is a shed, a makeshift thing constructed of odds and ends, warped half-planed logs and mill ends. She pulls into what might be the driveway, there are ruts anyway, and as she gets out of the car, the mother is peeking from around a vinyl-backed drape in what will turn out to be the bedroom, Lenore has seen enough of these units to know. She knows it's the mother, Darleen, because she stopped by once, attempting to establish contact between home and school, and was met by a slit-open door, the girl-faced woman peering through, piles of laundry blocking the hall, baby crying, the odour of dirt and male sweat, a fragrance she does not want to think about.

Today, again, the woman doesn't come out to greet her, although two boys, five-year-old twins, dart out from behind the trailer and turn and dart back, giggling and pointing. Lenore hates them suddenly for the pointing, but Elsbeth Jane in her gumboots takes her by the hand and leads her through the wood shavings and muck to the shed where the "dear littles" are kept. Lenore thinks she may faint from the stench in the dark interior of the shed, but for the sake of Elsbeth Jane she smiles, squeezes her hand, starts oh-ing even before her eyes have adjusted to the lack of light.

At the sight of Elsbeth Jane the pigs crowd around squealing, pushing against their small enclosure, and the other creatures, chickens and geese, penned in the shed are set off, squawking and clucking. Chaff floats in the air. Elsbeth Jane claps her hands. "What pretty noise!" she says, and then shyly to Lenore, "Do you like it?"

"I do," Lenore says. "Because you do." She wants to say more, about that's how it is with friends or people you love, something she wants to say, but the child has turned again and is leaning over the pigpen. Pulling ears and petting her "prides and joys." But, she explains, she doesn't give them names no matter how dear, because a pig is a pig. "Pigs are for eating, that's why God made 'em. You grow 'em, you kill 'em, and you eat 'em. That's what Preacher says." And then she asks if Lenore would like to pet one and Lenore wouldn't, not really, she is a little unused to pigs, but she thinks they're very nice, very special, very nice indeed. "You know my brothers? The ones that run when they seen you? They ain't even in school yet and they write their names real good. But I'm pretty aren't I? Preacher says I'm pretty, he says girls don't have to read or nothing, they just got to birth babies for the Lord and my time is coming." She pivots and, raising her face to Lenore, lowers her voice. "You know what? Mum's big with child again, he got her by the sink, I seen it. Most of 'em die though." She covers her mouth, eyes bright above a dusty hand, then cocks her head, suddenly hostessy. "Would you like a stool? Would you like to sit down?" and darts to drag a stool from somewhere, but Lenore is picturing "he got her by the sink." Who? The father? Preacher? One man or the other it was, who came at the woman, unzipped and ready in the child's pres- ence, apparently, and lifted her dress, perhaps pulled her back by the hips from where she stood at the sink? to make her bend over, her hands still dangling in the soapy water, holding a bowl, a spoon, a knife? A certain kind of woman she would be, who lets things take their course, her hands in warm water, absently rubbing the cloth over whatever it is she holds. A certain kind of woman so used to lovemak- ing, maybe, if that's what this is called, so used to, well, say it, fucking, that she even comes quickly, glazed-eyed as a bitch in heat, and then, while waiting for him to finish, turns on the tap and rinses a dish.

" — sit down?" the child is saying and Lenore smiles, oh, and sits, tentatively, testing the legs, and pulls her skirt into her lap to keep it from the dirt and cedar-chip floor which is, at least, dry in spots although it's obvious the roof leaks, you have only to look up. There is straw and mud and God knows what else stuck on her sensible shoes, she forgot to brush off the seat, she feels silly perched up on this little stool, oh, it doesn't matter, what matters is, leaning forward, asking, "You said they die?" and wondering what in the world the child really has seen, what in the world. It's dirty here, something dirty's going on. She would give her eyeteeth, her eyeteeth, Lord, to remove this one little girl from the primitive environment she was born into, with its coarse, uneducated people, where things happen in a kitchen that a youngster shouldn't know about, much less see. But she needs to find out if there's abuse here, if — "You said they die?"

"Oh, the babies. Mum don't 'specially want lots but Dad does, he keeps givin' 'em to her anyway, but mostly they get halfway" — one of the pigs starts up, a raspy, full-throated squealing, and Elsbeth Jane slaps it on the snout — "then die and Mum flushes 'em or Dad buries 'em and once, one got borned and Preacher baptized him, we just keep getting boys here, even though he was dead from the cord and now Mum has her hopes up again. She says this one's a keeper. It's special. Pigs like it, too. I watch 'em doing it, they got to be older though. I got three boys and three girls, except for the one gone off to be happy in Vancouver, like you. It's a boy."

Lenore is dizzy, there are spots before her eyes. The odour and the undercurrent of satisfied snorting and grunting from the pigs and a sort of busy rustling behind her from the other creatures in the shed is so bad she wants to leave, stand up and just leave, but Elsbeth Jane is happy, stroking the pigs, chatty and grinning over her shoulder at Lenore, and Lenore has her job to do, she needs to know things. Once the child says "Shoo!" and tosses a chunk of wood that bonks against the back wall, at the boys peeking through a slit, making Lenore clutch at her heart. She was lost in reverie there, for a moment, but she does wonder. She's curious and anybody would be: "How do you, how do you tell whether your pigs are boys or girls? I mean, I suppose you can. Tell."

Giggling, Elsbeth Jane tiptoes over and cups Lenore's ear. "Boys have those things, like twigs, that get hard. All boys got 'em. Mum calls 'em honey-sticks, but don't tell Preacher."

The boys come back, thunking rocks against the shed, and yell, "Mum says bring her on in." Lenore, her hand about to touch the child's sweet face, stands, upsetting the stool.

But of course she must see the geese first, the child insists. The two dozen or so white geese crammed into a pen start scuffling, wings pushing wings, pecking at each other's necks and making honking noises when Elsbeth Jane reaches into a feed sack. It takes Lenore a minute to realize their wings are clipped, which explains why, with no chicken wire over the pen like the scrawny chickens have, they don't just fly away. As Elsbeth Jane throws them some dried corn, she says they're having a killing when the rain stops but until then the geese have to stay in because Preacher wants the feathers nice. She says that she's hoping for the killing because last year she looked in the garbage can and realized about insides. She says, "You take their necks and wring 'em like Levis and then you axe 'em on a stump, that one there, whop, and the blood shoots out in gushes going bang, bang, bang, all over the dirt and the men are laughing, Preacher too, and the head lies there on the ground and the eyes close real slow."

Lenore turns to look through the doorway, at the stump the child has pointed to, and imagines the wild flapping of wings and the men laughing.

Boys are different. Boys are disappointing and angular. They push away when you want to hug them. Soon enough boys smell of dirty jeans and unwashed hair. They stay out to all hours, they come home stinking of beer and sometimes girls. Their underwear in the laundry basket is stiff with it, their uncontrollable juvenile sex. What is it with them? What is in boys that transforms them from sweet little things, she remembers Gary at two, three, four, he was sweet, his firm staunch little legs running, running, the way his cheeks became patchy red when he was excited, it almost looked like a rash, people commented on it, and then one day he picked up a piece of driftwood, they were on a picnic, Jack, smoking, gazing out to sea and she building a sand castle trying to interest the child, he picked up a piece of driftwood bent in the middle, a boomerang sort of shape really, and turned it into a gun, bang, bang he said, da-da-dat-dat, you're dead. What makes boys do that? What made Jack smile and shoot back with his fingers, pa-choo, pa-choo, and the two of them laugh, the boy and the man, leaving her with her foolish half-built castle, an outsider?

In her bedroom Lenore wonders what to say to Gary, now on unemployment in Vancouver, thinking about moving here. No, she doesn't want it, this heavy-set crude twenty-year-old that is her son, no way, as the kids used to say. No way José. Even after three months here she has boxes still to unpack, they line the back wall of the walk-in closet and are stashed in another room, too, what they call locally the "rec" room, she can't seem to get moved in. The overhead light in the master bathroom needs a fixture, and even though the house is fairly new, the trashburner has made smoke marks on the walls in the kitchen which needs fresh paint, oh, who cares. Lenore shoves a box back into the closet. Her feet hurt, her back hurts, crammed at that dinky table in the trailer kitchen, menopause has made her sweat, like a pig, just like one of Elsbeth Jane's pigs, menopause and tension, that's it, her body smell is changing, it smells old, an old female smell, it has been a long, hard day. Talking to Darleen was like talking to a brick wall.

She stares into the full-length mirror hanging on the door. Jack said that when she lost her breast to cancer he didn't love her less. He said that just because she was one-breasted, his love for her didn't change and wouldn't, that all he really, really cared about was her being cancer-free, but he was lying. In the year or so since her surgery, he has touched her, made love to her, less than a dozen times, and fast, with his eyes closed. It's ugly, all right, the scarred patch of grafted skin, shiny and poreless, where once a shapely breast hung, it's bruised-looking and makes the other breast seem ludicrous, some kind of vei-nous malformation attached to her chest wall. She's fat, gaining weight, her shoulders, her arms, her upper stom-ach, all pudging around the crater-like target zone. When she faces sideways to the mirror, turned to her breasted side, her belly is so big she looks pregnant, and far gone too. Bigger than Darleen, with her stupid knobby little bump, her sleepy eyes with their slightly Oriental cast, her red henna hair in bulky curls around her thin weaselly face. Not at all like bright-eyed Elsbeth Jane, thwarted in that place, with those people.

You must not try to teach her. That's all Lenore went there to say, but the work of it, explaining what a learning disability in a bright child is to a parent like that, trying to explain how endless copying (most of it backwards anyway) night after night doesn't do any good, does, in fact, do harm. The weight of what she needed to say to that young woman making the trailer shake as she came down the narrow hall, embarrassing to be so heavy, impossible not to whump, whump even when barefoot, out of respect she had removed her dirty shoes, whumped awkwardly down the hallway, nyloned thighs going swish swish, the bunions so obvious, so exposed, the little rip where one pinky poked through embarrassing.

Darleen had made instant coffee and set the mugs on the drop table in the kitchen and was sitting, waiting, head bowed Quakerlike at the neck, the neck itself thin and white, a scar on the throat to the left of the windpipe, the shape of a nick you'd take out of an apple with a paring knife, a placid tow-head baby boy on her lap. All we get is boys around here, Elsbeth Jane saying. The mother waiting, head bowed, as though maybe Lenore would axe her, one fell swoop and spurting.

She was wearing a bright-orange blouse with ruffles in a V around the neck that looked like she'd just finished making it (the scraps of fabric from the blouse were still strewn around the sewing machine, on the coffee table in the living room), and with the blouse she was wearing a pair of men's jeans, the kind with a button fly. As Lenore got settled, she put the baby on the linoleum at her feet and draped her hands over her small, hard belly. Lenore squints at her own belly before slipping a shift over her head.

Downstairs in the kitchen, she swallows a few more laxatives and moves the step stool over to reach the box of Wagon Wheels behind the supply of bran cereal on the top shelf. When Darleen automatically placed her large hands, bright-red chipped nails, on her belly, Lenore momentarily had lost track of what she was saying, was remembering what it was inside that nest of flesh.

Remembering what it had felt like to carry a baby and how Jack used to make love, when she was younger and thinner, and that made her recall what Elsbeth Jane had said one day about her mum bringing something to school that the child had forgotten, about her mum "having to get out of bed anyway." Shame on her, but Lenore wondered at the time if all the woman did was lie in bed and drip, semen sticking to her thighs. If you thought about it, you could wonder at some of the things that child said.

She puts the box of Wagon Wheels on the kitchen table, finds the deck of cards in the utility drawer and sits down. But how Darleen and what's-his-name pulled off such a bright child is a mystery, because no matter what you said, all that mattered to them was that the child had been "sent back" to Grade Two, the only one in the whole class. About the child's father, the woman said, "His patience with her is run out. Whatever the girl's got and being slow-minded means the same to him."

"I'm sure it does." But sarcasm was wasted, of course, on this young woman, and he, the father, whom Lenore had seen only from a distance in town one Saturday morning, seemed utterly typical of unskilled labourers in this coastal backwater: beer-parlour belly, Levis saggy in the rump. "Well," she said, "Elsbeth Jane certainly does love her pigs."

What else was there to say? She had been exhausted, suddenly, with the effort of the day. Darleen smiled then, finally, and Lenore noticed a missing premolar on the right side, top; being married to Jack tended over the years to make her notice teeth. "Preacher says she has a real gift with animals." Darleen was pleased as a child. Even her cheeks turned pink.

Lord. Preacher, Preacher. Shuffling the cards, she looks out the window at the big square plot of the summer garden. She had come up on a weekend in the spring, planted a garden, silly woman, trying to make the best of the move, and then in the chronic wetness everything rots, rots, rots anyway, and the soil was wrong, too acid, too alkaline, too something. The snaky squash vines are black, muddy tangles, puny tomatoes bloated, beans hard. Maybe Elsbeth Jane would want to help her clean up, do some composting. Maybe the child — but no, that's silly, all that child cares about is pigs. Pigs and babies, cute and cuddly, hadn't she said that? Let Jack take some responsibility. She brushes cookie crumbs off the table. To stretch the time it takes to play her three games of solitaire, she places the cards on the table methodically, seven across, counting aloud. Then she flips through the deck three cards at a time, makes her hands move slowly. It crosses her mind about Jack and his office girl, Jennie what's-her-name, the new one, alone together all day. Why not. No. She won't think about it, there would be real foolishness. The child patting her cheek, "poor girl, poor girl," sweet. She would give her eyeteeth to hold that little girl in her arms right now.

Game lost, Lenore takes the cards up again. Sometimes she can't remember the reasons why a person should read; sometimes she forgets what it is that Elsbeth Jane is supposed to lack. There are moments — listening to her carrying on about her pigs, or even something today — that Lenore thinks Elsbeth Jane needs nothing. Something about the way she looked at her mother. There was something sly about Darleen, she remembers now. One corner of her mouth twitched occasionally, as though she had secrets, or thought she had. Maybe just a tic, but maybe not. It was annoying, it annoyed her because it was as though the stupid twit had the nerve to imagine she actually knew something that Lenore herself didn't. Elsbeth Jane saying, pigs and babies, cute and cuddly. Elsbeth Jane saying, we keep getting boys around here.

When she picks up the cards again, her hands are shaking. She has her three games and puts the cards away. The day she's driven to twenty games in a row is when she'll know she's no longer coping. She takes the defrosted roast and the vegetables out of the refrigerator. Jack likes to eat promptly at six-thirty.

The day's laxatives start to gurgle through her bowels.

She remembers Elsbeth Jane in the doorway of the trailer, the woman's arm slack over the girl's shoulders. Both of them watching her. Waiting for her to leave.

The roast in the microwave, she goes upstairs to the bathroom, thinking of Darleen rooted to the steps of the trailer, her arm holding open the screen, her body leaning into it, relaxed, wearing the new, bright ruffly blouse, the man's Levis, the child climbing the steps toward her, being careful in her gumboots. Darleen looking at the girl, yes, Lenore recalls that now, the thin, scarred neck holding her fragile-looking head high but the eyes on the wispy-haired girl, the daughter, and she was beautiful, that was it, not flimsy or callow, the woman was beautiful, thighs thick in jeans too tight and her belly slightly swollen. Living in a man's world. Of smells and touch and bed-sheets sweaty with careless lovemaking, the slim woman-body filling with gurgling babies, warm and smelling of baby powder and milk, babies evolving into placid, grinning tow-headed children, until the trailer bursts with them.

Lenore sits on the toilet and waits. Her bowels are burning, her belly cramps so hard she is reminded of childbirth. She would like to close her eyes "real slow" like the heads of the geese, their decapitated bodies quietly gushing blood. It would be peaceful, to be behind those eyes closing on the light. She would like to sigh Lordy Lordy as her grandmother used to do, rocking in the dark. Just sit back and Lordy Lordy until the weight lifted from her heart.

JOHN NEWLOVE

QUATRAINS FROM A POEM IN PROGRESS

Up to a white world and it's still snowing.
　　Violence is reported but I didn't catch the details,
time for breakfast. My letter is in the newspaper,
　　dancing to someone else's loony tunes.

Bugdancing. That's the thing in town right now
　　and I think I'd better get going. Cabin-fever
and the forty-foot stare are getting me nowhere
　　but down and out. It doesn't look like up

to me. And so the distress, this distress,
　　opens like a slowly-photographed flower growing
into a velvet-wrinkled colour, centred in itself
　　brightly, all alone. Stick it in your mind.

I seem to be losing my life. I don't
　　care, I'm on nobody's side, not even my own,
I don't care for this place full of mumbling old men,
　　vain, fingering their eccentricities

like me. I want to forget my past selves
　　who cried in pain out of their rationality,
explaining everything, understanding nothing,
　　factual, weighted by false continents.

What has a Europe got to do with me? —
　　huge itching blood clot millennially slaughtering
itself so that generations fled insane from the plague
　　of culture, carrying the infection.

Snow covers the scars for a moment, sun
　　glitters without giving life to the philharmonia
of the endless earth I grew up on. Now mountains
　　choke me, postcards next to me stifling me.

John Newlove was born in 1938 in Regina. He has in his time been a bookstore clerk, cowboy, hobo, and senior editor at McClelland and Stewart. At present he lives in Ottawa and edits a journal called *Language and Society* for the Commissioner of Official Languages. "Newlove," says *The Oxford Companion to Canadian Literature,* "is Canada's most gifted and meticulous prosodist." The quatrains published here are the beginning of a long poem-in-progress. Among his books are: *Grave Sirs* (1962); *Elephants, Mothers and Others* (1963); *Black Night Window* (1968); *The Cave* (1970); *Lies* (1972); *The Fatman* (1977); *The Green Plain* (1981); and *The Night the Dog Smiled* (1986).

Into the plane, into the train, into
    anything including my bruised, used, abused brain,
that modeller of truth, trampler on reality,
    fabricating any world to live in

except the one it does, these landscapes, this
    body stumbling dumbly under itself, wanting
to leave, wanting to stay, wavering like a weed
    in the water. These weeds are flowers too.

We haven't found a use for all of them.
    No flowers in this whiteness except cut ones in vases,
silk flowers in department stores, blood flowers blooming
    vaguely in flesh. Where is this taking me?

Bring in the Spring by yourselves! This shabby,
    muddy dawn has nothing to do with me, I have
too much of a longing for colour, for green,
    to endure this slow mixture easily.

The mountains are remotely drifting by
    outside my window and, beneath the floating plane,
the notched scenery, ragged, unsentimental,
    without content. Once there was silver here.

Unsentimental: unlike the people,
    who infest the land with their wandering dreams
of peace and certitude, over which they quarrel
    communally, incessantly angry.

The dinosaur plane dashes on, fleeing east,
    first to the empty prairie airport full
of strangers being remotely polite to each other.
    This is not a journey to satisfy

my own curiosity at my own
    cargo. It is merely a trip, a temporary
escape, a hallucination of the freedom
    I cannot have and will not comprehend.

Why do I keep thinking of dead flowers,
    silk flowers, nylon flowers, she wore purple
flowers? There was nothing alive to the flowers
    except her underneath them. Who was she?

Who is *she*? I don't know. Only the wisps
    of memory tempt me to go further. I don't
want to. I would rather remember my father
    scratching his back like a bear on the door.

Who was he? I don't know. Back into
    the metal cocoon at 32,000 feet,
quarantined in the sky with water and rye.
    No one can walk in to analyse me.

Everything is a result of forcing.
    It is a makeshift world. What structure holds me
together? A coloured disease, a silk flower
    called life? Or the mere relativity

of the truth? Remembrance? Untrustworthy
    vision that it is: green fields variously
waving, gold fields variously waving,
    my friends variously waving, goodbye.

Don't talk about time to me. Any day
    in the life of the most retarded human
is worth a million years of stinking dinosaurs.
    Time to fill up a hole. Time to recall

whether this is poor white trash paradise
    or a geriatic eden we're going to
so slowly and by such diverse, wandering routes.
    Now is good. The sky is filigreed, white

with ranges of mountainous cloud, and blue.
    It is all emotionless, as music is
inarticulate. Damn the anthropomorphic myths,
    the dead crutch of the sentimentalists.

Beautiful, emotionless, and serene
    as untroubled ignorance always is: Is knowledge
ever untroubled? Or is always to be serene
    a sign of mountainous stupidity?

Only a disappointed optimist
    could feel so bitterly towards the world as it is,
and love it as it might be, dreaming impossibilities,
    dreaming peace, dreaming green, dreaming knowledge

deeper than, than . . . than what? No oceans here,
    only bewilderment, a seeming momentarily
to understand overcome by squalid facts.
    The ocean, the ocean, what world is this?

Driving into Tampa, passing houses
    for sale, unbuilt except for their surrounding walls,
an alien flatness, heavy air, and one thinks of
    the person oppressed by the place. There is

the rotting smell of the Atlantic. Palms,
    brown, vaguely green, tufty, comical to a Northern eye,
routinely line the avenues. There should be swamps,
    but I see none. The oyster beds are dead.

There is no idea of order here,
    no key in the west of this peninsula,
this ramshackle, depleted yellow and brown
    where all are polite, soft-spoken, remote

in their disorganized fountain of youth.
    I seem to be the youngest here. They are waiting
for death to pounce, waiting in a remote way.
    The approach of death is so casual.

America is truly beautiful.
    We drove so many laps to come back home again.
This is home. This is home. Is this home?
    I damn drove all over America

to come back. The grass is greener somewhere.
   That was a summer place and this is an arctic place.
Hello mom. I've been good. But I drink too much
   and my friends' love is unacceptable.

The wolves are out in the sagging landscape
   and to come back and to come back is unacceptable.
All over America it was being a stranger
   of an acceptable variety

entranced me, never to come back to face
   any sort of reality in that land
of new castles and sea coasts and oysters
   and never any stranger knowing me.

Waiting for rainbows that never come in,
   trying to find a word in this absurd, absurd game;
it's comfortable, I guess. I wish I had a vision
   that would explain, or something beautiful.

Love is a silk thing people say, like God,
   or I adore my shoes, or where is the softest path?
Who can believe any of that? It's all talking.
   They put kool-aid in your cereal here.

And now Vancouver's gutters will be full
   of clumped, sodden cherry blossoms and, walking
through another sea-city, it seems as alien
   as the stranger places were in sunshine.

I'm going off course, plants are exploding
   all over the earth, bursting green, bursting red,
these are the locust years that come to everyone,
   coming to this speckled, dying planet,

this earth of luxury, forgetfulness,
   and defeat. What has its stark, jangling music
for me, engrossed with my trivial sorrows?
   I see heroes grazing in my garden.

This wilful lack of will: I do know what
    I'm doing. I take risks too, as much as you
who have thrown away the past in disarray.
    Drunks get used to walking through everything,

including window panes and love, holding
    shells pressed to their ears, listening for the sound
of the day, the sea enveloping their swollen minds
    awash with failed dreams replaced by schemes

too transparent for tears, too ludicrous
    for laughter, wanting to lie down in the arms
of the day. It hurts: the shock of being normal. And who
    truly regards himself as exotic?

Loneliness drinks me. That's also a lie.
    I'm also tired of my cock falling in love,
of not knowing when someone loves me, not knowing
    what civilization I am part of.

You who lived desired and died lamented,
    the rubble of self-pity and frustration
still remains; but now for you there is no land
    uninhabitable. And, too, there is

nothing more to do but to let time have
    its way, to utter all the appropriate
sentences. The death chamber never empties:
    such a crowd! and such assiduity!

I'm having a difficult time, poem.
    Leave me alone and I'll tell you everything,
even the dumb things I make up, even poetry,
    even the truth. The truth! Who cares for that?

Everyone is wise. The idiot is
    a master in his idiocy and he
knows things he cannot explain to the others.
    We're just carriers for our genes anyways.

God only knows what they're up to tonight,
   those aids to eternity, to destiny,
manufacturing chaos into cosmos
   so that even I have observed myself

wrapped for a moment in the cold dark cloak
   of fate, always doubtful even of my own doubts.
How splendid, how pregnant, to feel persecuted,
   to be composed of vegetable peels.

How important it makes me in my own eyes.
   We live in a land of loonies, where to say
I don't like means I don't understand, in which
   the citizens are murderous and dumb.

Out of a long, dear association,
   making the alien recognizable
in ourselves — but I learned even first in school
   that our knowledge of ourselves is what we

should conceal. It is always the others
   who decide what we are, or will be, publicly.
We adapt to the disguises easily,
   adopting or discarding the many-

coloured silk, minds easily treacherous
   and flexible, stooping in humility,
dreaming revenge, justification, reply,
   victory, and to be ourselves again.

Were we ever? There are those who will find
   jobs but no comfort. Life being what it is,
we attempt to make our selves indiscernible.
   Honesty is praised and left to shiver.

The soul is crystallized. And now it is winter
   again. The snow will begin to fly, white lie,
another year has gone by and so few lines
   written down and so many of them dreamed.

And another day closer to death, said
    my father at breakfast. True enough, but
a hell of a thing to say over coffee
    and orange juice and eggs. But true enough.

I am killing time before time kills me.
    Even I have deserved myself, silkily
skirting memory, which will not recall itself,
    in favour of weather, whether or not

there is meaning in these dull mysteries.
    Most prospectors for gold find mud. Why should I
even want to be different? Klondike day
    of the soul! What fun! what gaiety! what

bullshit. There is a strange clear trembling band
    of interference across my vision. I
am a humourless and petulant baboon.
    Wah, wah. I hate you all. You all hate me.

This is just debris. This is you and me
    cuddling, out for a spree. If everyone my age
has the face he deserves then I don't know what
    I deserve, what any of us deserves.

On the road again. It's the easiest
    way to hide, always to be outside. Self-hatred's
funny too, and an easy thing to do. Better
    me doing it than you. O who are you!

Lord, give me the strength to see the angels
    moving in the confused welter of my life.
Do not let my eyes remain in this failing
    proportion to my loving heart always.

I could advance calmly toward my death
    if that were all. But there is still the green world
of those who love me, and whom I love, I do,
    but cannot tell. How sweet those flowers are!

I always walk on, hoping I'll meet friends;
    sometimes I do. Tonight everyone phoned me,
Vancouver, Toronto, Saskatoon, Toronto.
    And is it possible to be happy?

Benny Goodman is dead, is dead tonight.
    On the television an American
says the patients at Chernobyl will die
    and they know it. Sad? No. We are helpless.

'This is absolutely par for every
    accident we know about' — such as life itself,
I suppose. This whole world is mad and I have
    no neat silk sanity to supply it.

We've never been sure of ourselves, have we,
    despite the beatings, despite the love, despite
governing our lives, being the only child
    moving into the green obscure forest

of emotion? It is this other thing.
    If sex were all then every doll could make us.
Squeak. Everything's water. If you look long enough
    it's all plastic flowers, purple nylon,

and a slight hysteria seems to be
    growing here. Can you tolerate me? If you
look long enough? Sihanouk said, I could only
    see the flowers and hear the lies. These are

not soliloquies in hell, or eden,
    but on earth, surrendered, raped, mutilated,
rained upon with acid and rage, stripped bare, buggered,
    filled with sand, spat upon by lepers, green.

What a childish lament frustration is.
    I ought to make pretty pictures but it is
always better to travel on. And wiser.
    Wiser. Let us swaddle our minds in silk,

you friends, you enemies, you lovers . . . .

A SIMPLE STORY

BY *DIANE SCHOEMPERLEN*

O ne night in a small city a man and a woman went out to a restaurant to celebrate. On the way back, they were nearly run down by a car that went out of control and rammed into the window of an apartment building. They were lucky. They could have been killed.

Describe the night.

The snow begins in the early afternoon, big flakes falling like shredded paper and with purpose, patiently, so that by dusk it is drifting lackadaisically up against picket fences and unsuspecting parked cars. By the time the newspapers are delivered after supper, the wind is up and children all over the city are dawdling over their homework, peering outside every two minutes, praying that school will be closed tomorrow. Some men are already out shovelling. Others are generously offering to help with the dishes instead, feeling smug and practical because, if this keeps up all night and then the stupid snowplough comes, what's the point?

It takes this particular man, Richard, three tries to get out of his driveway in the suburbs, where there is always more snow anyway, according to a corollary of that law which causes tornadoes to hit trailer parks. He is one of those who will shovel in the morning, cursing and wiping his nose on the back of his gloves.

Born in 1954 in Thunder Bay, Ontario, Diane Schoemperlen graduated from Lakehead University in 1976 and moved west to Canmore, Alberta. She studied writing at the Banff School of Fine Arts and then worked as an avalanche researcher, bank teller, typesetter, newspaper reporter, and grocery-store clerk. She now lives in Kingston, Ontario, with her husband, Ron Paulson, and their son, Alexander. She teaches writing at St. Lawrence College and at the Upper Canada Writers Workshop at Queen's University. Her short stories have appeared in numerous magazines and anthologies, including *Coming Attractions 2*; *Double Bond: An Anthology of Prairie Women's Fiction*; *The Old Dance: Love Stories of One Kind or Another*; *Pure Fiction: The Okanagan Short Story Award Winners*; and *87 Best Canadian Stories*. She has published three books of fiction: *Double Exposures* (Coach House Press, 1984); *Frogs and Other Stories* (Quarry Press, 1986); and *Hockey Night in Canada* (Quarry Press, 1987).

This evening has required so many complicated advance arrangements that they are going anyway, come hell or high water. The dangerous driving conditions only add to Richard's pleasure, making him feel calm and committed.

This particular woman, Marilyn, is waiting for him in the lane behind her downtown apartment building, turtling her chin into her expensive fur coat, sucking on the collar. She is thinking of the time when one of her ex-lovers', Jim's, ex-lovers came for the weekend.

Describe the ex-lover Jim's ex-lover.

Predictably pert, still on the loose, blessed with a name like Amber, Angel, or Anemone, something like that, the ex-lover Jim's ex-lover spread her perfect thighs, boots, sweater, fur coat all over the ugly couch. Marilyn is thinking of what precise pleasure it gave her when the cat jumped up on the coat and sucked its heart out. She is still congratulating herself on the way she said, "Oh, isn't that cute? He thinks it's his mother! He must be part rabbit," and stuck her head in the oven to check on the chicken.

Marilyn is thinking that if Richard shows up now, safe, not dead in a drift, she will never be nasty again. She feels relieved but eternally obligated when he finally arrives.

Once in the car, she asks stupidly, "Can you see?" and tries to peer through the blizzard by tilting her head at an impossible angle and pressing her face closer to the windshield.

When Richard answers, "Sure, I can see. No problem," she settles back into her coat and sighs, giving herself over to the experienced hands of a God who can always make the visibility better on the driver's side.

Richard didn't buy her the fur coat, although that was the sort of gesture she'd expected at first. In the beginning, she had longed fleetingly for chocolates and flowers, arriving once a week, right on schedule, just when she was feeling the most guilty, the most neglected, or the most fed up with him. They both knew that he had to buy her something: the guilt-assuaging quality of gifts is universally accepted. She took to watching movies about married men, movies with words like "confessions," "secrets," and "lies" in their titles. But they never gave her anything to go on. The only thing these various married men had in common was that they were often found alone in shopping malls at odd hours, buying gifts for their wives and their lovers both, often on the same day in the same store.

Describe the gifts.

When Richard does bring her gifts, which is seldom enough, he brings her books or records which, he once explained, are more intelligent, more dignified, less likely to give credence to the inherent clichés of their situation. Marilyn makes him sign the books and then leaves them lying around for anyone to see. She doesn't read much but likes to dust them and study the authors' faces on the back jackets. She likes to hold them in her lap like kittens. She plays the records only when Richard is there, for fear of the sadness and regrettable phone calls they might elicit if played at three in the morning with a bottle of white wine. If mink has become melodramatic and embarrassing, hysteria is even worse.

So Marilyn bought the fur coat herself, with a small inheritance she received from her mother's sister, Aunt Louise.

Describe Aunt Louise.

The oldest in a family of fourteen, Aunt Louise was the one who never aged, bought a new bicycle at eighty, got up at six in the morning to bake blueberry pies for the kids, refused to go to the Senior Citizens Drop-In Centre because why would she want to sit around and play cards with a bunch of old people? Aunt Louise could simultaneously make every one of her nieces, nephews, and grandchildren, Marilyn included, believe that they were her favourite.

All of the women in Marilyn's family expect to be just like Aunt Louise: growing old without illness, complaint, or other damning evidence of decline, kneeling down dead one Sunday morning in the strawberry patch, the juice like sweet blood on her hymn book and hands.

Marilyn was completely surprised when the inheritance cheque arrived. It weighed heavily on her, crazily, dead money in a bank vault, growing interest effortlessly in the dark the way potato eyes grow those waxy white roots in the bin beneath the stairs.

At that time, Marilyn had been sleeping with Richard three times a week for about six months and it was hard on her. She knew she wasn't really cut out for this sort of thing. She was always wanting what she couldn't have: she was always wanting to go grocery-shopping with him on Saturday afternoon, to make him take out the garbage, to wash his socks, to wake up beside him in the morning and argue about whose turn it was to make the coffee. She was always wanting him to tell her how stupid his wife was this week, how she was always on him about something, how she didn't understand him, how she was mean to him for no reason. She was always wanting him to say that he was going to leave his wife and then she hated him for saying or not saying it. They took turns believing and not believing that he ever really would.

One day when Marilyn wasn't believing anything Richard told her any more, she went out and bought the coat without even trying it on. She wanted him to think some other man had bought it for her, some other man who really loved her and would quite happily crawl or die for her.

He said she was silly to squander good money that way. She said it wasn't good money, it was dead money.

She wore the coat with a vengeance, modelling herself after a young woman back home, Mrs. Greene, who, when her husband, a dentist, was killed in a car accident, took the insurance money and bought herself a $50,000 Turbo-charged Porsche. She cruised all over the country-side with the sun-roof open and the tape deck blaring rock-and-roll. The townspeople were collectively horri-fied, everyone keeping an eye on her now, asking each other knowingly, "Did you see Mrs. Greene today?" What did they expect her to buy: a hearse? Besides, it could have been worse: the Porsche could have been red instead of black. The more charitable among them suspected she was on the verge of a nervous breakdown, the rest thought she was glad he'd died.

All of these things happened in the small northern town where Marilyn was born and which now seems remote and symbolic, lush with significant memories, Gothic.

Describe the memories.

Street corners, weather, storefronts, furniture, meals: any of these are likely to come to Marilyn abruptly, whole and acute, when she is busy doing something else, not watching where she is going.

Waiting for the bus to work one night in front of Mac's Milk, she thinks about an old house on the corner of Cuthbert and Elm streets, close to her parents' house. She was just a teenager, running home late from a disastrous date with a boy named Desmond who would later marry a girl she knew slightly, Celeste, and who would still later be stabbed to death in a bar fight while Celeste, pregnant with their second child, looked on. The night she thinks about was in February and snowbanks were piled up against the old house. Warm squares of window-light were yellow in the middle of the night. Marilyn stood in front of the old house, lifting and putting down her cold feet like paws, wanting to go in and pour tea from the smoky blue pot she imagined on the table, wanting to pet the cat she imagined on the chair, a grey cat, the kind with fur like a rabbit. Next morning she heard the old man who lived there, Mr. Murdoch, had died in his bed in the night.

Aunt Louise said dreaming of snowbanks was a portent of death. But it wasn't a dream. Those snowbanks around that old house were real as pillows, real and meaningless as these ones piling up all over the city tonight.

Describe the city.

This is a small, old city which prides itself on its cleanliness, friendliness, and well-laid-out street plan, as most small cities do. Richard was born and raised here. His memories are pleasant but do not tell him anything in particular. He doesn't expect them to, being, as they are, a continuum. He couldn't tell you offhand what used to be where the Royal Bank building (twelve storeys, tallest in the city, an incendiary issue when the developers first moved in, but once accomplished, it was found to have disturbed nothing much and those who had voted "NO" in the plebiscite did their business there just like everyone else) is now, although, in fact, it was a fish-and-chip stand where he was always bugging his parents to take him and which still figures occasionally in his dreams.

Describe the dreams.

In the dream he is a tall teenager dousing his chips with salt and vinegar. His parents are standing behind him. His mother smiles indulgently, his father hands over a five-dollar bill. Behind them, over to the left, two boys he knows from school are fighting on the sidewalk, rolling over and over through cigarette butts, chocolate-bar wrappers, ketchup. He steps smoothly around them, pretends he's never seen them before, pretends the one boy, who will die the next spring in a motorcycle accident, has not reached out and grabbed him by the ankle. He shakes the boy's hand off like a puppy and thinks about fish, just walks away.

This is something that really did happen but something that Richard only remembers when he's sleeping.

He also dreams about going to the ballpark. In the station wagon on the way there, he is socking his fist into his new leather glove, breaking it in. Sometimes, after they get to the ballpark and his father parks the car, Richard turns into a grown-up and pitches a no-hitter, while the fans scream and scream, so hot and so loud that they melt.

Describe the ballpark.

The ballpark is just like any other, with a green wooden fence around the field and chicken wire around the dugouts, where the junior-high kids hide in the winter after school to smoke menthol cigarettes with their mitts on. Richard knows but has never examined the implications of the fact that this ballpark, where he first made love to a sixteen-year-old girl named Eileen who later became his wife, is now the Safeway store where they do their grocery-shopping on Saturday afternoons.

Richard is very comfortable in this city and everything about it is just fine with him. When the new shopping malls and suburbs go up, it seems to him that they've always been there. He believes in progress. A small businessman in a small city, he has never been accused of anything, least of all of being parochial. Sometimes he feels flawless. Even his affair with Marilyn seems innocent. They're not torturing anyone, not even themselves. They're not like other cheaters. They are in love.

They are driving in the snow past City Hall, a domed limestone building with pillars and coloured floodlights, a small fountain into which tourists and townspeople alike toss coins hopefully all summer long. Tonight the floodlights colour the falling snow red, blue, and green like some curtain poised to go up on a magic show. While they wait at the corner for the light to change, Richard gazes up at the dome with a great deep satisfaction, as if he'd built it with his own two hands.

"Beautiful," he says.

They have passed this building a thousand times and every time he says just that. It is reassuring somehow. Marilyn pats his hand on the gearshift and lovingly agrees with him. Force of habit.

Richard thinks that Marilyn doesn't know that his wife used to work there as a file clerk in the very early years of their marriage, in the happier times.

Describe the happier times.

The kitchen of Richard and Eileen's first apartment was always sun-splashed, the lemon light pouring in through frilly white curtains, running all over the black-and-white tile floor. There was no dust anywhere. Eileen was at the sink in her apron, the one with the enormous purple grapes embroidered around the hem. Her earrings sparkled and her painted fingernails flitted through the fragrant soapsuds like goldfish. She was always simmering something in a big black pot, spaghetti or chili — they weren't well off yet, they were still struggling, stirring up gallons of something spicy with hamburger and tomato sauce that would go a long way. They were tired, they'd worked all day. Gliding past each other like skaters on the shiny kitchen floor, they touched unconsciously, sweet pats and slow circular rubs across weary shoulder blades.

Over supper they talked about their friends, their jobs. She was still a file clerk, he was still a cook, frustrated and scheming, dreaming of owning his own restaurant some day. "Poor Richard," she said. On Friday nights they had a bottle of red wine and made love on the living-room floor in front of the TV which flickered like a fireplace. Richard covered himself with her apron when he went to get the cigarettes. Sometimes they talked about having children but Eileen never got pregnant, and, as the time for it passed, this was something they stopped discussing and just accepted, going on to other futures, other things.

Marilyn knows about Eileen's job at City Hall (although she doesn't know *how* she knows or why it seems like such a sadistic secret between them) but she doesn't know about the apron.

Marilyn alternates between trying to be more like Eileen (after all, he married her, didn't he?) and trying to be exactly the opposite. The stupid thing is: she has never met the woman, never hopes to, and yet she cannot buy a blouse without worrying that Eileen has one just like it, cannot make Richard a grilled-cheese sandwich without worrying that Eileen does it better, just the way he likes it.

Once Richard said, "You sound just like my wife."

They were talking about travelling, which Marilyn hates, Eileen too. Richard loves it. What Marilyn said was: "I hate living out of a suitcase and I get constipated in strange bathrooms."

So then she said, "Well, she can't be that bad. You married her, didn't you?" Which, aside from the obvious, also meant: You'll never marry me, will you?

Now she says, "I'm starving."

Richard says, "You're wonderful, you're always hungry, healthy," and Marilyn imagines Eileen existing on clear soup and green salad, pushing the lettuce listlessly around with her fork, looking pale. Eileen is probably one of those people who says, "Oh my, I forgot to eat today." Marilyn can eat a whole medium-sized pizza by herself.

"We're almost there now," Richard assures her.

The city and the streetlights end just past the new Ford dealership. They head north on the highway, singing along with the radio, thinking about how hungry they are, about having some wine when they get there. The restaurant is a new one in the next town where, hopefully, no one will know them.

Because of the storm, there is little traffic on the highway. The headlights of the few cars that do pass them look secretive, urgent or sinister. There is no ordinary reason to be out in this blizzard. Marilyn supposes that they must look suspicious too. Seen through the windshield, the snow appears to be coming and going in all directions at once, even up. It is narcotic and irresistible. She cannot help staring straight into it, as into a fire, until her eyes won't focus and all the flakes are coming right at her, the way the eyes in some pictures, the saddest, most dangerous pictures, are always looking right at you no matter what corner of the room you're hiding in. She wants to go to sleep. Richard, driving steadily, seems fortunately immune to this hypnosis.

Marilyn thinks lazily about driving one night through a snowstorm with her first lover, Luke, to the farmhouse where his best friends, Cheryl and Don, lived.

Describe the farmhouse.

Cheryl and Don had rented the farmhouse on Mapleward Road, fifteen miles north of town, for only twenty-five dollars a month as long as Don kept the place up. Luke's car was falling apart, backfiring all the way, machine-gunning through the snow. Luke was smoking a joint and turning his head every two seconds to say something to Marilyn. He was one of those people who cannot talk to you without looking at you. Marilyn was frightened, waving him away, pointing at the road which was indistinguishable now from the deep ditches on either side. She was angry too.

"What the hell do you mean dragging me all the way out here in a blizzard?"

It was something to do with money: Luke had some for Don or Don had some for him. Either way it was stupid and probably the result of something illegal they'd cooked up between them.

The farmhouse was set back from the road on top of a hill. The car wouldn't make it up the driveway, so they left it down by the mailbox and trudged up the hill towards the old house, which was glowing like a lightbulb in an empty white room.

Suddenly Marilyn wasn't mad any more. She threw herself down in the snow and made an angel, thinking of what a pretty and innocent gesture it was, something that Luke would remember for the rest of his life. They weren't very happy together any more and she supposed they were going to break up in a month or two, but still: she wanted him to remember her fondly forever.

Don was out in the driveway shovelling. Luke

grabbed up the other shovel and pounded Don on the back till the snow sprinkled off him. Don stopped for a few minutes to say hello to Marilyn, stamping his feet and slapping his leather mitts together like a seal. Then they went to work.

Inside, Marilyn and Cheryl played cribbage and listened to Janis Joplin over and over again. She was still alive then, not afraid of anything, they figured, showing few signs yet of letting them all down in the end. "Buried Alive in the Blues." The only heat in the house came from the big black woodstove and they stayed close to it, except when they had to go out back to pee in the snow. Cheryl was wearing a ridiculous outfit that looked beautiful on her: a red cotton dress over a pair of Don's longjohns, a purple vest with mirrors on it, rubber boots, and a headband. Cheryl made Marilyn feel uptight and out of it in her jeans and new ski sweater.

The men came in and dried their socks and mitts on the stove, drank coffee from metal mugs, made some plans for tomorrow night, nothing special: they'd all go out for a few beers somewhere downtown.

On the way home it was still snowing but Marilyn felt calmer — you were more likely, she figured, to die going some place else than you were heading home.

A man stood on top of a snowbank waving something at them. They stopped. He had his pant leg in his hand and there was blood dripping from the meaty inside part of his left thigh.

He struggled into the back seat and they drove off. He told them in an English accent over and over again the story of how he'd been just walking along minding his own business when a dog came running out of the trees, chewed off half his leg, and kept on running. It was a black dog. It hadn't even knocked him down. He was lucky. It was only one dog. They were said to be running in packs around here. He was just walking along a deserted country road in the middle of the night in the middle of the winter's worst blizzard. Minding his own business.

Marilyn watched him out of the corner of her eye. He was sweating and talking, bleeding all over the upholstery and apologizing. It was probably ketchup. He was probably going to kill them and steal the car. He was probably going to rape her and *then* kill them and steal the car. Luke was driving wildly and trying to think of everything he knew about mad dogs and Englishmen besides that Joe Cocker album. He knew they were supposed to come out in the midday sun. The men laughed at this and Marilyn kept her eyes squeezed shut till she could hear the blood in her ears.

When they dropped the Englishman off at the hospital emergency entrance, he gave Luke a ten-dollar bill and wouldn't hear of them coming in.

Without knowing why it was his fault or what she really meant, Marilyn said to Luke, "One of these days you'll get us both killed."

By the spring, Cheryl was pregnant and she and Don had taken an apartment in the Franklin Block downtown. After Luke and Marilyn split up, she and Cheryl became good friends. Marilyn often went over to the apartment where Cheryl sat in the La-Z-Boy with her swollen feet up, eating Vanilla Wafers out of the box, watching TV all day in her housecoat. Sometimes she would get sick and come out of the bathroom wiping her mouth and groaning. In the kitchen, she cursed and slammed cupboard doors, craving Corn Flakes. But all the dishes were stacked in the sink, dirty there for days, because washing them made her even more nauseated. So Marilyn would do them, also the vacuuming and the laundry. Cheryl would sit there eating, licking her lips and her fingers, burping occasionally, cradling her stomach in her hands.

One day Don came home from work early and Marilyn was still at the sink, rinsing and wiping and putting away. Cheryl was asleep with her mouth open. Don came into the kitchen and took the dishtowel out of Marilyn's hands. He put his arms around her waist and said, "Thanks. I should have married you instead."

Now Marilyn is deciding to tell this whole story to Richard because it just might make him see that there are things about her he doesn't know yet, things he will never understand, is not meant to. He likes to say that he knows her better than anyone else ever will. Sometimes she lets this go by, other times she says, "Don't be too sure," or, "Oh, you think you're so smart," which hurts him and he leaves her alone for a while. But the truth is: he is smart, he is handsome, he is a good lover, and if he hadn't gone ahead and married somebody else first, he might have been the man of her dreams.

Describe the man.

Richard is wearing a brown-leather bomber jacket and a multicoloured scarf which Marilyn knit him last winter to show there were no hard feelings when he took his wife on a ski trip to Banff. She tried not to think of strangling him with the wool or poking the needles up his nose and, sure enough, the scarf turned out perfectly.

Richard owns a bar and pizza place downtown called Poor Richard's. It is not a sleazy place — it has red-and-white-checked tablecloths and tacky Italian statues with missing arms and fig leaves, yes, but the cook doesn't wander around with tomato sauce splattered all over his apron and they don't deliver. They have an extensive wine list. They feature live entertainment on weekends which always draws a good crowd.

The waitresses wear tasteful black-and-red uniforms and do not chew gum, their pencils, or their fingernails. Marilyn has been a waitress there for three years. She likes the uniform because it saves her clothes, which will then be in good shape for occasions in her "real life" — which hasn't arrived yet, but it will. As a woman, she doesn't think of herself as a waitress per se. She never intended to work at the pizza place for this long. She still has a sense of waiting for something better to come along. She does enjoy the job though, working with the public, chatting with the regular customers who tell her their stories a piece or a drink at a time. Take Curtis, for instance. He owns racehorses. You'd think he was a stable-boy the way he comes bow-legged into the restaurant in cowboy boots and those tight jeans. Sometimes she thinks she catches a whiff coming off him of sweat and manure, some kind of liniment. He talks to her about odds, purses, jockeys, his lonely ranch. He has been telling her the story for a week now of how his wife walked out on him five years ago.

All Marilyn's customers have something about themselves that they've always been wanting to tell. She listens and gives advice when they ask for it. They say hello to her on the street. She is always a little surprised (but proud) that they recognize her out of uniform and without a tray in her hand.

As a twenty-seven-year-old woman, she doesn't like to think of herself as aimless, but sometimes, depressed, she has to admit that that's a good word for it.

Describe the woman.

Under her fur coat, Marilyn is wearing a shiny red dress she has been saving for months. It has silver buttons down the front and a black fringe at the yoke. She also has new black boots. Tonight is one of those real-life occasions she has been waiting for and she expects to feel satisfied and convinced by the time she gets home. She will not let herself consider the fact that she will be sleeping alone and Richard will be sleeping with his wife. Sometimes when they are together, she cannot enjoy herself at all for worrying towards that moment when he will look at his watch and say, "I have to get home." How does he say it? Afterwards, she can never be sure.

Because of Richard's irregular hours and his being in charge of setting up the work schedule, their rendezvous have never been difficult to arrange. Once in a blue moon, his wife decides to go to Poor Richard's with some of her girlfriends and then Marilyn gets an unexpected evening off. She sits at home in her housecoat, exploring this side of the "other woman" role, crying fitfully if she feels like it, imagining herself getting all dolled up and going down to Poor Richard's and sitting at Eileen's table, introducing herself, buying her a drink, a pizza, a dish of spumoni ice cream, imagining herself pouring a drink over Eileen's head, laughing in her face, telling her that she can have her stupid husband back, he's not that great, she never really wanted him anyway, imagining herself putting her head down on the table or in Eileen's lap (ample, she pictures it, aproned) and going to sleep. But more often, lately, Marilyn ends up having a long bubble-bath, reading and sipping white wine in the tub, admiring her legs as she shaves them, going to bed early and feeling obscurely pleased with herself. Then, in bed alone, she allows herself the short pleasure of fantasizing about Curtis.

* * *

Describe the fantasies.

She and Curtis are at the racetrack in the clubhouse, which is the exclusive area where the owners and the high rollers sit. He is wearing a white cowboy hat and rings on all his fingers. She is wearing a white dress and sunglasses. They are sipping tall frosted drinks with fruit in them. All of his horses are winning. He wants to buy her a red Porsche.

Or:

She has just impressed Curtis with a sumptuous supper and is piling the dishes in the sink. There is a saxophone on the radio. The steam from the hot water makes her hair curl prettily. Curtis comes up behind her and puts his arms around her waist. He kisses her ear and begins to turn her around slowly, gracefully. . . .

The fantasies are abbreviated and unconsummated, to keep the guilt at bay. She is, after all, supposed to be dreaming of Richard and the day he will leave his wife and become forever hers. So she does. All the quirks have been worked out of this fantasy by now, everybody knows their lines and everything fits, including all of his belongings into her little apartment.

Now Richard parks the car a couple of blocks away from the restaurant — a knee-jerk kind of subterfuge. Walking away from it, they hold hands and duck their heads down in the wind.

Describe the restaurant.

Decorated in the country style, with rustic furniture, old barn wood nailed imaginatively to the walls, quilted-gingham placemats and kerosene lamps on the tables, the restaurant is called The Square Dance Room. It is empty tonight, because of the storm, they hope, not the food. Marilyn is still shaking the snow out of her dark hair, thinking that she looks artless and adorable, when the waitress fairly jumps at their table.

Richard says, "You look like a drowned rat," to Marilyn, and "Slow night, eh?" to the waitress, who is wearing a square-dance dress of the same gingham as the placemats. The skirt sits straight out around her on layers of starched crinoline and bumps into everything: the table, the lamp, Marilyn's arm, as the girl bends to put down the menus and smile sweetly at Richard. Marilyn thinks meanly of a toy clown she once had, the kind with the weighted bottom that bobs and flops drunkenly around at all angles but never falls over on its fat red lips.

They order a litre of house wine and the waitress do-si-dos away.

Richard makes a toast. "Here's to our celebration."

Describe the celebration.

Tonight is the second anniversary of their affair. They aren't sure if they should be talking about their past (they've had their ups and downs) or their future together (they don't know what to expect).

When Richard takes his wife out to celebrate their anniversary, they talk about the past year (kind of an annual report) and their hopes for the next year (kind of a prospectus) and then they talk about other things, such as the new lawn-mower, the reason the car keeps backfiring, or what colour to paint the bathroom now.

At this moment, the food comes. In honour of the occasion, they have both ordered the prime rib, medium rare, with baked potato, sour cream. Marilyn likes it when they order the same meal in restaurants — it makes her feel like they are a real couple, a happy couple with no problems, not a care in the world. It makes her think of those old married couples you see waltzing together at weddings, so smoothly you'd think they were one body with two sets of legs. They dance with their eyes shut, humming.

The food, on plain white crockery plates, is so good they keep smiling at it as they dig in.

Richard says calmly, "I'm putting the house up for sale."

Marilyn thinks calmly, He's leaving her. He's all mine now. I will be stuck with him forever.

Richard says, "We're going to buy a new one, with a swimming-pool and a bay window. We're even going to decorate it ourselves this time."

Marilyn can just imagine Eileen squinting at paint chips, caressing upholstery swatches, studying weighty wallpaper books as though they were the Dead Sea Scrolls. She is sucking little mints and making little notes with a thin gold pen. Richard will let her do every little thing she wants and so he will never be able to leave her now. They will live perfectly ever after.

Over coffee and cherry cheesecake for dessert, Marilyn notices for the first time the country-and-western music playing in the background: "Your Cheatin' Heart," she will recall later, with satisfaction and some inverted sense of justice or triumph. For now, she supposes this is the kind of music that Curtis would like, would tap his cowboy boots to and tease her with when she tells him the story of her romance with Richard. The snow is still piling up outside, sticking to the windows in a festive Christmassy way.

They leave the restaurant and head back to the car. There is a sense between them, swinging somewhere in the vicinity of their clasped hands, hanging there like a purse, of something unsaid but settled. They step through the snow in silence, convincing themselves that it is merely companionable. They are so successful at this that soon Richard is thinking about how they will have just enough time to make love at Marilyn's before he has to go on home, and Marilyn is worrying that her new black-suede cowboy boots will be ruined for nothing in all this snow.

The car slides sideways towards them out of the snow slowly, so slowly, not like you might think, not like an express train or a charging wild horse. It slides sideways past them, just brushing the tail of Marilyn's fur coat, which has billowed out around her at this instant in the wind. It slides into the basement window of an apartment building across the street. The glass shatters all over the sparkling snow and the hood of the car is sucked into the hole. The tail-lights are red, the car is green, the snow is white, as Richard and Marilyn are running away.

Describe the car.

A 1968 Chevy Biscayne Street Racer Special with Positraction and a 425-horsepower solid-lifter 427-cubic-inch big block under the hood, the car is owned, loved, and now wrecked by a greasy teenager named Ted. He is an unlucky young man and this is just the sort of thing that happens to him. He has just been fired from his job at the gas station and has moved back in with his parents who think that all teenagers are like Ted so it's not really their fault the way he turned out. When he is not cruising in his car, which was a hunk of junk when he bought it for a song, he's working on it. Just when he gets it the way he wants it, he thinks happily of something else that should be done.

Before he hit that ice patch and drove into the window, he was on the way to pick up his girlfriend, who works at the Burger King three blocks away.

Describe the girlfriend.

Pinkie is waiting out front of the Burger King, sniffing her long blonde hair to see if the grease smell is gone. She's hoping the snow will wash it away. She has changed into her jeans and has her red uniform in a plastic bag. They are going to see a horror movie. She is thinking about getting a tattoo on her right shoulder, but she can't decide if she wants a butterfly or a unicorn. Either way, her parents will disown her but it wouldn't be the first time.

Ted is ten minutes late. Pinkie hears the sirens but is not old enough yet to be afraid for him. She is just plain mad. She stamps her little foot: if he doesn't show up in five minutes, she will break up with him. She will take a ride with Gerry, who owns a 1966 Dodge Hemi Coronet, candy-apple red, and who has been hanging around the Burger King all week, drinking chocolate milkshakes and pestering her to go for a ride. He would take her anywhere, even in this snow. This stupid snow. She can hardly wait till summer.

Ted is thirteen minutes late. Pinkie guesses he got the stupid Chevy stuck in the stupid snow somewhere.

Certainly she does not suspect that Ted has got the car stuck in an apartment building.

Describe the apartment.

In the living room of the cosy apartment there is a floral sofa and two matching chairs, rust-coloured shag carpeting, glass-topped coffee and end tables with doilies, needlepoint pictures of poppies and Jesus on the walls.

Mrs. Bernice Wetherby is sitting on her sofa watching TV and drinking lukewarm tea from a china cup. Her hair is permanently waved and rinsed to a bluish-white like mother's milk. Her bifocals are attached to a little gold chain so she will stop losing them all the time. She is just finishing up another needlepoint picture and thinking fondly of her dead husband, Albert. He has been gone, poor soul, for ten years now and Mrs. Wetherby has happily forgotten all about what a jerk he was.

The picture window which the green car comes through is right above the sofa. Glass and snow are twinkling, sprinkling everywhere and Ted and Mrs. Wetherby are both screaming but neither is really hurt. Painless pinpoints of blood well up on Mrs. Wetherby's left arm which was in the sewing basket when the car hit. One of the broken headlights springs out of its socket and dangles like an eyeball beside her. The needlepoint picture lands clear across the room under the TV set.

Describe the picture.

An arrangement of flat-faced purple pansies against a pink and green background, the picture will be a Christmas gift for Mrs. Wetherby's only surviving daughter.

Describe the daughter.

The daughter, Delores, is an ungainly woman, homely but kind, who lives three thousand miles away on the west coast but calls Mrs. Wetherby every Sunday night and writes when she can. She is a very good mother to her three children and a very good wife to her husband, Derek, whom Mrs. Wetherby has never really liked but she hides it well and tries not to interfere.

Describe the husband.

THE MAN OF MY DREAMS

BY *DIANE SCHOEMPERLEN*

ꙮ

"I dreamed of myself in a dream, and told the dream, which was mine, as if it were another person's of whom I dreamed. Indeed, what is life when thinking of the past, but dreaming of a dream dreamt by another who seems sometimes to be oneself?"
— *Stopford Brooke, Diary, June 8, 1899*

1

In the stories I read, the female characters dream in great detail of daring escapes from prisons, kitchens, and burning shopping malls; of reproduction, reincarnation, and masked terrorists tracking them through quicksand just when they are about to give birth. In these fictional dreams, the ex-husbands or -lovers are delightfully drowned in vats of warm beer or are pelted to death with wormy apples thrown by throngs of scorned women in their white negligées. These lucid dreamers wield axes, swords, scythes, and the occasional chain saw which lops off those unfaithful legs like sugar cane. The male characters in these clever stories dream muscularly about cars, hockey, boxing, and taking their mistresses and/or their mothers out for Châteaubriand and escargots.

All of this seems significant and makes good sense to me. I nod while I'm reading and often underline.

2

In the stories I write, the female characters dream about black stallions which burst into flames, carrying their young daughters to certain death in lakes a hundred feet deep; about alcoholic surgeons who keep taking them apart and putting them back together again like jigsaw puzzles, sometimes missing a piece; about bullfights at which they're wearing their wedding gowns and the matador rides the bull before he kills it and then a team of mules drags the dead bull away on its back like a giant insect and the crowd throws red roses, hysterical; about trains, catching them, missing them, chasing them; about babies, having them, losing them, selling them; about tunnels and eggs.

When they wake up in the morning, these women are gratified to remember every little detail of these dreams and tell them to their sleepy husbands or lovers who are not really interested but pretend to be as they slurp up their coffee and scratch. The women say, "Last night I dreamed you were dead," and the men say, "That's nice, honey. Where the hell are my socks?" And the women just hand those socks over without even having to think, they know where everything is, they just *know*, and they're talking about going into dream therapy and the men say, "Sure, that sounds like fun, honey. Go for it."

These male characters dream sturdily, if at all, about wrestling, drinking, baseball, sky-diving, and pouring vinegar on their fish and chips when they were happy little kids. More often though, they wake up in the morning with a simple erection and say, "Boy, I was dead the minute my head hit the pillow. I slept like a baby."

In the stories I write, I take it for granted that these men snore and roll over forty-seven times a night while these women beside them wander and moan, commit adultery, murder, and magic. This is along the lines of my mother always saying, "When men get upset, they drink. We women, we cry."

Of course, I write fiction.

3

In real life, I dream about telephone bills, frying pans, oranges.

The dream telephone bill is ten pages long, an astronomical amount, past due, which has me calling all over town trying to track down who owes me how much for which calls. Nobody can remember phoning anybody long distance on my phone ever in their entire lives. They tell me you have moved to a country where they don't speak English.

To dream of a telephone foretells meeting strangers who

will harass and bewilder you. For a woman to dream of using one warns that she will have much jealous rivalry, but will overcome all evil influences. If she cannot hear well on the telephone, she is threatened with evil gossip and the loss of a lover. If the telephone is out of order, it portends sad news.

The dream frying pan, red, Teflon-coated, is being returned to me by the man next door and it is three times as big as the one I loaned him in the first place, which was the one my mother gave me for Christmas three weeks before she died. He grins foolishly out from under a white baseball cap as I try to make him understand that this is not the right pan, this is not *my* frying pan. I give up eventually and get busy scrambling a dozen farm-fresh eggs for brunch.

To dream of pots and pans foretells that trivial events will cause you much vexation. To see a broken or rusty one implies that you will experience keen disappointment.

Oranges, twice I have dreamed about oranges.

The first orange dream, which I had when I was pregnant with Ben, is set in Atwater, the eastern town where I grew up. I am by the water around the docks and grain elevators. My friend Bonnie and someone named Lynn are there too, all bundled up in big coats and plastic hats because it is cold and raining. You are at work or in the bar drinking with the boys. We three women discuss this, shaking our heads and smoking in the rain. I go walking down to the water alone and then along the shoreline, which is icy and treacherous. I am thinking about a football star I knew in high school who got a summer job on the railroad and fell from a boxcar his first day out and got both his legs cut off at the knee. I am cutting up an orange with my Swiss Army knife and throwing the slices to the seagulls. I walk back along the shoreline, being extra careful not to slip on the ice because suddenly I am pregnant. I pick my way back to where Bonnie and Lynn are still huddled together on an iron bench.

I awoke then, suddenly and fully, as if at a noise in the night, breaking glass or footsteps, but there was nothing.

The second orange dream, which didn't amount to

much, is set in Hazelwood, the western town where you and I lived together. I am squeezing a whole bag of oranges to make juice for our breakfast. There are mountains out the window. You are at the kitchen table in your longjohns looking at the newspaper. I smell my orange-dipped fingers and you read me my horoscope.

To dream of eating oranges is signally bad, foretelling pervasive discontentment and the sickness of friends or relatives. A young woman is likely to lose her lover if she dreams of eating oranges. But if she dreams of seeing a fine one tossed up high, she will be discreet in choosing a husband from among her many lovers. To slip on an orange peel foretells the death of a relative.

4

In real life, I dream about my dead mother, young again in the garden there beside the peonies. Or I dream that it is my father who is dead instead.

5

In real life, I dream about grocery-shopping.

My parents, both of them alive in this dream, are here to visit Ben and me in this eastern city where we have come to live. I am at the A&P buying six ears of corn despite the fact that both my parents have false teeth and will have to scrape the kernels off the cobs with a fork, which is harder than it looks. I go over to the 24-Hour Deli Counter which features fresh peaches, three-bean salad, and pickled eggs. A woman slicing meat explains that everything on her counter is twenty-four hours old or less. "This beef, for instance," she tells me, waving a knife, "this cow has been dead for less than twenty-four hours."

I go around the store picking up the ingredients for Chinese Pork: pork tenderloin, three green peppers, mushrooms. I decide I will use fresh mushrooms. My mother, who gave me the recipe, always used canned, but now I will show her how much better it is with fresh. But all the mushrooms they have are brown and shrivelling, more stems than caps. Frozen lemonade, limeade, and orange juice cans go rolling down the aisles with messages on them.

To dream of pork predicts continued prosperity, whether you eat the pork, cook it, serve it, or buy it.

In the morning I dug out the recipe, one you always loved. It was written on a small blue-lined white card in my mother's neat, strong hand:

CHINESE PORK

$1/2$ lb. pork tenderloin
$2 1/2$ tspns. soya sauce
2 tblspns. flour
1 tblspn. butter
1 chicken bouillon cube
$1/2$ cup boiling water
1 green pepper, cut in strips
1 (10 oz.) can sliced mushrooms, drained

Cut tenderloin in narrow strips. Brush strips with soya sauce, roll in flour. Melt butter in fry pan, add meat and brown. Dissolve bouillon cube in $1/2$ cup boiling water, add to fry pan with other ingredients. Cover and simmer about 15 minutes. Serve with rice. (Serves 2.)

The recipe told me nothing about either you or her. It was just something she sent me once when she was dieting, a low-calorie one-dish meal that looked good on the table, good enough to photograph, good enough to eat. We traded recipes, she and I, just as I imagine other women do, but when I went back to Atwater for the funeral, I found the ones I'd sent (Sour Cream Meatloaf, Quick Spaghetti Sauce with Clams, Chunky Chili) not even filed into the box. She had never even tried them, so I made the meatloaf for my father, who liked it very much. Of course, he would.

This was the day before the funeral. My father and I had been out all morning making the arrangements and Sonja, the woman next door, was minding Ben. When I went over to pick him up, Sonja sat me down with warm spice cake and coffee. I remember her as cooking, always cooking, bringing over cast-iron pots and crockery bowls covered with tinfoil, still steaming.

That day she was making Sauerkraut Soup, which I said I had never heard of but it sure did smell good. So she told me the recipe, and also one for Perogies, which she'd been making twelve dozen of once a week for thirty years.

These were family recipes, passed on to her by *her* mother, who was still alive but laid up these days with a bad back. Sonja had never written them down herself but performed them magically from memory, like playing the piano without sheet music. I tried to follow her directions, scribbling them on the back of an envelope: a little bit of this, a little bit of that, simmer till it looks done.

Ben hopped happily around the fragrant kitchen, eating peanut-butter sandwiches and singing the *Sesame Street* theme song. Sonja and I smoked and drank coffee and talked about people I hadn't thought of for years, until finally she just wondered why my mother had never told her about Ben until he was nearly two years old.

6

In the dream about the bacon (this was years ago), you say, "I hate pork, you know I hate pork, why are you feeding me pork?"

I say, "You're lying, you asshole. You men are all alike," you being the one in real life who, every single time I made roast pork on Sunday, would say, "Oh goody, pork sandwiches for my midnight snack. They always give me the best dreams."

It makes sense to me that women should dream about food.

To dream of eating bacon is good if someone is eating with you and your hands are clean. Rancid bacon is a suggestion to see a doctor. Cooking bacon augurs a surprise or gift, which will please you very much.

The next morning I was still mad but could hardly explain myself, not sanely anyway, as I slammed around the kitchen, making lousy coffee and slapping together a cheese-and-tomato sandwich for your lunch, knowing full well that you hated how the bread would be soggy and pink by noon.

Either you were ignoring my mood or you were just getting used to me.

Your best dreams, your pork-induced visions, were all about work: the backhoe, the Cat, the scraper, the grader, you were operating all of them at once: knocking down trees, digging up boulders and whole mountainsides, grading steep slopes perfectly within an inch of your life so help me, loading twenty trucks a shift, unloading them all again at the other end, waking me up with your twitching as the dump truck bucked beneath you, box up, shrugging out the last of its load.

To dream of machinery foretells undertaking a project which will give great anxiety, but will finally result in good for you. If the machinery is idle or derelict, it indicates approaching family or employment problems.

I handed you your lunch and cursed you out for taking my last cigarette.

All you said was, "I'm so tired. I've been working all night."

I said nothing and glared at your hands, nicotine-stained and speckled with scabs and fresh scrapes which you liked to enumerate each evening over supper. Particularly purple and ugly were the two flat knuckles on your left hand, squashed one afternoon between a boulder and the tailgate, a story you loved to tell repeatedly in the bar, wrapping it up with, "Well, I guess that's what they mean by 'Caught between a rock and a hard place,' eh?" not mentioning how you threw up at the sound of your own bones grinding.

You were gabbing on about how in the dream you nearly rolled the truck and then the other guy just missed you with the bucket of the backhoe, until I said, gritting my teeth and spacing my words, "Can't you just be quiet for once?"

I always told you I hated to talk in the morning because, after sleeping for the last eight hours, I had nothing to talk about but my dreams and who wants to hear all that crap?

People change.

7

My best talking time was after we went to bed. We weren't having sex much any more by then so maybe my babbling was just a way of filling in the time. One night I remember we were talking about Italians, their industriousness, how they would come over from the old country with nothing and build up successful companies in concrete or construction. Then I told you about all the Italian women I'd worked with that one summer at the bank in Atwater. This covered lasagna (Angelina), Italian weddings (Loretta), arranged marriages (Teresa), and how some Italian women go so fat and sloppy after the first baby (Rosina) and how some Italian men fancy themselves such Romeos and like to let their chest hair show (Rosina's husband, Guido). Then I discovered you had lint in your belly button, which put me in mind of that girl I knew at the Atwater United Church who had no belly button and how we used to serve at church teas together.

And you said, "Sleep, sleep woman, I'm begging you to let me sleep."

That night all of my dreams were accompanied by organ music.

Pleasant organ music heard in a dream is an omen of satisfying sexual prowess. To hear doleful singing with organ accompaniment denotes you are approaching a tiresome task and probable loss of friends or status. To see an organ in church warns of despairing separation of family members and death, perhaps, for some of them.

8

I dreamed I was trying to steal another woman's baby from a furniture store. Then my mother offered me $3000 and a fancy orange sports car if only I would leave you and go live with her in a mobile home in Florida. She said, "If he really loved you, he'd marry you." We were in Sonja's kitchen, eating cabbage rolls and borscht, and the car was parked right across the street, running.

9

The reasons for our leaving each other are not especially clear. I wish you had left me for another woman. Such triangular situations are so common, so understandable. By way of compulsive comparison — myself to her, my hair to hers, my hips to hers, my cooking, my cleanliness, my clothes, my big eyes to hers — the pain would become so much more accessible, acceptable.

I wish you had left me for another woman or I wish I had left you for another man because then either or both of us could dream of revenge.

To dream of taking revenge is a sign of a weak and uncharitable nature, which will bring you trouble and loss of friends. Such a dream is a reminder that you must give consideration if you expect to get it.

10

I went to a dinner party at the home of another writer. We had a chicken, tender and meaty enough to have been a turkey, which she'd bought from the Hutterites. The other guests were writers too and one or two film-makers. They talked about people I didn't know, movies I hadn't seen, books I hadn't read. I couldn't blame them: they all knew each other, I was new in town and not about to admit that no, I wasn't especially fond of Henry James, and hadn't got around to reading Chekhov yet. Over dessert, fresh strawberries in heavy cream, they began to trade their dreams around the table like a deck of cards. They had earnest, intelligent dreams, intricate like lace or the way a prism in the window will cast colours on the backs of your hands.

"I was sitting with a group of Cossacks drinking black tea from a silver samovar. Then one of them turned into Dostoyevsky and we were debating crime and punishment until he wanted to know about Australian Rules Football and what does this word 'nuclear' mean? The windows were white with frost and a wolf howled."

"Oh, I've had that one too!"

"I was preparing Boeuf Bourguignon, sipping a good Chablis. Gurdjieff was coming for dinner. Afterwards we would play croquet and the sunset would be perfect."

"Marvellous!"

"I was having my first haircut, a child of two. Vidal Sassoon was the barber and I was reading to him from Sartre's *Being and Nothingness.*"

"Wonderful!"

"I was a peacock, preening."

"Oh, oh, we all know what that means!"

I felt inadequate and pushed the strawberries around in my bowl the way Ben does when he doesn't want to eat. But there was no escaping them.

So I told my recurring dream, the one where I am in bed, sweating and scared, trying to call for my father but the sound won't come out. Everything in this dream is detailed and true; it has recast itself into every bedroom I have ever lived in. Finally, after years of this, I woke myself up one night screaming, "Dad! Dad!" and you held me and I never had the dream again.

This was so obvious as to seem shallow.

11

The puppy, I assume, dreams about cats and other dogs, raw steak maybe on a good night. She twitches and whimpers, thumps her stubby tail on the floor.

The cat, I assume, dreams about birds, mice, and other cats, a nice fresh can of tuna. She sighs.

What does Ben dream about? I like to think he is dreaming about running, flying, cuddling, sailboats, ice cream with sprinkles, Big Bird, and lambs. I do not like to think he is dreaming about the time when he, at two months, cried all night and I whispered, hysterical at four in the morning, "Shut your fucking mouth, you little bastard!" and then laid my wet cheek against his monkey face and rocked him and watched till the streetlights went out, smelling his perfect skin.

He is too young, he will not dream about you. Oh, he may dream about your photographs, your guitar, your bald head, as I sometimes do.

To see a bald-headed man in a dream warns to guard against being cheated by someone you trust. For a young woman to dream of a bald-headed man means she must use her intelligence against listening to her next marriage offer. Bald-headed babies signify a happy home, a loving companion, and obedient children.

He is too young, he will not remember his grandmother either. For the rest of his life, he will suspect that all the strangers in his dreams are either you or her.

12

Often I dream that I am dreaming. But still, such knowledge does not keep me from the fear.

13

When I dream about you now, you are always wearing that red shirt.

14

Two months after my mother died, my father came here to visit Ben and me. The night before he was scheduled to arrive, I dreamed that when he did, my mother was with him, wearing her pink shortie nightie and a scarf. In the dream, I thought very clearly, *Well, of course, I should have known this would happen*.

I went to pick him up at the airport, the little old-fashioned kind where the passengers still have to walk down the steps and across the tarmac in the dark windy night. I stood behind the chain-link fence and watched for him, my tall father, thinking he would be wearing that stupid hat he always wears when he has to do something official like go to the doctor or fly. But there he was, coming at me bare-headed — and alone, of course.

An East Indian family got off the plane behind him. The man, in jeans and a plaid shirt, held a sleeping child against each shoulder. The woman behind took tiny steps in her purple sari, cuddling a wide-awake fat baby whose soother fell out of its mouth and rolled across the parking lot as she passed me. I was feeling too cruel or isolated to point this out to her and the taxi they got into backed right over it.

I had two dreams about planes while my father was here. In the first, a small red-and-white plane had crashed in my backyard, sending up fireworks instead of flames, and we were only surprised, not hurt or frightened. In the second, I was driving my father back out to the airport to go home but it ended up that Ben and I boarded and he stayed behind, waving. I knew it was all a mistake but there could be no turning back now.

I told my father this one at breakfast as he held Ben on his lap and fed him toast with strawberry jam, but I never told him about the fireworks.

15

During my father's visit, I had one of those dreams where you keep coming almost awake but you don't want to, so, miraculously, you are able to swim back down and pick up where you left off.

In the dream, you and my father are in my kitchen, talking about fishing. Your father, you are telling him, tied his own flies. I am making hamburgers and salad, bringing you both another beer. My dead mother, I discover, has been laid out in my new queen-size bed. I try to walk into the bedroom but see her folded hands and think I am going to throw up. I back away, then force myself forward again and then again, gagging. I never do get into the room before I wake up.

There was something in this dream about lettuce, about peeling away all those pale-green leaves. Or was there? Maybe I just made it up, searching for a symbol, trying to get surreal.

16

Four months after my mother died, Ben and I went back to Atwater to visit my father. Each day he said, "Maybe we should go out to the cemetery this afternoon," until finally one day we went. I took pictures of her headstone with the lilies in the rain, something which did not strike me as an odd thing to do until after I got the prints back and could not think where to put them.

When we got back to my father's house, Ben fell asleep and I lay down too, on my parents' bed. There was thunder and lightning all afternoon. I am still afraid of storms, not the lightning so much, which is swift and can kill you instantly, but the thunder, which is unpredictable and makes you hold your breath waiting for it.

In the long dream we are driving in from the country, my mother, father, me, in a taxicab at night. I am obsessively worrying that I will have to drive in the dark, will wreck the car and kill us all. But no. It turns out that the cab driver will take us all the way to wherever we are going.

We stop at a supper club on the highway, eat steak, treat the cab driver too because he's such a nice guy. He holds my hand on the way back to the car. Then we are just travelling for a long time.

When daylight comes, I am alone in the seedy downtown section of a strange city. I walk along slummy streets looking for a bookstore. I even climb over a chicken-wire fence. I pass a little old lady in a green dress who says, "It's hard to get around these days," so I help her over the fence.

I go below street level into a narrow room and find it filled with colourfully dressed people and bikers. I meet a young blond man wearing an Indian shirt, the embroidered kind with mirrors.

He says, "My name is Chris. I've fried my brain. I

used to be a Hare Krishna and they killed my brain. Look into my eyes, they are dead, empty, insane."

We make love and I say, "No, your eyes are beautiful, neither dead, empty, nor insane."

A short blonde woman with a shirt just like his, dirty little hands and feet, comes over and watches us. She is his girlfriend, Kathy. She leaves.

Making love again, he says, "I'm dead, I can't feel anything."

I say, "I'll make you feel it."

He is on top, I climax, he doesn't, but says, "Still, you made me feel something, more than Kathy can."

We make love once more, I'm on top, I come twice, calling his name. He comes too and cries on me, with love and relief.

Back on the street, I'm waiting for a bus at a huge complex intersection where eight streets converge. Behind me is a Safeway store, an A&P and an IT&T. My watch reads 10:17 A.M. I am being blown around in the hot wind and, hanging onto a parking meter, I tell the man beside me that I wish I had a pen so I could write down the street names to find this place again.

But I've lost my purse and I panic, until I look in the pockets of the green army parka I've acquired. There I find my wallet, cigarettes, address book, and two library books: *Disturbances in the Field* by Lynne Sharon Schwartz and *Technique in Fiction*.

The bus comes and I am riding to my parents' house, thinking of how mad they're going to be that I stayed out all night. So I decide to let my mother help me choose a dress for the dance tomorrow night. This is bound to make her happy again.

It was the kind of dream that you think takes hours, the kind of dream that makes perfect sense when you first wake up and then proceeds to mystify you all day long.

17

I have never dreamed about the lilies.

To dream of a lily denotes coming chastisement through illness and death. For a young woman to dream of admiring or gathering lilies denotes much suffering coupled with joy. If she sees them withering, the sadness is nearer than she suspects. To dream of breathing the fragrance of lilies denotes that sorrow will purify and enhance your mental qualities.

18

From my mother's closet, I chose a green linen suit and a white blouse, and put them in a brown paper bag. I did not know beforehand that I would also have to give them her underwear: a slip, bra and panties, pantyhose. Shoes, they said, were optional. I didn't put them in because I couldn't bear to think of anyone putting them on her feet. My father at the last minute put in the emerald earrings and pendant he'd given her for Christmas three weeks earlier.

As we shuffled past the coffin, he moaned and held his arms out, leaning forward as if to kiss her. I pulled him back and led him away because I was afraid.

After the service, everyone went to Sonja's for sandwiches and dainties, dark rum and beer. Sonja gave me a huge pot of spaghetti sauce which I served with salad for supper that night to the relatives gathered in my father's house. You called long distance with your sympathy.

That night I slept in the bed of my childhood and my feet kept bumping the borrowed crib where Ben slept at the end. He sighed and said, "Sorry." I counted the books on the shelves like sheep.

That night I dreamed of your lips, which I was always fond of.

Sweet lips in a dream signify a successful sex life and happiness in love. Thick, overly sensual, or ugly lips forecast failure in love but success in business. Sore or swollen lips denote deprivation and unhealthy desires.

At breakfast, my father said, "I had a kooky dream last night. I dreamed that your mother had left me and they said she was living with some guy on Market Street. But I said, 'No, she's dead, it can't be true, she can't be over there with him.'"

I kept on scrambling farm-fresh eggs for Ben.

19

The only childhood dream I can still remember is the one about the giant camel. I am in the school basement, wearing my black patent-leather shoes and my new tartan skirt with the gold pin. I am hiding in the bathroom, where all the toilets are short and the concrete blocks are painted pink. The camel is upstairs in the kindergarten room. His hooves come through the ceiling like shovels. I am washing my hands and there is hair on the soap. There is never any doubt that the camel will get me.

To dream of a camel means you will have to work hard to overcome your obstacles. If the camel bore a burden, unexpected wealth, possibly in the form of an inheritance, will come your way. If you rode the camel, your future is bright indeed.

20

I often dream about Lake Street in the east end of Atwater. In this dream nothing happens and I'm not in it. In this dream it is always five o'clock in the morning and raining. Cars with their headlights on pass each other all up and down the wet street, swishing and splashing to a halt, idling and waiting for the light to change. The tavern has its windows bricked up. The Chinese grocery and the pawn shop are bankrupt, vacant, the apartments upstairs condemned by the health department. Winos lounge and sleep or die in the doorways of warehouses filled with washers, dryers, fridges, stoves, dishwashers, and stereos. Bats cling and swoop. The rain stops, the sun comes up hot, and the sidewalks stream.

There is in this dream a persistent and clammy sense of danger which does not materialize and is never explained.

21

I dreamed about buying a refrigerator in the chocolate-brown colour no longer popular among major appliance purchasers (so the salesman informs me while eating a peanut-butter and banana sandwich) but I just have to have the brown anyway. Then I call Annie Churchill, who I graduated from high school with and haven't seen since, although I seem to know that she is married to a dentist now and happy about it. I tell them what I've just bought, how much I love it, how much I've changed. "You're getting so domestic in your old age," he says or she says.

After a grainy digression that has to do with a party and changing my clothes, there is a slow-motion section about an enormous mound of cocaine being kneaded into a pound of raw hamburger and stashed in the fridge door behind the eggs because the cops are coming. I can hear the sirens.

To see a refrigerator in your dreams warns that your self-ishness will injure someone trying to gain an honest livelihood. To place food in one brings the dreamer into disfavour.

22

I thought I was coming down with something, so I lay on the couch all afternoon, aching and feverish.

I dreamed that my friend Bonnie was running a home for retarded deformed children.

I dreamed that I went to see a lady who had advertised for someone to walk her two white sheepdogs.

I dreamed that you went to Texas and shaved off your beard for the first time in fourteen years.

I dreamed that my mother was finally teaching me how to iron a shirt properly.

Just before I woke up, I dreamed about Janet, who is married to your friend Roger now. She was always wearing blue jeans, bow-legged, flat-chested, a real tomboy, always playing in mixed softball tournaments. They had such a good relationship that she could stay out all night drinking with the girls and Roger didn't mind. In the dream I am at the ballpark with hundreds of other fans waiting for the game to start. I am alone and searching for someone to sit with. Janet is the only person I know. As I make my way towards her, she says to someone else, "I've gotta go to my feminist class. 'Bye now." I am carrying my new puppy in my arms and suddenly baseballs are being thrown at us. I am running away, shoulders hunched to protect the puppy, who has turned into a rabbit. The baseballs bounce off my back like ping-pongs.

23

I have been, among other things, giving Ben his bath before bed, watching a made-for-TV movie about a compulsive gambler (female), pushing Ben's stroller up a steep street in the heat and feeling profoundly sorry for myself, when a certain sneaky word has come to me without warning:

CHIMERA.

It is one of those words which, for years, I've had to look up every time I come across it because I keep thinking it has something to do with water or light, shimmering.

> **chimera** *n.* 1. (Gk Myth.) A fire-breathing monster with the head of a lion, the body of a goat, and the tail of a serpent. 2. An impossible or foolish fancy. (Gk *khimaira*, chimera, "she-goat")

The image which invariably follows is of a gorilla straddling a silver airplane wing, beating its hairy chest and roaring in at the innocent bug-eyed passengers. The airplane is flying low at night through fraying cloud cover and the eyes of this gorilla are red.

This doesn't shake me up nearly as much as it used to and I am able now to wonder maturely how this gorilla got into my head in the first place. Was it a movie or a dream? Who can I ask?

> To dream of a gorilla portends a painful misunderstanding, unless the animal was very docile or definitely friendly, in which case the dream forecasts an unusual new friend.

This is like thinking of that November night in the Hazelwood Hotel, you and I drinking draft beer because we were broke, and some guy came in and said there was a dog frozen dead out front, said it was Bonnie's dog, Blitz. The entire bar emptied and outside we found that someone had let Blitz off her chain and put in her place a dead Doberman, frozen, its throat slit. So then we all got talking about that crazy guy in town for a month or two last summer, the one who always carried an empty pizza box under his arm and who chased his Doberman down Main Street with an axe that one time when the dog wouldn't mind.

So then it was last call and you and me and our friend Mike bought a case of off-sales and went over to his place for a sauna. I think of the three of us running naked in the backyard, rolling around in the snow like puppies, having heard that's how they do it in Finland. And in my drunkenness, Mike with his bulging eyes and acne-ravaged skin was starting to look pretty good to me. And I was ranting on about Remembrance Day, which had just passed, and how I was so proud of my father for what he had done in the war, fairly weeping with the intensity of my unexamined admiration, and Mike said, "I don't believe in war," and tried to talk me out of it, but I said, "I don't either but still . . ." and would not be swayed. So then Mike went and called his mother long-distance in Ontario at three in the morning and told her how he loved her.

You said, "It's time to go home, I'm seeing triple and I might call my mother too, she's been dead for years," and when you tried to stand up, you knocked over the lamp, spilling kerosene all over our clothes, and I was screaming, "How stupid can one person be!"

The next morning we soaked our clothes for a while in the bathtub, then gave up and threw them away.

I don't think this was a dream but it should have been. That time I called you to check, you said you didn't remember any of it. Sometimes you're no help at all.

What I really want to know is: how did we get home without our clothes?

24

I got my hair cut. That night I dreamed of going back to the beauty parlour, wanting to show the nice lady how good the new style looks. My mother is with me. This lady has light-red hair, long red fingernails, and freckles all over her hands, what my mother called "age spots." She is talking on the phone and smoking when we go into the shop. All the chairs and dryers have been removed — all that remains is the reception desk and this French Provincial telephone.

The hairdresser recognizes me immediately, puts her hand over the mouthpiece, and asks, "Did you ever figure out how John died?"

What on earth is she talking about? Then I remember that while she cut my hair we talked about *Another World*, her favourite soap opera.

I say, excitedly, "No, no, I didn't, but here's my mother." She is standing near the glass door in a red pantsuit. "She's been watching *Another World* since before I was born, she'll know." I turn to my mother and ask her how John died. She's looking right at me but she can't hear me. I am yelling but still she can't hear me.

When my mother was here for Christmas three weeks before she died, I was always angry because she couldn't hear the doorbell or the telephone and the TV was too loud. She might get a hearing aid, she said, some day.

When my mother went into the hospital the first time, she got my father to tape *Another World* on the VCR every day so she could catch up on the action when she got home. This last time, when the doctors were still trying to figure out how to tell her she was dying, she told my father not to bother. He told me this when he came to visit Ben and me, he told me this was how he knew that she knew. "Remember how mad she used to get when they put the ball game on instead of her show?" he asked.

Remember how when the U.S. bombed Libya and I called home to say I was watching the news all day and I was scared and she said, "Well, if you don't like it, change the channel." And the next morning I went down to the A&P and bought a case each of baby formula and cat food, praying, *Please God, let Ben live to be old*.

If you were here with me now, would I tell you all this in the morning over breakfast, fresh-ground coffee and brown toast, soft-boiled eggs?

You were always trying to figure out how to get the eggs just right at the high altitude of Hazelwood. "It's perfect, it's perfect!" you'd say before you tasted it, and then you'd say, sadly, "No, no, thirty seconds more, just thirty seconds more, and it would have been perfect."

Until finally one winter morning you were satisfied, so I got out the Polaroid and snapped a shot of it: The Perfect Six-Minute Egg. We kept this picture on our bulletin board for years. I study it now: egg in the egg-cup, a half-eaten piece of toast on the Blue River plate on the wicker placemat on the blue tabletop, a coffee mug with a bottle of Baileys Irish Cream beside it, also dental floss, a dirty ashtray, and a pink pepper shaker which is one my mother gave me when I first left home, called carnival glass, which used to come in boxes of detergent.

25

The dreams I hate the most are those in which every person, place, and thing keeps changing into some other person, place, or thing and then back again. Even the ground seems to shift and bubble beneath my dreamy feet and occasionally it disappears altogether.

26

You become my father watching the ball game and drinking frosty beer, he becomes my mother melting, she becomes Ben eating ice cream with his fingers.

27

The coffee cup in my left hand becomes a piano and the cigarette in my right a spatula.

28

The front step of my father's house becomes a conveyor belt and then the house itself a restaurant.

29

Ben becomes a kitten even as I hold him in my arms which are turning into saxophones.

30

Waking, I open my eyes and cannot imagine for a minute where in the world you or I might be.

31

I used to dream that Ben was crying in the night. I would wake up, get out of bed, go to the kitchen, take the bottle out of the fridge, heat it to exactly the right temperature by instinct, and when I got to his room, there he was fast asleep. He'd never moved, never cried, never made a single sound.

32

Sometimes now I am pregnant in my dreams, but the pregnancy is never what the dream is about, is merely the condition I happen to be in as I board buses, go to parties, make pizza, or fly.

33

When Ben was three weeks old and I could almost sit down normally again, I had an erotic dream about Dr. Long, the one who delivered him, the handsome one who interrupted his Sunday-afternoon golf game three times to come to me in the delivery room and listen to me hollering, "Do something, do something, can't you do something? What kind of doctor are you anyway? I don't want to do this any more, I want to go home now." The one who said, "Wow, look at that, the blood squirted right across the room!" The one who handed Ben to me softly and said, "He's perfect like a flower," even though when the nurse said, "Look, look, it's a boy!" I wailed, "I don't want to look!" because after eleven hours on that table and everything going wrong — monitors, oxygen, Demerol, forceps — I thought he was going to have a big purple birthmark all over his face.

In the dream, Dr. Long was caressing me in his surgical greens, spreading me open gently on that table and burying his face in my milk-filled breasts. I awoke embarrassed and disgusted with myself.

Some time later, in a confessional fit, I told this dream to Bonnie, who is my best friend and so I can tell her anything, disgusting or not, and she will still like me. Dr. Long had delivered her baby too. And she laughed and said, yes, yes, she'd dreamed of making love to him too. We snickered and compared details.

Some time later still, here in this city, I was having lunch and white-wine spritzers with two other women I hardly knew. I was making fun of my former self by telling them this dream and they marvelled and said, yes, yes, they'd had it too about their obstetricians and never told a single soul till now. One of these women had had four children, grown now, all delivered by the same fat, fatherly man who had also taken out her tonsils when she was six. She had dreamed of making love to him in the laundry room. We were so relieved, the three of us, to find ourselves feeling normal for a change that we laughed and laughed, hugged each other round the table, and sat there drinking all afternoon.

34

I have not slept with a man in over ten months. Every night for a week I dream of sex. I have perfunctory sex with everyone but you, including Roger who married Janet, Mike who had the sauna, David Coleman who was in my grade ten Health class, and the man in front of me in the checkout line at the A&P on Wednesday, buying Kraft Dinner, Oreo ice cream, and a comb. I have elaborate and extended dream sex with the man next door who borrows my frying pan and lifts weights in his front yard in his small red shorts. When I see him in the bank the next day, I blush furiously and fidget. But he does not seem to recognize me from either the street or the dream.

35

There are whole days when nothing goes through my mind but you. Then I lie down and dream all night of shopping with my mother, buying a bag of potatoes and a pair of blue high heels. What does this say about me? I wonder, I worry. Am I missing something serious in my psychological makeup? Am I missing the point? What's wrong with me anyway?

36

The night you left I dreamed about washing the kitchen floor.

LATE SUMMER DINNERS

By David Donnell

My father sits across the dining-room table from me, his neat Oxford stripe shirt sleeves tucked up at the elbow with silver sleeve bands, gold signet ring winking in the early evening light. He is barely concealing his gargantuan impatience with me. It flickers around the corners of his mouth. The fury seems to move back and forth like a coal car rocking on steel ball bearings somewhere in the dark middle of his head. His mouth is firm, his hazel eyes, which used to remind me of August flowers growing wild in the back yard of our friends the Rices' cottage, now seem almost dark blue-grey. He bends his great head over the steaming bowl of vegetable soup my mother has spent part of the afternoon preparing, while he has been teaching at the Collegiate, classics, history, and inhales briefly. Then he takes the giant ladle and dishes out a full bowl for himself, passes the tureen to my older sister; she is sitting across the table from me with her dark gaminish head cocked to one side, delicately chewing her thumb.

He proceeds to eat, precisely tilting the large spoon into his mouth without spilling a drop, and without schlurping. His hair is short and well brushed. There is a touch of grey above the ears. His black ebony-handled brushes sit one beside the other on top of his bureau every morning when I walk past their master bedroom on the second floor to wash,

David Donnell was born in 1939. His book of poems *Settlements* won the Governor General's Award for 1983. He has published since then a story collection, *The Blue Ontario Hemingway Boat Race*, and is currently working on a new book of poems and a detective novel.

brush my teeth, and run a comb through my hair. His hands are extremely clean, nails cut evenly and short like a surgeon's. His eyes are hazel one minute, then cool as ice. He doesn't look at me.

Sometimes I stop across from the St. Marys Ice-House on Main Street after school. I like to watch the men with their quilted shoulder reinforcements, ice picks dangling like pistols or fish from their belts, loading the trucks for the last afternoon run. The ice smokes in the fresh butter-soft afternoon sunlight as the men load it into the trucks with tongs. My father doesn't smoke. He has never smoked. He was far too much of an A student and college athlete to get involved in pennant-waving, tobacco or random parties with flasks of Canadian rye and model A Ford roadsters. My father isn't strict, he's exact: not stern, merely correct and explosively forceful.

I sit with my large mouth open in trepidation above my untouched soup, although I am hungry, and wait for him to speak. He has no intention of speaking until my mother brings in the main course, sweet moist ham with mounds of fresh mashed potatoes and smart crisp green snap beans from the garden at the back of our house. The dog is out there. It is still light. There is a patch of sunlight on the dining-room windowsill. I will be allowed to go out and play after supper.

"Don't squirm; keep your head up, be calm." I was told this as soon as I was allowed to eat dinner with my parents at the huge mahogany dining-room table. So I never do. I sit openmouthed in trepidation, but I'm very calm, hands plain as mushrooms on the table in front of me. Calm, I sit frozen. Thinking about my grandfather, Duncan. Duncan was superb and died recently: a few years of gladioli and summer elm trees and winter snow on spruce trees.

Duncan was tall and rawboned and elegant, tanned and casual, ruminative, hands in pockets; odd things in pockets, Irish Twist tobacco, small bars wrapped with gold-foil seals with sharp stickers at the ends, which he used to give me to play with while he took out one of his favourite jackknives and pared off a small palmful of shavings for his pipe. I was seduced by those seals, those seals and the smell of tobacco. My mother says I am very much like my father: obsessed with exactness; but I am also very much like Duncan: fond of fishing, auction sales and old prints.

The Spartan hoplites were like this: young boys with their shirts rolled up at the wrists, overturning cars in the streets, eating dark bread and honey with bowls of goat's milk, invading gymnasiums, illuminating the Collegiate in the middle of the night with electrical cords.

When he does speak, the silence is more terrible than clashing brass instruments. First, he puts down the soup spoon very precisely at the edge of his plate. Then he stares down the long mahogany length of the table as if his eyes were piercing straight through the south wall. The blood rushes into his face like rivers. His eyes flex. Then he tears off his tie, which was tucked into his shirt, rips open his shirt and roars: "I want to buy something. I want to sell things I already own. I want to sell the Collegiate I teach in and buy five brand-new Pierce-Arrows. I want to sell my family and buy a large granite library like the Widener Library at Harvard. I want to sell this house and buy a Mausoleum."

My father is frothing at the mouth. His hair is disarranged. He pulls out a handful of hair and throws it in the soup tureen. His eyes crackle like electrical storms. His face is like the dark summer night sky on the 24th of May, in Haliburton where we go for vacations. His hands are like deranged picnic tables. His fly bursts. His cock emerges huge and wet as a wriggling fish.

I am embarrassed. My mother will get up and leave the room. My sister will comfort him. I stare into the faint steam of my soup. I see alphabets and continents and legions in the small white x's and y's and the celery and carrots. I have been taught to think, to take values seriously; I have been taught to be calm. I say nothing.

I am frozen like winter light on the panes of a public building at night, with the overhead electrical lights left on. The cleaning staff mops the floors with their pails of steaming water. A man called Marconi is sending radio signals across a pond. A photograph of a Canadian called Alexander Graham Bell talks to a city in New York State over a black Bakelite device called a telephone. I am rapt. I love my father, but I am weighted with the importance of the values he has taught me. My intestines bleed but I say nothing. I sit quietly and stare past my sister's beautiful dark head out the open dining-room window at the garden.

"Bring me home something I can buy and sell, for Christ's sake," he says to me. He has not taught at the Collegiate for several months. They discovered he has a heart condition when he went for his general checkup.

I say nothing. I resolve to bring home a pair of rubber-handled pliers, some wrenches, a medicine ball.

My mother gets up and leaves the room. She returns with a fresh napkin in her hand. Yellow flowers curl up at the corners of her mouth like a summer field. My sister smiles at her.

"We forgot to say grace before the soup," my mother points out. She is gentle but formidable.

"Are we going to say grace?" says my sister. She giggles.

The summer air is as thick as pollen. My left shoulder is full of light. There are small bits of yellow flowers in the soup. My heart is like a football. I hear one of my father's students at the local Collegiate say something like, "Throw me that pigskin. Go for it, babe." I lower my head slowly over the cold soup and pray for alphabets.

DESIGNER DEATH

BY JAY SCOTT

Well, darling, Darla's fabulous, I mean, her hairdo, it's fabulous, I mean, we trade petite quipettes at Vidal Sassoon's and we pretend at Hazelton Lanes to be attracted to each other's persons but what we're really after is not anything so low as the unfashionably physical, I mean, ish, getting physical destroys the LOOK, which is a no-no, you know, and you never know just *what* you're going to get if you so much as suck a straw after someone else, do you?

So at Sassoon's Darla sits in her chair, Sean does her, always, and Sean's got great teeth and a great earring and a great LOOK that just looks different every week, Sean's LOOK is Giorgio Armani Uomo *Vogue* today and Ralph Lauren Coors Beer tomorrow, but tasteful, toujours tasteful, and Liz does me and Liz has got a great LOOK too, I mean of course she does, she has a nose jewel, oh darling, she was just in pain over it for so long, but it was worth it of course, and she always thinks so, except maybe when she has a cold, and she has punkadoodle hair, she calls it that, it just changes colors more often than anything and she's very spiritual, she's like been to Nepal, she got a horrible virus there, they told her at Toronto General when she got back that it was toxic-shock syndrome and she said, "So why did my 75-year-old guru in the Himalayas have it too?" but even when she's bad, and she can be mucho bad,

Jay Scott *usually* reviews films for the *Globe and Mail*.

she's still very spiritual, I mean she knows about herb teas and things.

So one day Liz was like trimming my tresses, she says that to me, she says, "Time to trim those tresses, sweetheart," and I asked her why she wore so much skin, like lizard skin and leopard skin and I don't know what, and she said, "That's because in a past life, I was a snake," and well, I just didn't know WHAT to say, I was just so taken aback, I mean I just sat there, like a veg brain, imagine being able to KNOW that! and so I said, "Liz, these tresses are HONORED to be trimmed by hands that were once a snake's," and I started to wonder about my past lives and Liz promised to introduce me to somebody who would read the reincarnation beads for me, at least some of them, and I can't wait, and she said, "You wear a lot of denim and wool, sweetheart, you're a designer-jean sweater queen, you were probably, oh, I don't know, a cotton gin, or maybe a cocksucking sheepherder."

Liz can be wicked, I mean, she knows all my sweaters are mohair.

So by the time Darla and I left Sassoon's, we were in love with our shells, I mean we were hot over our styling gels, her hair was modified Mohawk, très *present*, brown and bossy, and my hair was yellow and spiky, post-punk prickly, just so *now*, and I was wearing my tight black jeans and my sexy Issey Miyake tuxedo-type top and she was wearing earrings big as Rosedale chandeliers, and that's because we'd just seen *Subway*, which is just too-too demi-monde Deco for words, and we'd realized that Christophe Lambert and Isabelle Adjani are just the fashion statements we want to make this week, I mean, as Tarzan, he brought nipples back, because of him I got my left tit pierced, well, not just because of him, Richard Harris in *A Man Called Horse* had something to do with it too, and so did the guy I saw one night at The Tool Box, all in leather with both tits pierced and a chain hanging down between them but two pierced tits and a chain is not knowing when to cease and desist, n'est-ce pas? and I don't know what I would have done with duo anyway, because this one little hole in my left nip where they put this one little gold stud, yeeps, it hurt just like Liz's nose, I have never had pain like that, but at least a tit can't catch cold, so the worst is finito, and it made Darla jealous beyond belief so she wanted to get a nose job because of Isabelle Adjani but the doctor told her she was too young, that she should wait until her cartilage had set or something, until she was like twenty-six or something, and he said there was nothing wrong with her nose anyway, that it wasn't very big anyway, and it's not, even if it isn't as small as Isabelle Adjani's, which is smaller than a jelly bean, so Darla took French lessons instead.

So over at Hazelton Lanes, we ran into Jason and Rick, poor us, and they were doing the usual, they were talking about the big gay dance at the Masonic Temple and all the dope they did and all the unmentionables they did and then they started talking about IT, The Disease, and who they knew who had it and who they knew who was going to get it and I just don't see how they can talk about it like that and then keep on doing what they do, I am speaking of sexual activity and drug abuse, and they start to get all wrinkly serious and like who needs it, wrinkles wreck the LOOK, unless you're D.V., and Darla and I were just too bored for words and it certainly put Darla off her appetite and that's too-too gruesome because she just like recovered from anorexia and then those two started talking about the sixties, I mean they're old enough to remember them, and all I know about the sixties is paisley and that Janis Joplin had a fashion sense, I mean she was the Madonna of her day, and I also know, because Darla and I dragged ourselves to *Woodstock* out of duty to Jason, that no one else had any fashion sense at all, nada, I mean, shudder, natural hair and beads, when you saw that LOOK, well, you just wanted to look away.

So Darla and I left and I was feeling depressed, I knew I was just going to have to buy a Saint-Laurent at least and maybe a Hermès to get myself out of it, so I said that to Darla and she said, "What about your credit cards?" and I blew up at the bitch, but it was all copacetic lickety-split, I mean très vite, I mean I explained how those dizzy sixties queens had just put me off *everything* and Darla said, "You're jealous," and I blew up again and I said, "Jealous of what?" and she said, "That they have a good time," and I said, "Good time? GOOD TIME? Darla, they are flirting with DEATH. And it makes them wrinkly serious," and she said, "Safe sex is possible, you know," and I said, "Sex in the eighties is unsightly, it has no

LOOK and that's all there is to it and every newspaper and even Dr. Ruth, well, tous les monde, they all make the recommendation that you choose your sex partners carefully and I for one am not choosing a sex partner until I know that he is the right one, I mean forever," and she said, "Well, roar away, aren't you just the Cowardly Lion?" and I didn't say anything because I wasn't sure what she was on about and then she said, "What if the right man has IT?" and I said, "It would be humanly impossible for the right man to have IT, because if he did, he would not be the right man and that's that. I am not about to care for an unhealthy person who got that way because he lacked self-discipline, nor am I about to care for the friends of Jason who are wasting away like Auschwitz or something because they could not control the placement of their orifices on the open market and that's that again, un point finale," and she said, "Well, wasn't that a fine little speech, Doris Day?" and I thought so too, but fuck you, Darla, for Doris Day.

And then she said, "I have AIDS."

We were on Bloor, I was heading for Holt's to look at the limited-edition leathers, I mean I was *that* depressed, and I stopped dead and I said, "What?" and even before I said it, it all made the most awful sense, the way Darla got sick about a year ago and could not be dragged out, not even to shop, and then started wasting away and would not eat, not even champagne truffles from Teuscher which are just the best chocolates in the whole world, oh God it all made the most awful sense and I thought all in a rush I thought IT'S NOT HER FAULT MAYBE IT'S NOT ANY-BODY'S FAULT MAYBE IT DOESN'T MATTER ABOUT FAULT MAYBE IT DOESN'T MATTER HOW OR WHY WHAT AM I GOING TO DO WITHOUT HER THIS IS THE MOST AWFUL PAIN IN ALL THE WORLD WORSE EVEN THAN THE TIT-PIERCING OH GOD DARLA WHAT DO I SAY WHAT DO I DO WHAT DO YOU DO WHAT DO WE DO I HAVE TO TALK TO JASON.

She said it again, "I have AIDS."

And then she opened her purse and I thought HER ARM IS SO SKINNY OH GOD and she took out a little package and she handed it to me, a little cardboard box, and it said Ayds on it and she said, "I hear it helps you lose weight," and that evil cunt started laughing and I started laughing and I bought a $2,000 Claude Montana leather jacket at Holt's and I don't know how I'm going to pay for it but you only live once.

A BIRD STORY

BY TERRY GRIGGS

(for Don McKay and Nancy McLeod)

Terry Griggs was born in 1951 in Little Current, Manitoulin Island. She has an M.A. in English and lives in London, Ontario, where she is working on collections of stories and poems.

You weren't born, you were hatched, Henry's father used to say. Henry's brother Arnie they found behind the couch, a ball of dust and dog hair and thread loosely hanging together the way Arnie does when he shuffles into town on a Saturday night. Muriel came in a basket of apples, a fresh red-cheeked child with a swirl of golden delicious hair. Phyllis scooped her up out of the basket and shouted down to Dayland who was making whirligigs in the basement, *It's a girl*. Arnie too had been a surprise. *My goodness*, Phyllis said as she slid the couch aside during spring cleaning and Arnie rolled out, *a big one*. But Henry was another story — a long, difficult birth. He sat on the kitchen counter for two years in a homemade eggcup, one of Dayland's old bowling trophies, picking up coffee stains and specks of grease from the fry pan. He annoyed Phyllis. He cluttered up the counter, he got in her way. He was *useless*. Eventually she quilted a cover for Henry and stuck him between the toaster and the blender. There he hummed quietly to himself and in a manner of speaking cooked.

Then one night, the moon a bulging eye weeping silver on bats' wings, a night so clear you could hear snakes singing arias on the rocks, Henry, egged on perhaps by this sorcery in the air, finally cracked. *I'll be damned*, said Phyllis as she flapped into the kitchen the next morning and saw him wriggling helplessly on the counter. She washed him in the sink, diapered him in a gingham tea towel, then placed him on the porch nestled in an eyrie of blankets. He jerked and waved his little starfish hands at the two curious faces bobbing in front of him. Arnie's slapdash features — lopsided smile, boxer's nose, odd-coloured eyes, red-springing Dagwood hair — cadged a first delighted chortle from baby Henry, and Muriel's face, round as a dish and rosy, dimpled with mischief, unwhorled his heart like a fern. *This is great*, he thought, settling in, lulled by the comforting sound of his mother breaking dishes and smashing pots in the kitchen, when suddenly Dayland emerged from the basement. A monster with hair on his face and a full black shadow trailing like a garbage bag behind him. He loomed and leered, wanting to get a good look at his son, and Henry couldn't help himself. He screamed. A wild shriek, a thin shrill wire of sound that strung their ears together. Honey the cat, a sunny blaze of fur, hit the screen. Dust and dander began to boil off Arnie like a beaten rug. Henry screamed again and his cry, amplified, skipped around the perimeter of the bay, hemming it like a huge skirt. Dogfish whimpered like spaniels. Terns picked up the fear in it and carried it for miles.

Dayland trudged back downstairs. He snapped on the light and it buzzed like an angry bee. *Why*, he addressed his whirligigs, Wily Coyote, Sylvester, Elmer Fudd, *why can't we have normal kids? Why*, he asked the furnace, *why can't they be like the Priddles'? Every one of them straight out of Vergie's potato patch. Nice kids. A little thick you got to admit, but nice.* He grabbed a hammer and scratched his head with the claw, thoroughly perplexed.

Like any mother worth her salt, Phyllis blamed herself. If every dead moth and fungus spore gravitated to Arnie and encircled him like a planetary ring, it was her fault for not vacuuming high enough. If Muriel had little leaf-shaped ears that listened too intently, that was because a drop of Irish blood, green as chlorophyll, had worked its elfin mischief through Phyllis's side of the family. As for Henry, well, that was as plain as the tuberous nose on Elsie Priddle's face. Phyllis's childhood nickname was to blame. *Bird Legs* her brothers called her when she was a tiny chattering thing with sticks for limbs. *Bird Legs* they taunted, and it stuck. Other names applied in malice or in fun, flicked idly at her like beer foam, simply melted away. Bird Legs alone twirled in the dust and flew through childhood, emerging in high school transformed. No longer a skinny sparrow-faced girl but a larger blossoming creature, warm and full-bodied as a cinnamon teal. *A looker*, said Peal Lewis. *A real dish*, according to Harless Lozier. Both grade nine boys at the time making their own transitions from BB guns and gobbing off the town dock to dances at the Shaftsbury Hall and puking a purée of lemon gin and hot dog down the back steps. At these dances it was apparent that Phyllis's nickname had grown up with her; it rolled off people's tongues like praise. It buoyed her up as she swept around the hall, feet flying, heart pounding, chrysanthemum curls bouncing. She rarely sat down to catch her breath, the boys wouldn't let her. It was not for Bird Legs to know the anguish of wall-flowers, girls like Maisie Blue or the Wood sisters, who sank deep coiling roots into the sidelines and soured there like old milk.

Phyllis met Dayland at the Shaftsbury. He was from the west end of the island and looked it. He was darker, denser, greasier than the boys from the east, who carried a certain light in their eyes and on their skin. Dayland was a bear out of a cave and just as grumpy. His fists sprang into the air and hovered like birds of prey at the slightest provocation. Like hapless Buddy Worth stabbing him in the ankle with his new pointy-toed shoes and almost getting his block knocked off. Phyllis intervened and Dayland was hers. He tagged after her the rest of the evening, persistently cutting in on her other partners. She disliked him. But that summer night handfuls of stars had been tossed like confetti into the sky and a slow kind of magic rose off the lake and drifted into the hall where it moved lazily among the dancers, relaxing their clenched hearts and lavishing them with gifts. Fred McClay, two hundred pounds teetering on two left feet, suddenly couldn't be touched for agility and grace. Flashes of beauty redefined homely inbred faces and currents churned in minds that had long been pools of floating duckweed. As for Day-land, something about him diffuse and wayward came together, like darkness condensing into mystery, that gave him an edge, a lure, a strange unprecedented attraction. Put off by his gruffness, his fat grasping fingers and barnyard smell (*pigshit*, her heightened sensitivities told her), Phyllis nevertheless found herself drawn to him as a mouse to the ghostly heart-shaped face of a barn owl. As she left with him that night — he took her home by way of twisting dirt roads and a field with rushing waves of grass and blue pools of chicory that whispered against them — someone called her name. A disembodied and sorrowful voice followed her down the steps and into the dark cab of Dayland's truck. And it followed her still. Doing the wash or the ironing she'd hear a faint *Bird Legs, Bird Legs*, like a waif calling. A small disquieting voice that sang its disappointment and mourned her loss. That cooed and scolded, pulling her back in time, leaving her staring into space. That wove an ever-tightening noose around her life.

So Phyllis often stood watching her youngest swooping around the yard or singlemindedly digging for worms in the garden, and a portion of guilt, about the size of an ostrich egg, would roll off the roof and land on her head. Or sneak up from behind like a gigolo and give her a big squeeze. Because with Henry it was never airplanes, but swifts; never cowboys and Indians, but sharks and shearwaters. When most toddlers were babbling *birdie birdie* at any creature with wings, Henry would say of a speck miles away on the rocks, *Look, black-crowned night heron*. He knew chickens the way most boys know hockey players. *Andalusian, black Spanish, blue Orpington, Jersey white giant, speckled Sussex*. He recited long lists happily to Arnie, who accepted any kind of information, no matter how peculiar, from anyone. To Muriel, swaying in the treetops, he told secrets about local birdlife, matters of sex and family, shamelessly revealing even the tiny skeletons in their closets. She envisioned a vast and resonant soap opera taking place all around them with episodes begun in the bushes concluding romantically in the clouds, or along the lake in huge drifting kettles.

Dayland on the other hand viewed ornithology as an overlong and obscene word. *All you got to know about birds*, he would say, *is some are yellow, some are brown*. Muttering to himself over breakfast, he threatened to take Henry into town to see a doctor. Phyllis stood firm in the doorway, a block of stone, saying that if he took Henry he'd surely have to take the others. Wasn't Arnie just as bad with his hoard of empty spaghetti tins and shampoo bottles, or Muriel, who was no end of trouble, practically living outside. Not that Phyllis wasn't worried about Henry. Oh no, worry was a piece of work never finished. He was enough to drive a brood of mothers to distraction. When he wasn't jumping head first nighthawk-style off the shed, he was practising mating displays in front of her bridge club, or risking his life at the supper table by parroting everything Dayland happened to say. His moods were as erratic as the flight patterns of swallows. He suffered migratory restlessness in the fall. A week of frenzied activity, stockpiling food and packing his knapsack, was followed by a sudden swing into depression. As the flocks gathered and left one by one for the Bahamas and Mexico, a sickness seized him. He spent days sitting by the picture window in the living room, staring out, the sky unyielding as a test pattern. His only consolation was Honey, a mass of gold curled in his lap, purring out her own nostalgic longing for the savoury taste of meadowlark, the succulence of dove.

Then duck season opened. Night after night Henry dreamed he was falling. Dreamed of pain shooting through him like an electric wire as he plummeted into black water. His father the shadowy figure that splashed toward him, gun in hand.

As always it was a relief to see a skin of ice forming on the lake and the first flakes of snow jiving like midges above it. Winter would enter with a slap and set Henry to rights. His forlorn face took on a pale saintly expression. Meagre rations kept him alive: the friendly buzz of a chickadee, starlings squabbling over a crust, the disappearing wingtip of a snowy owl, white as an apparition. His passion went underground and germinated there like the sprouting plants and grasses that were tickling the great duck-soft underbelly of snow that covered everything. He descended into the basement and worked beside his father *like a real boy*. Together they made Tweety Birds and Woody Woodpeckers to give away for Christmas, while the furnace ate enormous helpings of coal and pitched heat around the room like an old demon.

As long as winter ruled, butting up against the house and freezing the plumbing, the family huddled close, tightly packed as a pod. Oddly, under these conditions, they fit more easily together. While the cold drove hungry wolves around the lake and mixed cruel concoctions of ice and wind, they felt safe, nestled in self-generated warmth. But at the first microscopic hint of spring in the air, solidarity began to thaw.

Ambling into the kitchen one morning frowzy as a hound dog's bed, Arnie would catch an evil look from his mother, or get a slap on the head from Dayland, who would claim to have seen a pair of flies screwing behind his ear. Muriel might start flipping soggy cereal at him, or Honey arch her back and hiss. Would this upset Arnie? Not in the least. This was a sign. The season, however imperceptibly, had changed. Almost within reach, below thinning layers of snow, lay a bounty of last year's refuse, discoloured, swollen as the drowned, though to Arnie's eyes as lovely and artfully arranged as any spring floral display.

Henry, tuned in to a collective idea swelling in the south like an enormous sun bulging below the horizon, was already pacing the floor. He'd been on the alert from the moment the first whistling swan, gliding majestically across a lake near Lumpkin, Georgia, raised its long neck, pointed its slender black beak north, and thought *hmmn*. By the time the sky was filled with the ocean roar of beating wings, excitement had driven him into a frenetic, twittering state. He was unable to sit or eat, or even speak without tearing his words into syllabic shreds. And then there was the other problem. This was the time of year when boys from town rode out on their bikes, later in cars, to court Muriel — they'd swing like monkeys from tree to tree trying to catch up with her. Arnie was gone for days, returning home even scruffier, with weeds in his hair and shirt buttons swinging loose on single threads. An outbreak of spring fever meant they had to put up with the nuisance and embarrassment of Henry's infatuations. One year a pretty little warbler might catch his eye, the next an indigo bunting or a Baltimore oriole. He fell for flashy tanagers and yellow dancers, flittering redstarts and duplicitous catbirds. Once he was smitten by a common weather-worn gull and spent the summer madly filleting fish while it stood on the dock and screeched at him like a querulous wife. Some of these heart-throbs lived on in family memory: the dissolute Bohemian waxwing that devoured fermented berries, then flew in crazy drunken circles trilling loudly until it smacked into the side of the house; the unrequited turkey vulture that hovered and hovered and would not go away; the much lamented European goldfinch that Honey ate, colourful fieldmarks bleeding like paint out of her mouth. Certain special ones Henry alone cherished, like the timorous loon that called to him every evening over the moon-streaked bay, the flirtatious tail-wagging phoebe, the thrush that wanted his hair for her nest, his lips for her fledglings, and the hummingbird, a Cuban emerald, that materialized like a quivering jewel before his eyes, then vanished forever.

An endlessly unfurling list, a lifetime of fowl fancies and flames might have been Henry's lot if it hadn't been for Raphael. Admittedly, neither fanfare nor flashing lights marked his arrival on the scene, but for the family, soon to be unwittingly herded into their renaissance, it was a significant event.

Henry discovered him on the shore one morning, lying limp on a rock. *Hurt*, he immediately concluded, whereas Raphael was simply indulging in one of his favourite activities: sleep. When Henry burst into the kitchen carrying his newfound treasure (what to Phyllis looked like a huge pair of argyle socks rolled up into a ball), Dayland had a fit. Cigarette smoke pouring out of his nostrils, beads of dribbled coffee rolling down his chin, he shouted, *Jesus-another-goddamn-dead-bird-get-that-thing-out-of-here*. At which point Raphael cocked open a dark defiant eye and stared straight at him. He leafed quickly through Dayland's mind as if it were a grade-one primer. Then he surveyed the whole sorry lot, shaking his head sadly as one would at the victims of some unspeakable disaster. Slopping up cereal, sucking on toast, snarling at one another, they stirred in him a sense of mission. They *needed* him. It was obvious. They needed him as an infant needs a mother, as a body needs a soul. This must have been the moment that *the wild kingdom* (as Raphael was to hear it described on TV) planted one large webbed foot immovably in the door.

Raphael's own mother wasn't surprised when she heard that her son had wormed his way into a human household and into human hearts, small as they are. He'd always been the odd one out, a snot from the word go. Even as an egg he tried to roll himself away from the others in the nest. He had the vanity of a peacock, the cunning of a crow, and he was lazy like his father, forever squawking to ride on her back while Gavriel, Euphemia, Ora, and Umbriel paddled behind. He used to pester her with questions about them. *What do they do in those houses? Do they have any kind of spiritual life, any capacity for thought?* She hadn't been the one to encourage him. She told him the truth. That they're sick. The species has an incurable illness which makes them unpredictable and cruel. One minute they're studying you, worshipping you, painting eggs and wearing feathers, and the next they're wringing your neck and making gravy to pour over your carcass. Might as well go and live with ogres as far as Raphael's mother was concerned. *She* would never sink so low.

At first the family didn't think much of it. They tolerated him. He was quiet, and *kinda cute*, though always underfoot. In the basement he was an attentive audience to Dayland's soliloquies, and in the kitchen he watched as Phyllis sobbed into the cake batter (tears being the secret ingredient that gave her baking that special tangy flavour). He listened carefully to confidences from Muriel and Arnie, but especially from Henry, who seemed to interest him the most. Empathetic, loyal as a winged Lassie, he ascended through the ranks. Companion, analyst, mentor . . . double agent.

He infiltrated the family's dreams and worked there with a viral intensity. He dove below the surface of their lives and rode the undercurrent, ducked below the swampy miasma of emotion and probed where sensitive roots were knotted into a ball. He undermined their sadness, strong in humans as musk, and diffused the anger that made them blow apart then come together again like hands squeezing and kneading. He introduced the comic element. Humour travelled around the supper table like salmonella. They began to find one another mildly entertaining, then ridiculously funny. Indeed, a bright and whimsical mood took hold, as though a narcotic spice had been slipped into the familial stew.

Phyllis lightened up and nibbled with more amusement at her life. She lost weight and dyed her hair. She stopped hearing those voices, or at least if the Jell-O salad addressed her its message was not unpleasant. The nattering past slid off her back like an incubus tired of the game. She bustled blithe and unburdened into home renovation: knocking down walls, stripping wood, hanging plants, painting ceilings blue as a budgie's nostril. She threw open the windows and light splashed in like bleach. It chewed up the shadows and spit them out as lace. Dayland's shadow like a bride's frothy train swishing behind him as he wandered outside to gaze at the sky. This a newfound pastime. For heaven no longer gaped back at him the way it used to, but had taken him under its wide arching wing. Sent him blessings in warm caressing breezes and showers of inspiration. Ideas jammed into his mind like a multitude of stations vying for one channel on the radio. He hummed, he whistled. Then, picking up a distress signal, he'd rush back inside to open another can of peas for the cat, who lately had become a vegetarian.

Nor were the others immune to this new ambience. In it, the shards and fragments of Arnie's creative genius cohered. The mass of odds and ends he'd been collecting all his life began surging like an enormous river into place. He built a car out of broken hockey sticks; a patio out of dixie cups and those flat wooden spoons. Anything missing, he supplied; anything broken, he fixed. He was invaluable, ever ready with ancient furry bottles of glue and used bits of Scotch tape to mend and hold in place a disintegrating material world.

Parental pride swelled, and even Muriel pleased her mother by dropping out of the trees one night like a ripened spy and landing in the arms of Curtis Mead, a budding naturalist out studying the effect of moonlight on the reproductive cycle of the firefly. The family welcomed him wholeheartedly into their midst. *She might have brought home a squirrel*, Dayland pointed out philosophically.

As for Henry, why he became his mother's favourite, her darling, her pet. She now greeted friends in the grocery store by digging in her purse for show-off photos: One of Henry rowing on the lake with Raphael perched like a figurehead on the bow; one of him clowning, fanning Raphael like a sultan and feeding him chocolates; and a more recent picture of him on a beach in Florida where he drove Raphael every winter.

Miraculously, Henry's nature had settled; his obsession came to roost, tucking and folding itself almost invisibly away. It took a rare bird these days to move him over to the window from his comfortable perch in front of the TV. Dayland, gesturing generously, laying before his son wonders freshly gleaned from the sky, could scarcely stir an ember of interest. Henry was like a monk or a holy man whose meditative investments had finally paid off in cool tranquillity. Contentment surrounded him on all sides, enclosing him completely.

Given an aerial view, a bird's-eye view if you will, you could say he looked happier than most, like a child reading a story, absorbed, and totally at ease with whatever anthropomorphic detail might crop up.

DAVID MCFADDEN

A VISIT TO THE ZOO

David McFadden was born in 1940. He is currently working as writer-in-residence at Hamilton Public Library, the city of his birth. His most recent book of poems is *Gypsy Guitar*. His most recent novel is *Canadian Sunset*. Forthcoming is the third novel in his Great Lakes series, *A Trip Around Lake Ontario*.

Thirty minutes to feeding-time in the cathouse at the Granby Zoo, and the lions, tigers, pumas, panthers, and assorted passionate, beautiful, and mindless carnivores explode and explode again with wild and furious insanity. In the wild they'd be consuming all this intensity in the hunt. Here the bars and the sliding doors of inch-thick glass are preserving them from the extinction they'd face in the wild. But they don't know that. How amazing! Such enforced patience! Such suffering! And above all, thick electrical clouds are massing and it's about to rain huge globs of steaming adrenalin. How removed this was, I thought, from Zasep the Tibetan lama, who is totally celibate and always has been, and three times a week since childhood has performed a special yoga technique for relieving sexual tension, a technique involving violent exhalations and so on, and it may be noted that he eats no meat and little of anything else. And how far removed from us, grazing sweetly on each other's memories since you appeared at my door like an angel with no luggage.

You should come back tomorrow, says the keeper, with his pails of raw and steaming horsemeat from the horse farms of the Eastern Townships. We don't feed them on Mondays and things get really tense. . . . Whew! That's it, they think this might be Monday, they don't even have the satisfaction of knowing for certain they're going to be fed on any given day. Cats can't count to seven. In the air is no love, there is only passionate hunger, and not the passionate hunger that can sometimes be mistaken for love. And even us, we argue mildly about the weather. And about whether or not to leave immediately. And I wonder if I'm fooling myself when I think I understand what's in your heart and mind.

ELEPHANTS

Knoxville, San Diego, Winnipeg, Buffalo, Granby, Toronto: a list of zoos I've visited this year. And anyone could see the gorillas at the Toronto Zoo were conscious, deliberate philosophers with no vocabulary, sitting in the glass house pondering ambiguity, paradox, and absolutes. At Granby the gorillas were of a decidedly lower class. I hope they don't read this. Two big ones studiously ignored a tossed banana for several tense minutes until finally the male broke down and flickered with interest and the female leaped from her perch, pounced on the banana, then ate it herself while the male tried to pretend he didn't care. And an American eagle attacked his mate over a gerbil tossed in their cage.

Viciously too, all heaven in a rage. But when I held out a handful of nuts to the bull elephant he took only half, then slowly backed up so his mate could have the remainder. The eyes of these sad spiritual lovers in leg chains checked to see if I understood and appreciated their little gesture of kindness and love, and I felt I'd been blessed by the Pope. They knew there was nothing I could do to free them, though when two doves were presented to Pope John Paul II in Montreal he released them — and they didn't fly away, just sat there in transcendental splendour in the middle of crowded Olympic Stadium, little haloes radiant. And people who live in the vicinity of the Granby Zoo when you get to know them will shyly confide in you that late at night after they turn off the television they lie in bed listening to and feeling the earth and sky quivering and murmuring with the mammoth heartbreaking hour-long orgasms of the elephants.

SHANTIDEVA

Every day I try to do something that would make my mother proud of me if she knew about it. God, what's this guy going to say next? Oh, life is so embarrassing. I am only as innocent as you are. Never thought of that, didya? You know how much I smoke and what a hyena I am at the table. Well, when you were a kid did you sometimes think your mother could read your mind? It's true; even when you were at school she could tune into your thinking whenever she wanted and she often wanted. If you ever become a mother you'll be much the same. I somehow was burdened with knowing Mom was listening in. You spend the first twenty years of your life only thinking thoughts your mother would approve of, it does something to you. Sort of ruins you forever. Makes you want to devote your life to writing poems or something. Repairing toasters. Any anguished priesthood you could name. Then at a certain point you do a flip-flop, turn into a veritable lamb of warmth and softness. The universe begins to resemble a Superheroes comic book, and you are the reader. Taking away the sins of the world. For years you were plagued by impressions that there were certain important things that you weren't supposed to know. Now you know those things are unknowable. You know everything you need to know the moment you need to know it. But you don't need to know that. As for me, I thought my parents were conspirators on a global scale, in league with all of nature and all of humanity dragging me down screaming from heaven. Now I look at them and smile deeply. I'm my only conceivable enemy and we're going through a period of détente.

Cute little two-bar saxophone riff in the middle of a boring piano solo. Today I walked for miles on the hot pavement, barefoot, holding my sandals in my hand, my feet bleeding and dirty, and thought about my mind, as if it were my brain that had broken, not my sandal strap. An unchained elephant is a dangerous thing. They'll uproot parking meters, trample flowerbeds, crash through the windows of healthfood stores. Chained, they become sad and deep and wise and gentle. A sort of Stalinism of the self. Now and then a mother discovers her own mind.

The eighth-century Buddhist poet Shantideva likened the mind to a wild elephant.

TERRIBLE STORM ON LAKE ERIE

It was Father's Day at the Seaway Hotel and everyone had the chicken cordon bleu special. Mom didn't have anything to drink, but Dad and his two grown sons drank two beers each. Dad asked if I had a five on me. I did. He said give it to Jack, so I did, and Dad handed me a neatly folded ten. He said he found it on the street and when he found it he thought I'll give it to my sons the struggling artists, so he did. Mom said Mr. Silver had a heart attack and died, and I remembered scenes from his terrible marriage. The time for instance he and his wife had a terrible fight and he took his little motorboat straight out into Lake Erie in the middle of a terrible storm. Everyone on the beach in silence watched him disappear behind the black waves over and over again, his wife sobbing and being held by neighbours and the minister. But that was years ago when Mr. Silver was young and had a romantic little moustache like Clark Gable or Errol Flynn. He finally divorced his wife and married again and now he's dead and his first wife is in a nursing home in Vancouver.

Mom and Dad looked so wonderfully happy sitting there, white hair, happy after forty years of marriage's ups and downs. I wondered why the waitress didn't seem to be more thrilled to be waiting on them. She didn't seem to notice their rare and simple beauty. There was a little orchestra playing songs from old Fred Astaire movies and there were other little families celebrating Father's Day but we were the best.

BLUE IRISES

It makes me feel lonely when I realize the past simply does not exist, we simply talk as if it does. And of course there is no future. Nothing but now, nothing ahead, nothing behind. There was a time when I felt that writing was my life, now I don't know what I think until I think it. My friend Rodney says there is no subconscious, so that if you do something and only later find out why, you are fooling yourself. If a man chooses blue irises to send to someone he loves and later remembers she associates blue irises with someone else, he'd be a fool to berate himself, or bother to look more deeply into the case, for it's simply that he forgot. Who was it who said that he who knows there is no past and no future has control over both? Perhaps it was my friend Rodney. It's hard for me to believe the things my inadequate mind tells me I used to believe. It's hard for me to imagine anyone being the kind of person I remember having been and later becoming the kind of person I now imagine myself to be. No one can talk as if there is no future, is no past, the future and the past have to be invented before we can begin to speak. Don't be misled. As if. There's no reason for you to know that I am sitting here writing this and resisting editing the movie currently running in my mind simultaneously, resisting slowing it down and running it frame by frame. It's true the sadness in my mind interests me, but don't expect me to try to figure out why I'm sad. Nothing can be anybody's life. Peace to all!

Rodney says he wants to be remembered for his poetry, he likes to think of academics in universities a hundred years from now looking at his verse and discovering hidden meanings. He says there is no subconscious and I say there is no past or future, I'm not sure about the present, I'm the man who sent blue irises to you and recalled too late you hate blue irises.

DERK WYNAND

RAILING THROUGH EUROPE

A sters rocket toward the sky with the dahlias and burst into flame when they reach it: these concussions in September and October knock the finches out of the air, the bees out of their routine dance. On the edge of his second-class seat, a civil servant loosens the chain that binds him to his briefcase. Yes, a bird only stunned, bird that will fly again, and bees too dazed to sting are a good memory we all draw on often, whenever the shoes are blasted from the feet of women and children in Paris, city of light, or a diplomat in Bonn, cool to the end, learns the limits of language there. Denunciations drift in the air and come apart slowly, denials, reservations, feathers. The illustrated papers are folded, picked up, and read again or looked at by others. Sometimes we're quite content not to have such a variety of songbirds back home. The dogs in their cages drop their heads into their paws. In the houses along the tracks, the eiderdowns, plumped up and beaten, spill with the geraniums over the balconies and explode. Everything follows its own inclination: live grenade hidden in the peat moss, incendiary bomb in a cushion. Any passing bush could shelter a man who'd die for the cause gladly, and die twice if only he could take you along. You in the headlines . . . me . . . all of us. Yellow fields turn to black ones, the storks alone constant, on top of chimneys or hanging back in the haze. We keep an eye out for abandoned pieces of luggage, for the briefcase no one claims. The autumnal flowers are cut, bunched and tied, then tossed onto the street where the bodies have finally been pieced

Derk Wynand was born in 1944. He teaches writing at the University of Victoria. Recent books are collections of poetry entitled *Second Person* (1983) and *Fetishistic* (1984). His most recent collection is called *Heat Waves*.

together again. The light on their faces in the light of the cameras catches the clouds from below and softens them further, opens their bellies, the cloudburst not dousing the fire at all. Impossible to breathe in these stations, so much burning up in its own gases and still pushing on, wave upon wave of green shooting into the blue ozone. We never see the insects, but hear them. Waiting for our train, we shut our eyes, pinch them tight until the memory of a better sun lights up the blood of our eyelids.

EARTHQUAKE

Last night, the earth took our house and gave it a good shaking: the European skylarks started up from the TV antenna; the vertical hold did not hold; the mice stopped rolling walnuts down the aluminum ducts in the basement. Doors rattled in their frames as though someone desperate wanted in or out and we refused to open; the windows threatened to shatter. On the high shelf, a ceramic pot began to vibrate closer to the edge; on the wall, a picture swung on its wire and did not fall. The rocking chair rocked before the fireplace, no fire in it, but only the soot drifting down. The pipes played a new tune behind the walls.

As our bed shook, we clung to each other because, for the first time in our life, our lives seemed to depend on it. The bed shook; the chair at its foot shook; the lamp, tungsten buzzing, swung back and forth on its chain. We held on tight, labouring to breathe, neither of us able to come up with a word that could correctly name the situation in which we suddenly found ourselves. The bed shook and we refused to be shaken off. Your slip trembled toward the edge of the chair and over, your dress after, my shirt, pants, socks. The light flickered and did not go out entirely. As flakes of paint began to cover us, we gasped and did not let go.

I'm not sure *when*, only *that* we fell asleep. Maybe you dreamed, as I did, of a couple on a long voyage, he by air, she by sea, nothing but cloud and water around them, no land to be seen. I dreamed that our bed was moving in the same direction as their vessel in the dream. When I woke up this morning, your eyes were closed, but following something quick beneath the lids: only then did I know we had reached solid ground once again.

ONE VERSION OF LOVE

Tablecloths of the second-best Irish linen and what looks like the silk of parachutes have been tacked to all our neighbours' windows except the one with its Japanese sunburst: what wars have been fought all these years behind them without our knowing?

One perception immediate on another sounds more like an ordinary life than a structure, but we keep our eyes and ears open.

The letters that need to be written have not been written. All the creditors and friends have not pressed hard enough. Lately, nothing but the simple gets done and the rewards do not last long. We waste too much time reconstructing bad dreams in painstaking detail, as though they proved how crazy we were *or could be*. We call nothing nightmare. If the writing came easy as that.

Often, you think me grandiose, though I approach you on my knees. You never tell me what's roused your suspicions. Often, my rage has no purpose, though it's seldom without effect.

Behind the tablecloths, parachutes, and the flag of the emperor, the shadows of our neighbours make their move. They bluster and strut. Just for us?

So the night has fallen again, all the house lights around us full up. We concentrate on the shadows, thinking maybe of Narcissus, increasingly paralytic, barely able to utter his lie of an active love, eager to believe the lie.

A DEAL WE COULD LIVE WITH

And though no one suggested it, they threw in the kitchen sink for good measure, the hammock, the smoke coil and mosquito-proof netting, the collection of Botticelli prints — or was it only the promise of even more breathless descriptions of the back of her knee? They said, "Take the surfboard, the surf, the spindrift on otherwise quiet nights, spoondrift, the sound of one or the other, whichever you prefer, or both, the arabesques on the hand-mirror held in her hand whenever she looks for something she's not sure of — Venus in the foam — whatever her own eye is window to, reflected light, some lucky gnat blinked in."

In the distance, what must have been sunlight bounced off the chrome fittings or glass of a boat in distress, its paler electric light and horn spelling out the novice captain's idea of Mayday or SOS. "Take it, too," they said, "if you want, the boat, the light, the horn, the SOS. Take the sun beneath which she often lies tanning, and the whitecaps, and the captain's wife not trembling below deck, holding her fear in, saying nothing to alarm her two children. We assume," they said, "you would have no use for a man who'd allow matters to get so out of hand."

We agreed, not blaming him especially, but distracted by the inevitable thoughts of our tenuous hold on everything. Maybe that's why we could not help but conjure up the woman coming ashore, hair and hips swinging as we followed her, her dress foaming high to expose her legs, spindrift, substance we could more willingly drown in, and her daughters as beautiful, almost adults, but sticking close to her, unaware of the close call they had had, the dangers still ahead, and we nodded, nodded, perhaps too eager, saying, "Done!"

DRAWING OF A DESIRABLE WOMAN

The pencil falls from beneath her right breast. She stoops to pick it up — a trace of graphite marks the carpet — and places it beneath the left, nearer the heart. It holds. So there she pouts, a pencil trapped against one rib by the weight of her flesh. Biting her lower lip, the disappointment hardly bitten back, she finds what solace she can in the lack of witnesses to this ludicrous test. She stretches, folds her hands behind her neck, tenses. She cheats. Has the alignment of earth, moon, and sun conspired against her? Has this relentless heat — what dog days — altered the nature of her all too delicate tissues? Has she been too tolerant of the men in her nights, all of them with their urgent, clumsy, heavy hands? Their bodies and predictable gravitation? Because she must think these questions through, she does think, clasping her hands together before her and flexing them all the while, flexing and relaxing and flexing again. Thinking. Flexing. Throughout the evening and for much of the night, she refuses to acknowledge the knocks at her door and the persistent male voices that call out her name.

DERK WYNAND

WOUND, CLOSING

One day, you said, *All right*, simply, and simply disappeared, as promised. For a time, we saved your place. You had never said how long you intended to be gone. Bit by bit, we let it go. Things kept crowding or falling in: mysteries, Hieronymus Bosch, excellent seafood in restaurants in Lisbon or Cascais, *Dr. Fischer of Geneva*, first in English, four months or so later in Portuguese, a monument to nobler causes, these navigators marching up the steps of their monuments, mother and son, the Common Market, changing rates of exchange, frigates now armed with the latest in weapons, insomnia, wasps that would not be chased from the breakfast table, all the knives in a museum, avenues without signs, the cobblestones broken or breaking out underfoot, traps, the details of which we cannot go into, wasps that did not sting, euphemisms too late at night and long into the morning, the possible influence of everything we have ever watched on TV, euphemisms in the late afternoon, sleeping much of the day away, forty, forty-one and still counting, now beginning to talk openly about all these things, still finding no answers, everything that we said and could have said the last time we spoke on the telephone, buzz of wasps, not one of the knives sharp enough to cut us free from the line.

Sam Tata

MAVIS GALLANT:

A PROFILE 🍁 *BY JANICE KULYK KEEFER*

Mavis Gallant really *is* unique among contemporary Canadian writers in the English language. For nearly forty years she has been making her living simply by writing — unsubsidized by any government grants, any stints of creative-writing teaching, any descents into the lucratively sub- or pseudo-literary. Although her stories have appeared elsewhere, *The New Yorker* has been her main venue for publication, an arrangement for which most Canadian writers would kill. And if she is not as publicly prominent a writer as Margaret Atwood, for example, one gets the feeling that she's not only reconciled to but also content with this situation: she simply hasn't permitted herself or her fiction to fall victim to the vulgarity of a media blitz. Over the last ten years a great deal of critical attention has been paid to her work, starting with the special issue of *Canadian Fiction Magazine* devoted to her in 1978, followed by a rash of scholarly articles, and reaching a peak now with at least two book-length studies of her fiction in the offing. Gallant has been awarded the 1981 Governor General's Award — for *Home Truths* — has had a play, *What Is To Be Done?*, produced at Toronto's Tarragon Theatre, and has even spent a year as writer-in-residence (a consultative rather than pedagogical position) at the University of Toronto, which is now in possession of a considerable number of her papers.

Gallant is respected by critics and readers for the sheer quality of her considerable oeuvre; relished for the elegance, wit, and formidable cut-

Janice Kulyk Keefer was born in 1954. She lives in Annapolis Royal. She has published two collections of stories, *The Paris-Napoli Express* and *Transformations*, and a collection of poems called *White of the Lesser Angels*.

ting edge of her fiction, and for the fluent intelligence of her many reviews and essays, of which the recently published *Paris Note-books* gives a fair sampling. Yet reading reviews of her work, one is struck by a certain reserve — the respect so superb a stylist commands is tinctured with something very like resistance or even fear. The clarity of her vision is often described as chilling; she is accused of unduly constricting the range of possibilities open to her characters, of loading life's dice against them. Under-lying such complaints may be the suspicion that Gallant's fictions entrap and expose not just her characters but her *hypocrites lecteurs*, as well. What makes us ill at ease is not merely Gallant's decisive wit, her acerbic vision of human possibility, or the strongly political nature of the sensibility at work in her fiction — such a list could, after all, as readily describe Margaret Atwood. True, readers of *The Handmaid's Tale* may be left looking warily over their shoulders on finishing that book, but it is to the world outside the book, irrevocably altered by their reading of the book, that their gaze will be directed. In Gallant's case, however, readers may be left not only with the desolating sense that the world is a much harsher, cramped, impoverished place than they'd like to recognize, but also with the unsettling sense that the author is laughing at them for ever having thought it otherwise. Stories such as "Its Image on the Mirror," "The Remission," or "A Recollection" disconcert the reader with a paradoxical sense of Gallant's presence — ironic, amused, even arrogant in her sum-mary dismissal of certain characters and situations — yet also of her absence. There's a troubling opacity about her fiction in its refusal to overtly discriminate between good and bad, wise and foolish — or, more importantly, in its disinterested delineation of the various ways in which we helplessly confuse these different things in our own interests. In this sense a work such as *The Pegnitz Junction*, that baffling mix of literary pastiche, love story, historical précis, and narrative interruptus, is poles apart from such a straightforward, Manichaean fiction as *The Handmaid's Tale*. Yet surely the fascination and, more importantly, the challenge of Gallant's fiction lie precisely in the puzzlement it creates, the paradoxical nature of the gifts it bestows. One is left richly satis-fied in terms of the artistry employed; radically disturbed by a deliberate insubstantiality — not lack of substance — vis-à-vis the experience it conveys.

What fiction is about, Gallant has said, "is that something is taking place and that nothing lasts. Against the sustained tick of a watch, fiction takes the measure of a life. . . . The watch continues to tick where the story stops.'' Gallant, then, concedes the inherent limitations of her chosen art: her own fiction does not produce meanings, but rather, takes the measure of the evanescent — and takes that measure through a detailed observation of gesture, manner, and the nuances of context. Yet anyone who has read Gallant will attest to the fact that she's prone to take her measure of any given life with a razor for a ruler. Gallant's vision of reality, of human possibility, can be compared to that of Marguerite Yourcenar,² a writer whom she greatly admires, and for whom she coined the term "Limpid Pessimist." It is a vision which scarcely warms the cockles of one's heart. Can the world be as bleak, comfortless, unnurturing a place as Gallant's fictions delineate, with parents forever abandoning or damaging children, and with lovers, husbands, and wives doing endless dances to the music of loss, betrayal, and bewilderment? Must all illusions be picked clean as bones, and must all laughter be self-consuming? We want to say no — but Gallant's prose, by its sheer excellence, possesses an extraordinary authority, compelling our consent to her vision, at least in the process of reading her fiction. On finishing a collection of her stories, one may be left asking, "What is at the heart of this fiction — is there any heart at all?" When one of Gallant's characters, having been beaten and raped in the northern bush, is made to declare, "My heart is broken" (not because of the violence she's suffered, but because her assailant hadn't even been "friendly" or even "liked" her), what are we to make of the statement? (Particularly as Jeannie is preoccupied by applying a coat of polish to her nails immediately before she makes this declaration, and is then described as "serene" as she listens to the nagging warnings of her confidante.) It's not only the prison of context which Gallant so persuasively details — the tawdry, petty "women's world" within the dreary northern mining camp — that makes the reader uncomfortable, but also the equanimity with which Gallant situates Jeannie at this moment in a life so obviously headed from bad to worse. And this equanimity, this authorial neutrality toward the fate of incarcerated characters, is typical of Gallant: she makes her men and women wriggle on but never free themselves from the various pins with which she impales them.

Yet it is untrue to say that Gallant's fiction lacks heart; that heart, however, is less like a valentine, or even a fiery furnace, than a Promethean liver, interminably savaged. Or, to be less romantic, we can image the concept of heart as it emerges in a story like "My Heart Is Broken" not as something warm and pulsing and messily red, but as a fractured crystal whose transparency serves to reveal a maze of cracks and flaws. After a prolonged reading of Gallant's fiction, one rushes to a writer like Margaret Laurence or Alice Munro. Munro is as fine a stylist, as accomplished a word-artist, as Gallant, but there is a saving, softening element of mystery to the world of horrible, yet necessary, peculiarities her fiction reveals. And Margaret Laurence's best work has a breadth of moral vision, a magnificent passion, which transcends any structural faults or stylistic lapses to be found in her novels. As importantly, both writers command not only our admiration but also our affection: a sense of closeness develops between writer, character, and reader, not so much complicity as camaraderie. We form a bond with Vanessa in *A Bird in the House*, Dell Jordan in *Lives of Girls and Women*, a bond impossible to forge, for example, with Jean Price in "Its Image on the Mirror," or even with Linnet Muir in the final stories of *Home Truths*. Mavis Gallant, it would seem, has carried her project of "personal independence"[3] to its consummate conclusion: a penumbra of unknowableness surrounds herself, her characters, and the fictive worlds which author them.

With Gallant, this categorical imperative of distance, difference, otherness between writer, character, and reader is achieved by that paradoxical mix of clarity and opacity so distinctive of her fiction. Jean Price's observations about her equal desire and incapacity for love are devastatingly precise, yet the overwhelming sense the reader gets from "Its Image on the Mirror" is one of impenetrability: not revelation but protective disguise is the novella's keynote, ending as it does with the images of falling snow, unending night. And though Linnet Muir is the most sympathetic of Gallant's first-person narrators (largely because Gallant's habitual acidly ironic tone is deflected in the stories this character narrates), Linnet withholds as much as she reveals to the reader. In reading her character we take our cue from Linnet's own response to the mystery of her father's death — did he die of T.B. or did he commit suicide? Unable to get firm evidence for either, Linnet subsumes both possibilities in a fiction of her own making: "I thought he had died of homesickness; sickness for England was the consumption, the gun, the everything. . . . Once I had made up my mind, the whole story somehow became none of my business: I had looked in a drawer that did not belong to me."[4]

Ultimately, characters like Jean Price and Linnet Muir are similar kinds of drawers: we are allowed a look inside, but only to permit us the realization that what we see we cannot solve; cannot understand and thus appropriate as our own. Over and over again Gallant's characters — Flor in *Green Water, Green Sky*, Bernadette in the story which bears her name, Carmela in "The Four Seasons," the narrator of the "Magdalena" stories in *Overhead in a Balloon* — create a sense of bafflement which becomes all the more acute the more precisely such characters are drawn. The measure of their lives is the measure of human life itself: the razor may cut deep, but it possesses no reassuringly recognizable units of measurement. Not transcendent mystery but inescapable bewilderment is the locus of Gallant's imagination: if her artistry in the narrating of this condition gives us great pleasure, it does not make bewilderment any less painful to acknowledge. In this way the reader's own frustration with the opacity of Gallant's fiction becomes a metonymy for the experience of her characters themselves.

This bafflement and sense of paradox may well be the reason that so many critics and interviewers are driven to dig and delve into Gallant's private life as if her family background, her various relationships, or the sum total of her laundry lists would furnish the psychic key to fit the intransigent lock of her fiction. And the fact that Gallant guards her privacy with the verbal equivalent of Doberman pinschers, and that she repeatedly warns us against reading any of her fiction as autobiographical — even the Linnet Muir stories[5] — would seem only to fuel beliefs that we can crack her fiction's code — frustrate, in effect, the project of her fiction — by using the hidden facts about her life as an interpretative grid for her oeuvre. Gallant is at present writing her memoirs for Oxford University Press, driven, one suspects, as much by the need to have done with irritating invasions of her privacy, and with fatuous or else damagingly false assertions about her character, as by any compulsive fascination with her own past. Consistent with her practice of impersonality/invisibility in her work (a practice which extends to a refusal to comment on interpretations of her fiction) is her belief that curiosity about the writer's life kills interest in the work itself — she has cited the recent biography of Katherine Anne Porter as a case in point.[6]

How does one respond to Gallant's refusal to talk about her private life; her insistence that the work speaks for itself and that it is not the writer's place nor is it worth her time to talk about that work in any literary-critical way? One responds with a round of applause. For it's doubtful that intimate knowledge of Gallant's own life would in any authentic way illuminate her work.

For one thing, her fiction is rich with dreams and images, recurrent motifs and situations which work supremely well within the fictive structures she creates — we have no need to drag in biographical fact to improve their eloquence. For another, Gallant's an artist of negative capability in true Keatsian style,[7] assuming the persona, or exposing the consciousness, of a considerable range of characters with whom she can have no more than fragments of experience and desire in common. Think of Bonnie — and Wishart — in *Green Water, Green Sky*, Netta in "The Moslem Wife," Sandor Speck and Lydia Cruche in "Speck's Idea." The Linnet Muir sequence in *Home Truths* is an exception to the rule, and the *caveat* Gallant issues regarding any one-to-one identification between herself and the character Linnet would no doubt be doubly extended to Jenny and Molly in *What Is To Be Done?*, the play set in that wartime Montreal Gallant knew so well. Moreover, Gallant has already provided us with an entrée into something at least as important as her personal life, her "life of the mind": the recently published *Paris Notebooks* reveal those political, social, and literary sympathies which are the foundation for the fictive worlds she constructs. (Gallant, after all, is as fine a writer of non-fiction as she is of fiction: her forthcoming book on the Dreyfus affair may turn out to be as important as any of her collections of stories.)

Most importantly, however, the "true confessions" biographical approach would afford false satisfactions to Gallant's readers, permitting us to substitute facile psychological explanations such as "she writes so pessimistically about marriage because her own marriage failed so quickly" for the less consoling apprehension that marriage, by its very nature, constricts and condemns us. Gallant's fiction would not succeed unless it were both crystalline and opaque, ruthless and yet disinterested: her best work operates on those same principles of attraction and repulsion that Lucian Freud evokes in his comments upon painting: "The task of the artist is to make the human being uncomfortable, and yet we are drawn to a great work by involuntary chemistry, like a hound getting a scent; the dog isn't free, it can't do otherwise, it gets the scent and instinct does the rest."[8]

The business of this essay is not to analyse Gallant's oeuvre, or to tease out intimate aspects of her personal life, but to approach Gallant as someone who has succeeded in making writing a way of life. I recently talked with Gallant in Paris — on the understanding that we would discuss her writing life and nothing else. For all her reputation as a *farouche*, she was as courteous and informative an interviewee as could be wished. What follows, then, will be an account of this writer's life drawn from information I received directly from Gallant,[9] and supplemented by facts which she has disclosed in previously published interviews.

In the interests of "placing" this most atypical of Canadian writers, one might begin by invoking the writer who is her polar opposite: Elizabeth Smart. Both women had mothers who can be most charitably described as impossible, and from whom relations had to be completely severed so that any independent life could take place at all. Both spent most of their adult life away from the country of their birth. Here the resemblance stops short. For Smart produced one significant work of fiction, *By Grand Central Station I Sat Down and Wept*: a disastrous, even masochistic, choice of lover — the poet George Barker — led not only to the necessity of her raising, singlehandedly, four children, but also to the thwarting of her own desire to create fiction for a period of some thirty years. What Elizabeth Smart accomplished: imperfect self-immolation in the name of "the myth of romantic love,"[10] the blighting and wasting of her gifts as a writer, entrapment within the most cretinous premises of the feminine mystique — Mavis Gallant avoided with precision. What is most astonishing about Gallant, given the pre-feminist context of her most important decisions, is her early establishment and brilliantly successful enjoyment of independence — from parental control and from the personal and professional entanglements which would have prevented her from pursuing her vocation. From 1950, when she quit her job as a journalist at *The Montreal Standard*, until the present, she has made the writing of fiction her profession. At sixty-five she is the author of a play, two novels, seven books of short stories, a collection of essays, and numerous reviews for prestigious magazines, as well as a staggering number of uncollected stories and prose pieces published mainly in *The New Yorker*. More importantly, she is still at work: on a new novel, on her memoirs, and on a monumental account of the Dreyfus affair, not a historian's but a writer's evocation and interpretation of an entire era.

There may well be a myth in place that, after her first publication in *The New Yorker*, Gallant was assured of a steady income and venue for her fiction: that hers was a royal road to the realization of her desire not only to write, but to write as confidently as she does. The reality is significantly different. After publishing a few stories in small Canadian journals, Gallant tried her luck with the most prestigious magazine in America: "I just wanted to be published," she recalls, "and *The New Yorker* had very good writers — I thought it was a nice place to be, if I could get in." Get in she did, but one gets the impression that her success was somewhat spoiled for her by ambivalent responses from her peers. She was earning, she recalls, $50 a week when she received her first cheque from *The New Yorker* — a cheque for $600. "It was a lot of money — I don't think I'd ever had $600 together, ever. I don't know anyone who did. I made a great mistake — I thought it was $60 . . . it never occurred to me it might be so much. The mistake I made, quite truthfully, was showing it to people — [they] thought I was showing off. But I know I was very excited. I was twenty-seven years old." In the daze of her excitement and disbelief, Gallant went round the newspaper where she worked, telling her colleagues of her good fortune. "A couple of my friends were very pleased for me — others, I learned later, were very resentful." Not so much of the money she'd earned, but of the fact that now she really could follow her plan to travel and write. "I'd quit my job, I said I was leaving in the autumn of that year, and suddenly I could say, 'Well look, all right, I can do it.' "

This anecdote of Gallant's first grand success in print reveals key elements of her persona as writer: amazing bravado or *chutzpah*, an extraordinary degree of discipline and determination, and, rather surprisingly, prudence. She gave herself two years to succeed at a decidedly risky business — the writing of excellent fiction which would yet be lucrative enough to support her — while leaving open the option of returning to Montreal and the practice of journalism should she fail. Yet failure, one comes to understand, would have resulted in more than a blow to her pride. For she confesses that during those probationary years she was "haunted" by the fear that she might be like her father, whom she describes as "a virtually untalented painter who passionately lived for this thing for which he had no gift."

Gallant survived with "great difficulty" during her first three years of "feast or famine" in Europe. She came first to Paris, stayed the winter, and then left for the Midi. She sojourned — and wrote — in Austria, Rome, and Sicily, poked round Switzerland, and finally went to Spain both because it was "rock bottom cheap" and because of overwhelming curiosity about the Spanish civil war, which had been a "myth" to Gallant and her friends during the war years. Although she kept coming back to Paris, she spent the greatest part of her time — two years on and off — in Spain. "I went back because it was cheap," she reiterates, describing how she kept company with other hard-up people, the kind mercilessly delineated in her story "When We Were Nearly Young." "It was up and down a great deal" — penury in Madrid and comparative luxury in Majorca, where, for practically nothing, she rented a house for a whole summer. Radical financial insecurity, however, did not put a crimp into what one realizes was a native generosity or lavishness of spirit: "I invited friends [to Majorca], I invited people and they came until I had no money." Back in Madrid she sold her clothes to raise ready cash, ate in dirt-cheap restaurants, or at times didn't eat at all, staying in bed till the afternoon because she didn't have the money to get through a normal waking day. She admits to having destroyed photographs of herself from the period, so emaciated had she become: "I associate being thin — for me — with being desperately ill — it's a neurotic thing."

When I expressed my admiration for her tenacity, her sticking it out through thin and thinner, Gallant's reply was revealing of her extraordinarily focussed and tenacious character: "It was my decision, so I couldn't worry about it — because you can't make yourself sound like someone demanding sympathy for this. All I had to do was stay in Montreal, where I had a very good job. It was my choice, so I couldn't sit and weep about it and get people to weep with me because everyone would have said, 'You were wrong.'" Gallant permitted herself neither self-pity nor indecisiveness; she obviously made it through those difficult first years due to a strong fighting spirit and a rather magnificent pride. "If you give yourself two years, you have to take two years. To go back beaten — I would never have written another word. I would never be a Sunday writer. I would have gone back to journalism, which I liked — I liked the life. I would have done it and swallowed the rest. But I wasn't willing to, and the alternative seemed to be so mediocre." Yet Gallant is honest about the consequences of her successful independence. "You pay for it. It's a choice of what you want to give up. I don't know any writer who has total security. . . . You can't live off books, you know."

Gallant's insistence on her financial independence brings us back to the uniqueness of her position as a Canadian writer who has always paid her own professional way, and who, thanks to publication in well-paying (American) magazines, hasn't had to depend on that staple means to eke out income, creative-writing classes. She described to me how her most promising students at the University of Toronto went to such classes and henceforth ceased to be promising. "They picked up expressions like 'creative flow.' " She alludes to problems faced by *The New Yorker*: fiction from the creative-writing courses of the seventies is now streaming in — instead of the "stacks and stacks of good stories" the fiction editors previously had to choose from, they are stuck with what Gallant refers to as the "homogenized" results of creative-writing degrees. The results are predictable: "Creative-writing students get resentful if their work isn't published." They expect, Gallant implies, that whatever erupts from their pens or processors is publishable, and thus worthy of state funding. "Some students I've addressed thought that the fact I supported myself was against me. They thought I was writing for money, and that if you were writing on grants and scholarships you weren't writing for money but for — they never used the word 'art,' that was beyond them — you were writing out of your need to 'communicate.' But if you're constantly writing out of grants, how do you know if you're going to sink or swim? What about readership?"

Gallant's attitude to what many Canadian writers have referred to as "The Canada Cow" may indicate an indifference to or simple distance from the present realities not so much of Canadian writers' lives as their possibilities for making a living without leaving Canada or Canadian publishers. In her introduction to *Home Truths* she declares, "I distrust and reject absolutely" the concepts of nationalism and patriotism, which she distinguishes from "the national sense of self."[11] Gallant's first submissions to *The New Yorker* were rejected as being too Canadian in their settings, and she did respond by sending the magazine a story set in Connecticut,[12] but after this initial compromise, she seems to have suited herself as to the locale and dramatis personae of her fictions. The characters of her stories of the fifties and sixties are often American — but they are Canadian, British, German as well, and the hero of her second novel, *A Fairly Good Time*, is decidedly Canadian. Like other writers more or less of her generation — Hugh MacLennan and Morley Callaghan, for example — Gallant has a natural attachment to the United States as the "great good place" which made her financial survival possible. She also has personal reasons for this attachment: "It was in New York, at fourteen, that I understood for the first time there was a possibility in life of being happy."[13] Yet Gallant also recalls refusing to salute the American flag when at school in the States — not out of any resentment, she insists, but because "I was not an American, the Stars and Stripes was not my flag, and that was that. I resisted a change of citizenship when it was offered me because I knew the result would be fake: whatever I was called, I would continue to think of myself as a Canadian."[14] Perhaps such an unproblematic sense of national self is only possible to the expatriate: certainly Canadian artists living in Mulroney's Canada will be decidedly out of sympathy with Gallant's lack of animosity, or at least of wariness, towards the United States[15] and the cultural implications of Manifest Destiny. Yet it is refreshing to find such a superb artist taking her Canadianness for granted, pointing us beyond the tediously dated "Canadian identity" preoccupation and towards the apprehension that what's of signal importance in our writing is not its quota of Canadian content, its degree of conformity to the so-called Canadian archetypes, but simply its inherent excellence.

Gallant's attitudes and sympathies, however, are enmeshed in her point and place of view: she has made Europe her home for thirty-seven years, and it is with her European experience as it permeates her fiction that I wish to deal. One of the most striking features of Gallant's vision is its inclusiveness, its awareness that there is more than one class, gender, religion, or race. She is no F. Scott Fitzgerald writing of the gilded few: her fiction deals as persuasively with an illiterate Italian peasant girl as with a spoiled American divorcée. The range of her sympathies and interests was made possible by the kind of life she led those first few years in Europe: the hard times she went through and the nature of the people she chose to know. For these reasons, it's worthwhile to examine in some detail the context and circumstances of Gallant's first years abroad.

Though The New Yorker was taking many more of Gallant's stories than they rejected, she was still hard up. "The reason was that you would fall behind, and you would really need . . . about six cheques (at once) because you're behind with everything — it's winter and you've only got your summer clothes. I had fallen into a world of refugees and I was helping them out a lot — people of my own age, late twenties — they looked on me as someone with a lot of money."

Quite apart from these acts of philanthropy, Gallant's income was minimal simply because she was not being paid for the stories she published — and for no fault of The New Yorker. The experience she has to relate on this subject softens the usual portrait of her as a street-smart artist, born knowing exactly what she wants and how to get it. She relates how she picked, almost at random — because he wrote such a charming letter —

one particular agent out of all those who contacted her after her first publication in *The New Yorker*. "What I didn't know was that he was a crook; he'd taken in any number of young writers, but I had no one to consult. So I wrote to him . . . and, between 1951 and 1953, sent him twelve stories, all of which he sold and for none of which he paid me. He told me that none of them had been taken. And there was a point in Madrid in '52 when I was in complete despair, because I thought my work wasn't being published and I thought I'd have to give up — because I'd given myself two years. And I was desperate. . . . Finally he was unmasked. Somehow I got a copy of *The New Yorker* and saw the story of mine called 'The Picnic' — I didn't even know it had sold. I didn't write to them saying, 'Where's my money,' I said, 'I'm very upset that you didn't show me the proofs.' They immediately wrote back and said, 'Thank God we've heard from you, your agent said you were off somewhere in Capri and he couldn't get in touch with you. Did you get the money for this story, and, more important, did you get the money for the other two stories?' I had no idea any of this was going on. Finally *The New Yorker* said, 'It's time for you to make up your mind about this agent because we don't want to deal with him.' And I was dilly-dallying: I couldn't believe it. And I'd made a mistake, because I didn't know you never signed a contract with an agent."

One of the reasons she is so devoted to *The New Yorker*, Gallant explains, has to do with the magazine's helpfulness in disentangling her from this extremely sticky web. "They said, 'We can never get your money back for you but we can break the contract for you and get you your stories back.' . . . " This they did, for a minimum of legal fees, and Gallant's consequent loyalty to the magazine is due, perhaps, as much to relief at her liberation from the emotional implications of her situation as to gratitude for its practical remedy. For she describes herself as having been "in agony" in Madrid. "I wrote in my diary, 'I walk like an old woman.' I was thirty, I was so discouraged, I had this awful feeling that if [my writing] really is nothing there's nothing else I want to do. You musn't imagine it [was] easy."

This appalling chain of circumstances — grinding poverty stemming from her supposed lack of publication, pointing to the abject failure of her plan to live by writing and to a consequent near-collapse of her very sense of herself as a writer — obviously has much to do with the fact that, despite her protracted period of residence in Spain, she has published surprisingly little to do with the country. Thus the only literary testimony to her Spanish days are the stories "When We Were Nearly Young" — a relation of the penury shared by the narrator, a foreigner temporarily down and out in Madrid, and a number of endemically impoverished Spaniards with whom she finds herself associating — and "Señor Piñedo," which has to do with the occupants of an illegal boarding-house in Franco's Madrid, and finally, a novel which she describes as "a piece of junk," but which she can't somehow bring herself to throw away.

In Spain she discovered that what she and fellow leftists in wartime Montreal had made into myth was, in fact, the life of real people. "I had the same shock in Italy," she adds. "It was the time of the Vittorio de Sica films. . . . And when you saw the reality it was so much more sad. God knows the films were sad, but the reality was worse, more humdrum. . . . I realized how much one is cheated in art. It was a great shock. . . . Just getting in a train — I was travelling third or fourth class — and there'd suddenly be all the workers going to work in Salerno and they were all this high, and I thought . . . [de Sica's] cheated us because the reality is much worse, there's nothing pretty about it. You know, there's pretty-sad and ugly-sad. Art is essentially a cheat . . . being a displacement. I don't mean that Rossellini or de Sica prettied up reality, my God they didn't, but you left the theatre, and when you saw the reality outside —"

Art is a cheat, a displacement of brute by aesthetically possible reality. Her own art is no exception to this rule, Gallant insists. Yet perhaps her recognition of the sweet cheat involved in her calling gives the clue to a subtle yet pervasive shading in Gallant's fiction — an acrid, brittle quality that lingers like an aftertaste, for all the deliciousness of her phrasing. Gallant can be savagely funny, and to come across one of her stories in *The New Yorker* is like coming across a marvellously witty, maliciously intelligent acquaintance in a room of drearily pretentious or just plain silly bores. Yet to read an entire collection at a go, to plunge into Gallant's entire oeuvre, is a different matter. With few exceptions her stories deal with privileged characters in archetypally glamorous and sophisticated settings — Paris, Venice, the French or Italian Riviera — yet her narratives disclose how the most superb surfaces and enviable reputations are disfigured by tawdriness, pettiness, selfishness, and greed. Gallant, in fact, is not just a realist but something of a moralist as well, relentlessly tripping up our expectations and desires that things should be as we wish them, not as we've made them. To put it crudely, her stories reveal that one can be as miserable, as cruel, as ignorant in Paris,

France, as in Paris, Ontario. The whole myth of the romantic flight abroad is not only defeathered but dismembered by Gallant's unsparing pen. Whatever illusions about the old world she may have had while still in Canada were certainly shattered by her experience of life in immediately post-war Europe. And here is a telling point of difference between Gallant and other expatriate writers such as Mordecai Richler and Norman Levine, a simple, yet profound, difference in the company each kept.

Coming to Europe, Gallant shunned the company of other North Americans, or even English-speakers, and found herself in a floating circle of exiles and refugees. "You just naturally fell into that world, particularly as I didn't want to go into the . . . expatriate Anglo-American thing — I rather avoided it. For one thing I had no money. And they were all people who were . . . either bums or deadbeats, and I really didn't want to fall in with [them]. . . . There's a difference between a refugee who's hard up and a deadbeat . . . there's a great difference. But I knew refugees, Hungarians, Eastern Europeans, who were about my age and younger, and I did help them. They all came to something but in different ways. . . . The Anglo-American world was very different, I wasn't drawn to it. [The well-off ones] were either salaried or in embassies. In Madrid, there was no embassy, because Canada was the last country to recognize Franco and we just had a man from some commercial centre. I went to see him on some matter or other, and through him I was invited to tea with some Canadian people. And do you know that these people — honest to God — came from small towns and sat talking about the servants. I was furious, because with the poverty of Spain at that time, you'd be ashamed to have a servant. . . ."

Talking of her Spanish stories, she utters a characteristic proviso: "You mustn't take these things to be autobiographical or you're going to fall flat on your face. These are background, it's not straight autobiography. It's the common nature of people and cognition of circumstances." Yet it's more than an absolute insistence on privacy that makes Gallant refuse any autobiographical interpretation of her fiction. Historical perspective and an admirable honesty play their parts as well. "I wasn't a victim of history. If you are Arthur Koestler, young, you can say, 'I'm a victim of history, I've been thrown around Europe.' But I wasn't, I chose this, and I knew I had to go through it." To go through it meant not only experiencing her own abject poverty, but also observing and recording the more horrific sources of impoverishment of those whom she calls "the victims of history." Recording them, moreover, with a strict disinterestedness which precludes the dishonesty of sentimentality or Chadbandian humanitarianism, and which, in her finest stories — "The Four Seasons" for example, or "The Latehomecomer" — creates a rare compassion, all the more moving for its restraint.

Gallant, in fact, appears as a "selfless" writer when her fictions are placed next to those of her more egocentric compatriots. She herself distinguishes her practice as a writer of fiction from that of Richler and Levine in three words: "I'm more political." Referring to current events and the acts of the powerful, she adds, "Every so often it comes over me, something happens — by God, I was right — they really are bastards." She comments that when she was in the process of rereading certain of her essays for publication in *Paris Notebooks*, she was "struck with how much to the right everyone had moved. And that shift to the right one finds constantly in life and that's why young people are left, I suppose, because they'll go to the right. People who were kids then are now married with children and are very much more conservative than they were. Hardly anyone has stayed as they were. . . . Even I sound somewhat unrecognizable to myself — so *passionnée*. . . ." She relates an incident concerning her yearly application for the permit which all resident foreigners must possess in France. "I gave [*Paris Notebooks*] last time I was in the Préfecture to the supercop I was dealing with. And when I saw him again he said, 'Vous êtes insurrectionnaire, madame,' and I said, 'Oh, monsieur, si peu.' . . . And he said [that he hadn't had] this feeling of insurrection [in 1968]. I said, 'We were in the streets and all we had were the rumours — you were in the Préfecture and you had the facts.' . . . A year ago I was sitting at dinner with Canadians from the Embassy . . . and two of the men there who are now officials in our embassy had been students in Paris at the time — at ENA, that's the School of National Administration — and they were just completely scornful of the '68 thing — but they had been living in the Seizième Arrondissement at the time. They said they used to stroll out and look at this nonsense and then they'd stroll back to the safety of the Seizième where things weren't on strike. Of course they weren't on strike, the Seizième [never is]. And I said to myself, 'How funny,' because my whole world was in it, and all of my friends, even in the Seizième, because their children were in it. And here were these two Canadian students . . ."

Gallant's intense involvement in the events of May 1968, as recorded in *Paris Notebooks*, gives the lie to any contention that because she's an exile and expatriate, she must preserve a necessary distance and detachment from the life around her, and from the responses of those who hail from her country of origin. Her ironic appraisal of the way in which the two Canadian officials had disremembered the past, or at least refused to concede any reality to an alternative version of May '68, recalls her indignant response to the small-town Canadians who sat in poverty-stricken Madrid discussing the servant problem. Disinterestedness does not mean indifference: rather, it is the condition of genuine as opposed to fashionable or "politically correct" sympathy for those who are "other," particularly in terms of social class and historical experience — the Carmelas, Bernadettes, Jeannies, and their like.

One of the distinctive tasks of Gallant's writing is to set down the lives of people who are other, different from herself, and from the majority of her North American readers. Her choice of subjects predates her European years: her first published stories dealt with refugees from Nazism who found themselves utterly dislocated in Canadian cities and homes. Undoubtedly Gallant's early fascination with the physically as well as psychologically displaced and homeless can be traced to her own childhood experience: after her father's death she was shipped off to seventeen schools in a number of different cities. Yet what's more important to note is that in her fiction, physical dislocation almost always has political and historical resonances. The first stories she published in *The New Yorker* had to do with the daughters of wealthy parents engaged in adulterous affairs or marital shuffles. Yet in one of them, "Madeline's Birthday," a young refugee from Nazi Germany works his way into the margins of the text.

In subsequent stories such as "The Other Paris" and "The Old Place," Gallant would bring North Americans to Europe in order to pit the romantic ignorance engendered by "Fortress America" against the reality of lived history — not memorized facts and dates but the tangible results of bombing, deportation, and genocide. Later still, in collections such as *The Pegnitz Junction* and *From the Fifteenth District*, she would deal almost entirely with "foreigners" from within the assumptions of their own cultural, historical, and social experience, without any North American observers to mediate "the other." (The exception in *Fifteenth District* is "Potter," a story told from the perspective of the perfectly realized Pole, Piotr, to whom the spoiled Canadian girl Laurie is enchantingly unfathomable.) Gallant has proved equally adept at exposing the ethos of the expatriate, déclassé British on the French or Italian Riviera, and of Parisiens in their native habitat, as in her latest book of short stories, *Overhead in a Balloon*. Those critics who persist in judging Gallant's "Canadian" stories to be, *a priori*, her finest, are guilty of more than cultural chauvinism. For in her uncanny ability to present the lives of "foreigners" from within their own social and psychological context — to do so as a disinterested observer rather than as a perplexed outsider — Gallant resembles Henry James, who went beyond the limitations of the "international theme" to produce some of his finest work, fictions as varied as *What Maisie Knew* and *The Turn of the Screw*, *The Awkward Age* and *The Princess Cassamassima*.

Over the years, Gallant's interest has quite naturally shifted from a preoccupation with the effects of the Second World War to an interest in more recent history and politics — the emergence of the extreme right, for example, as registered in stories like "Speck's Idea." In her interview in *Canadian Fiction Magazine* she described the devastating effect of being shown the first photographs of Nazi extermination camps — devastating, she insists, because these things were not then the données and clichés they are now. "I was fascinated by Germany," she relates, "but the funny thing is that when I finished [*The Pegnitz Junction*] . . . I lost interest — not in history or anything, but that overwhelming curiosity I had — just deflated." So, seemingly, did her *Wanderlust*. Once Gallant's problems with her crooked agent had been sorted out, and the days of abject uncertainty were past her, she settled upon The City of Light as a permanent home, and for the most prosaic of reasons. "I wouldn't have stayed in France if I couldn't have had a normal bourgeois life. I'd never have stayed if I was going to have a marginal life. And that's why I didn't go to live in Rome, because a foreigner's always marginal there. I was very torn, I loved Rome, but a woman would always be *en marge* and always with foreigners. . . . I wanted a normal, what I call bourgeois, life, where people get married and have children . . . and so forth."

Yet for all her fidelity to the bourgeois code, Gallant has consistently refused to acquire the usual appurtenances of the *bourgeoise* — a husband and children. "I'm not really a very marriageable person," she asserts. "And every time the question came up I always found that I was thinking, 'Well, whatever happens, I wouldn't abandon children, that's absolutely out. And I wouldn't take children away from their father, as I was taken away from mine. . . . So I'm walking into a trap.' So — I said no, no, no, because I could see myself in this awful dilemma. And unless you go on writing, [marriage] takes up more and more of your life." While talking of the difficulties women writers face in reconciling the needs of their vocation with the demands of their children, Gallant warns, "You mustn't be surprised if your children resent your work, and won't read it. Colette's daughter never read a word Colette wrote."

Obviously Gallant is not "the compleat feminist" — she rejects perhaps not the movement so much as the label as "utterly meaningless." "To me," she asserts, "the only feminist thing is economic — it's to get the same pay [as men]. . . . When the movement began and I read the first things of Kate Millett, I was pleased, because there were things I thought too — Hemingway, and the whole Freudian thing where they always would go on about the little baby boy and his Oedipus and his mother, and then the girl would get that much. . . . And [Millett] brought that out — all babies are *not* boys. . . . But then something happened and I completely lost it. . . ." Here is the point at which one can hypothesize a crucial difference between the writer Gallant would have been had she remained in North America, and the writer she has become by living in France for the past thirty-odd years. For her fiction, and even her essay on Gabrielle Russier, the young lycée teacher hounded to her death for having an affair with one of her male students, could not remotely be described as feminist in vision or ideological orientation. Of feminism in France, Gallant remarks: "I don't see the results here, it's never taken hold here, everything becomes intellectual, of course, but that's all, there's nothing else. But in Canada the only result I saw [of the feminist movement] was that nobody held open a door for me." Of the movement's effect on ordinary life in North America she recounts one illuminating incident. When she was taken into one of the faculty lounges at the University of Toronto to be introduced to the professors, nobody stood up at her entrance. "In France even women stand up to meet a woman, which is much more feminist, I think. You *always* stand up. . . . I was rather amazed, partly because I'd become used to [the courtesy] and also because of my age; they were much younger men." The anecdote points as much to Gallant's profound respect for the gestures and customs which make civilized life possible as to her fundamental lack of interest in and sympathy for what she describes as the "foreign territory" of the feminist movement.

As for English-speaking radical feminists and their projects of creating a new, non-patriarchal language in their writing, Gallant dismisses them succinctly: "They have no grasp on English — read their work. And it's marginal." Rather an abrupt dismissal of a brave new wave, yet one which gives considerable pause, considering the absolute mastery of the language Gallant possesses. She is very much a woman of her formative years, the age of the feminine mystique, in which women had black-and-white choices presented to them: either marry, have children, and spend your life ironing, or else stay single and have a successful career — as long as you're careful to make men think you're doing nothing of the kind. True to her early experience as a working woman — her journalist days on *The Montreal Standard* — Gallant shares one fundamental concern with all feminists: what she describes as "the economic issue," equal pay and status for work of equal value. But social complexities, she insists, cannot be tackled in the same way: "I don't think that the couple can be solved by legislation, that's absolute nonsense. What goes on between men and women goes on between men and women, *et ça c'est tout*. But — and these are trivial things — when I go to a restaurant with another woman, for example, I want the same attention as if I were a man. And I do insist. I've said in restaurants, "If we were men you wouldn't bring this wine." But that's economic again. Apart from that — there are men and there are women." As far as the overt influence of feminism on her fiction, she points to her new novel: "There are two couples, and it's the women who leave their husbands, for a pleasant change."

Paradoxically, it was as much the recognition that single women were not perceived by the French as the intellectual or social equivalents of doorstops, as it was fluency in the French language (which she's spoken from early childhood), and a passionate interest in French literature and politics, which led Gallant to make her home in Paris. And it is from her Parisian vantage point that she has written some of her most important work — not fiction, but what we might call social narratives — the journal she kept during the events of May 1968 and which was published almost by accident in *The New Yorker*,[16] and the lengthy introduction she wrote to a book on Gabrielle Russier. Gallant's "Immortal Gatito: The Gabrielle Russier Case," reprinted along with "The Events in May" in *Paris Notebooks*, is a miraculously direct and incisive threading of the labyrinth of French social practices, legal codes and institutions, and cultural données. This essay and "Paris: The Taste of a New Age" (also included in *Paris Notebooks*)

bear witness to Gallant's enviable position in her environment of
adoption: she is neither slavishly attached nor irremediably alien
to the daily life going on around her. Rather, she is sufficiently at
home to be able to criticize the shortcomings of French society
— while remaining enough of an émigré to perceive those shortcomings in the first place.

For all her familiarity with French society, politics, and
culture, Gallant has kept her distance from the Parisian literary
scene. "I do know some writers," she admits, "but they're just
friends. I think I've the same mix [of friends] I'd have had if I'd
stayed in Canada. And don't forget I'm getting pretty antique.
The people I know are older, so that you're not really rattling
around as you were thirty years ago. My friends are really quite
old, because when I came, I tended to meet people who were
much older than myself, who were interesting. . . ."

For a long time, in fact, few people knew that she was a
writer. "The French are not inquisitive," she observes. Only when
she began to inquire into the Russier case and needed to get
precise information from friends and acquaintances did the nature
of her professional life become known. "It wasn't that I made a
secret of it. If asked what I did I said, 'J'écris.' The French love
writers . . . they don't ask what you've done — they just love you
for writing." She offers a rather piquant observation about the
changed habits of Parisian writers (as opposed to literary theo-
rists). "Writers here aren't part of a group. That doesn't exist any
more — it existed when there was a café life. And a café life for
writers existed when there was no place to live and houses
weren't heated and people needed to keep warm. Now people
are at home with their television — and I mean it — and their place
in the country. Older writers need each other, but I don't think
the young ones do, now. They have agents and they want to to go
on TV, because there's a TV program for writers [*Apostrophe*]. It's
no different from writers in America. I do know that flocking
together is the last thing writers should do — it's different with
painters, they have to go to each other's studios to look at the
work [each is doing], but I don't think writers have any particular
conversation. Particularly nowadays when they talk about publishers and grants."

The overwhelming impression one receives, however, is
that Gallant has always been too busy producing books to spend
much time talking about writing. Apart from the novel-in-
progress (the first instalment of which appeared in the May 18,
1987, issue of *The New Yorker*) and the memoirs which she's

compiling from her journals for Oxford University Press, her chief labour is the book on Dreyfus which she's writing at the request of Random House. She makes it clear that this book is not the product of any private obsession: "I didn't have any interest in Dreyfus, it was *sur commande*. I'd turned down a lot of things on Dreyfus because I wanted to write fiction." And she admits that she didn't know what she was getting into with the Dreyfus book: "All the research is done, it's completely blocked out — and I just want to do it. I didn't realize how long it was going to take — it's like a thesis." She confesses to being apprehensive about the book's reception in certain quarters: "All the historians are going to be gunning, because I'm not a historian." Yet the fact that this account of the Dreyfus affair relies on the truth of the imagination and a passion for human observation would seem to make it, *a priori*, as valuable as any orthodox history.

As Gallant describes the book, it is a study of context and character — much as is her essay on Gabrielle Russier: "The first part is a long, long essay which just sets the thing in its time, Paris of that period, and the early life of Dreyfus and of Esterhazy, back to back. Their childhoods, and their marriage contracts . . . and [backgrounds]. It's all very well to say [Dreyfus] was an Alsatian Jew, but what was an Alsatian, what was a Jew, at that time? Then I take it year by year from 1904 till he comes back from Devil's Island in 1909; every one of those years is a chapter. [The narrative] is what happened, as far as I know, and when I don't know, I say. . . . It's all from books and from what people told me — I was lucky enough to get the children of these people."

The heart of the work, at least so far, would appear to be the introductory essay, in which Gallant records and interprets the minutiae of ordinary life for one segment of late-nineteenth-century French society: "what people ate for breakfast in Paris at the time. . . . The literature, the paintings." Yet she is also concerned to combat the stereotypes about Dreyfus, and to avoid the polarizations which characterize most discussion of his case: "He was just a man, he had all sorts of flaws and failings. But one hardly dares [to discuss these] because of the stereotype. . . . But he became very sympathetic to me." So *sympathique* that for Gallant the boundaries between history and memory, fact and imagination, became curiously and productively fluid: "I lived it so completely that it was in my dreams." As she relates in the introduction to *Home Truths*, the Linnet Muir stories grew out of her research on Dreyfus: "I had thought of [this book] sometimes as a river where I was drifting farther and farther from shore. At the same time . . . there began to be restored in some under-ground river of the mind a lost Montreal."[17]

As to when Gallant will complete the Dreyfus manuscript, and how many more "lost cities" and "underground rivers" it will uncover, we can only wait and see. In the meantime, Gallant is at work on her memoirs, her new novel, and, perhaps as a necessary respite from the arduous task of revisioning history, the occasional humorous prose piece. In the latter line she has produced, among other things, a series of surreal letters between Lewis Carroll and Maurice Ravel, a satirical sketch of the relations between various tenants in a Parisian apartment building, a spoof of an émigré review, and a pastiche of confessional writing with the splendid title "Dido Flute, Spouse to Europe."

One cannot imagine Gallant not writing: nor can one imagine her writing life being affected by questions of how popular or pushable her fictions are. "I knew from the beginning that I would never have a large readership. But I still thought I might be able to live from [my fiction]. In fact [my readership] is larger than I thought it would be. I had no illusions . . . that three million people would have heard of me. But I knew where I'd succeed, if I were to succeed at all. I've not been disappointed."

Neither, one need hardly add, have we.

---

[1] "What Is Style," *Paris Notebooks* (Toronto: Macmillan, 1986), p. 177.

[2] See Gallant's essay on Yourcenar in *Paris Notebooks*.

[3] Gallant chose this line from Boris Pasternak — "Only personal independence matters" — as the epigraph to *Home Truths*.

[4] "In Youth Is Pleasure," *Home Truths* (Toronto: Macmillan, 1981), p. 235.

[5] She states in the preface to *Home Truths* (p. xxii), "The character I called Linnet Muir is not an exact reflection. I saw her as quite another person, but it would be untrue to say that I invented everything."

[6] A comment made during the interview I conducted with Gallant in June 1987.

[7] Stephen Spender quoting Keats — "The poetical character is not itself — it has no self — it is everything and nothing — it has no character" — comments: "In this way it enters into the nature of things and people outside itself." (Introduction to *The Notebooks of Malte Laurids Brigge* [Oxford: Oxford University Press, 1984], p. xviii.) Spender goes on to liken Rilke's task

in his *Notebooks* (written, incidentally, when Rilke was living in Paris) to that of Keats: "the transformation of the world of reality into language capable of comprehending that reality. The poet . . . must be one of 'those to whom the miseries of the world/Are misery, and will not let them rest.' " As with the poet, so with the writer of fiction, and especially so in the case of Gallant, who, when asked whether she had any religious beliefs, replied: ". . . I can't completely . . . take seriously a philosophy that excludes the possibility of Divine Intervention. On the other hand, I find it hard to believe we're in a world where God walked. . . . Look at us. Awful. Dreadful. Get in the Métro and look at people." (Interview with Geoff Hancock, *Canadian Fiction Magazine*, November 28, 1978, p. 35.)

[8] Quoted by Robert Hughes, "On Lucian Freud" in *The New York Review of Books*, XXXIV: 13 (August 13, 1987), 57.

[9] Material in quotation marks is a transcription of Gallant's comments made during an interview recorded in June 1987 in her Paris apartment.

[10] See Rosemary Sullivan's article "Muse in a Female Ghetto: A Portrait of Elizabeth Smart," *This Magazine* 20:3 (August-September 1986), 22-4. Sullivan declares: "Elizabeth was the kind of person one puzzles over: to understand her life seems as important as understanding her writing." (p. 22)

[11] *Home Truths*, p. xv.

[12] See Geoff Hancock's interview with Mavis Gallant for the special Gallant issue of *Canadian Fiction Magazine*, p. 32.

[13] *Home Truths*, p. xiv.

[14] *Ibid.*, p. xiv.

[15] See, for example, Gallant's response in "The Events in May: A Paris Notebook II" to anti-Americanism manifested by the striking students, in *Paris Notebooks*, pp. 63-4.

[16] "The Events in May: A Paris Notebook" I and II were published almost by accident in *The New Yorker*. When editor William Maxwell telephoned Gallant during May 1968 and learned that she wasn't writing stories at the time, but was preoccupied with recording what was happening on the streets of Paris, he asked her to put something together on the subject for his magazine.

[17] *Home Truths*, p. xxii.

THE CHOSEN HUSBAND

By Mavis Gallant

Mavis Gallant was born in Montreal in 1922. She worked for a short time for the National Film Board and as a journalist but in 1950 decided to live and work in Paris, where she has remained ever since. Her stories are usually first published in *The New Yorker*. Canada has been slow to recognize her as one of our most accomplished and sophisticated writers. Her books include: *The Other Paris* (1956); *Green Water, Green Sky* (1959); *My Heart Is Broken* (1964); *A Fairly Good Time* (1970); *The Affair of Gabrielle Russier* (1971); *The Pegnitz Junction* (1973); *The End of the World and Other Stories* (1974); *From the Fifteenth District* (1979); *Home Truths* (1981); *Overhead in a Balloon* (1985); and *Paris Notebooks* (1986).

In 1949, a year that contained no other news of value, Mme. Carette came into a legacy of eighteen thousand dollars from a brother-in-law who had done well in Fall River. She had suspected him of being a Freemason, as well as of other offenses, none of them trifling, and so she did not make a show of bringing out his photograph; instead, she asked her daughters, Berthe and Marie, to mention him in their prayers. They may have, for a while. The girls were twenty-two and twenty, and Berthe, the elder, hardly prayed at all.

The first thing that Mme. Carette did was to acquire a better address. Until now she had kept the Montreal habit of changing her rented quarters every few seasons, a conversation with a landlord serving as warranty, rent paid in cash. This time she was summoned by appointment to a rental agency to sign a two-year lease. She had taken the first floor of a stone house around the corner from the church of St. Louis de France. This was her old parish (she held to the network of streets near Parc Lafontaine), but a glorious strand of it, Rue St. Hubert.

Before her inheritance Mme. Carette had crept to church, eyes lowered; had sat where she was unlikely to disturb anyone whose life seemed more fortunate, therefore more deserving, than her own. She had not so much prayed as petitioned. Now she ran a glove along the pew to see if it was dusted, straightened the unread pamphlets that called for more vocations for missionary service in Africa, told a confessor that, like all the prosperous, she was probably without fault. When the holy-water font looked mossy, she called the parish priest and had words with his housekeeper, even though scrubbing the church was not her job. She still prayed every day for the repose of her late husband, and the unlikelier rest of his Freemason brother, but a tone of briskness caused her own words to rattle in her head. Church was a hushed annex to home. She prayed to insist upon the refinement of some request, and instead of giving thanks simply acknowledged that matters used to be worse.

Her daughter Berthe had been quick to point out that Rue St. Hubert was in decline. Otherwise, how could the Carettes afford to live here? (Berthe worked in an office and was able to pay half the rent.) A family of foreigners were installed across the road. A seamstress had placed a sign in a ground-floor window — a sure symptom of decay. True, but Mme. Carette had as near neighbors a retired opera singer and the first cousins of a city councillor — calm, courteous people who had never been on relief. A few blocks north stood the mayor's private dwelling, with a lamppost on each side of his front door. (During the recent war the mayor had been interned, like an enemy alien. No one quite remembered why. Mme. Carette believed that he had refused an invitation to Buckingham Palace, and that the English had it in for him. Berthe had been told that he had tried to annex Montreal to the State of New York and that someone had minded. Marie, who spoke to strangers on the bus, once came home with a story about Fascist views; but as she could not spell "Fascist," and did not know if it was a kind of landscape or something to eat, no one took her seriously. The mayor had eventually been released, was promptly re-elected, and continued to add lustre to Rue St. Hubert.)

Mme. Carette looked out upon long façades of whitish stone, windowpanes with bevelled edges that threw rainbows. In her childhood this was how notaries and pharmacists had lived, before they began to copy the English taste for freestanding houses, blank lawns, ornamental willows, leashed dogs. She recalled a moneyed aunt and uncle, a family of well-dressed, soft-spoken children, heard the echo of a French more accurately expressed than her own. She had tried to imitate the peculiarity of every syllable, sounded like a plucked string, had tried to make her little girls speak that way. But they had rebelled, refused, said it made them laughed at.

When she had nothing to request, or was tired of repeating the same reminders, she shut her eyes and imagined her funeral. She was barely forty-five, but a long widowhood strictly observed had kept her childish, not youthful. She saw the rosary twined round her hands, the vigil, the candles perfectly still, the hillock of wreaths. Until the stunning message from Fall River, death had been her small talk. She had never left the subject, once entered, without asking, "And what will happen then to my poor little Marie?" Nobody had ever taken the question seriously except her Uncle Gildas. This was during their first Christmas dinner on Rue St. Hubert. He said that Marie should pray for guidance, the sooner the better. God had no patience with last-minute appeals. (Uncle Gildas was an elderly priest with limited social opportunities, though his niece believed him to have wide and worldly connections.)

"Prayer can fail," said Berthe, testing him.

Instead of berating her he said calmly, "In that case, Berthe can look after her little sister."

She considered him, old and eating slowly. His cassock exhaled some strong cleaning fluid — tetrachloride; he lived in a rest home, and nuns took care of him.

Marie was dressed in one of Berthe's castoffs — marine-blue velvet with a lace collar. Mme. Carette wore a gray-white dress Berthe thought she had seen all her life. In her first year of employment Berthe had saved enough for a dyed rabbit coat. She also had an electric seal, and was on her way to sheared raccoon. "Marie had better get married," she said.

Mme. Carette still felt cruelly the want of a husband, someone — not a daughter — to help her up the step of a streetcar, read *La Presse* and tell her what was in it, lay down the law to Berthe. When Berthe was in adolescence, laughing and whispering and not telling her mother the joke, Mme. Carette had asked Uncle Gildas to speak as a father. He sat in the parlor, in a plush chair, all boots and cassock, knees apart and a hand on each knee, and questioned Berthe about her dreams. She said she had never in her life dreamed anything. Uncle Gildas replied that anyone with a good conscience could dream events pleasing to God; he himself had been doing it for years. God kept the dreams of every living person on record, like great rolls of film. He could have them projected whenever he wanted. Montreal girls, notoriously virtuous, had his favor, but only up to a point. He forgave, but never forgot. He was the embodiment of endless time — though one should not take "embodiment" literally. Eternal remorse in a pit of flames was the same to him as a rap on the fingers with the sharp edge of a ruler. Marie, hearing this, had fainted dead away. That was the power of Uncle Gildas.

Nowadays, shrunken and always hungry, he lived in retirement, had waxed linoleum on his floor, no carpet, ate tapioca soup two or three times a week. He would have stayed in bed all day, but the nuns who ran the place looked upon illness as fatigue, fatigue as shirking. He was not tired or lazy; he had nothing to get up for. The view from his window was a screen of trees. When Mme. Carette came to visit — a long streetcar ride, then a bus — she had just the trees to look at: she could not stare at her uncle the whole time. The trees put out of sight a busy commercial garage. It might have distracted him to watch trucks backing out, perhaps to witness a bloodless accident. In the morning he went downstairs to the chapel, ate breakfast, sat on his bed after it was made. Or crossed the gleaming floor to a small table, folded back the oilcloth cover, read the first sentence of a memoir he was writing for his great-nieces: "I was born in Montreal, on the 22nd of May, 1869, of pious Christian parents, connected to Montreal families for whom streets and bridges have been named." Or shuffled out to the varnished corridor, where there was a pay phone. He liked dialling, but out of long discipline never did without a reason.

Soon after Christmas Mme. Carette came to see him, wearing Berthe's velvet boots with tassels, Berthe's dyed rabbit coat, and a feather turban of her own. Instead of praying for guidance Marie had fallen in love with one of the Greeks who were starting to move into their part of Montreal. There had never been a foreigner in the family, let alone a pagan. Her uncle interrupted to remark that Greeks were usually Christians, though of the wrong kind for Marie. Mme. Carette implored him to find someone, not a Greek, of the right kind: sober, established, Catholic, French-speaking, natively Canadian. "Not Canadian from New England," she said, showing a brief ingratitude to Fall River. She left a store of nickels, so that he could ring her whenever he liked.

Louis Driscoll, French in all but name, called on Marie for the first time on the twelfth of April, 1950. Patches of dirty snow still lay against the curb. The trees on Rue St. Hubert looked dark and brittle, as though winter had killed them at last. From behind the parlor curtain, unseen from the street, the Carette women watched him coming along from the bus stop. To meet Marie he had put on a beige tweed overcoat, loosely belted, a beige scarf, a bottle-green snap-brim fedora, crêpe-soled shoes, pigskin gloves. His trousers were sharply pressed, a shade darker than the hat. Under his left arm he held close a parcel in white paper, the size and shape of a two-pound box of Laura Secord chocolates. He stopped frequently to consult the house numbers (blue-and-white, set rather high, Montreal style), which he compared with a slip of paper brought close to his eyes.

It was too bad that he had to wear glasses; the Carettes were not prepared for that, or for the fringe of ginger hair below his hat. Uncle Gildas had said he was of distinguished appearance. He came from Moncton, New Brunswick, and was employed at the head office of a pulp-and-paper concern. His age was twenty-six. Berthe thought that he must be a failed seminarist; they were the only Catholic bachelors Uncle Gildas knew.

Peering at their front door, he walked into a puddle of slush. Mme. Carette wondered if Marie's children were going to be nearsighted. "How can we be sure he's the right man?" she said.

"Who else could he be?" Berthe replied. What did he want with Marie? Uncle Gildas could not have promised much in her name, apart from a pliant nature. There could never be a meeting in a notary's office to discuss a dowry, unless you counted some plates and furniture.

The old man may have frightened Louis, reminded him that prolonged celibacy — except among the clergy — is displeasing to God. Marie is poor, he must have said, though honorably connected. She will feel grateful to you all her life.

Their front steps were painted pearl gray, to match the building stone. Louis's face, upturned, was the color of wood ash. Climbing the stair, ringing the front doorbell could change his life in a way he did not wholly desire. Probably he wanted a woman without sin or risk or coaxing or remorse; but did he want her enough to warrant setting up a household? A man with a memory as transient as his, who could read an address thirty times and still let it drift, might forget to come to the wedding. He crumpled the slip of paper, pushed it inside a tweed pocket, withdrew a large handkerchief, blew his nose.

Mme. Carette swayed back from the curtain as though a stone had been flung. She concluded some private thought by addressing Marie: ". . . although I will feel better on my deathbed if I know you are in your own home." Louis meanwhile kicked the bottom step, getting rid of snow stuck to his shoes. (Rustics kicked and stamped. Marie's Greek had wiped his feet.) Still he hesitated, sliding a last pale look in the direction of buses and streetcars. Then, as he might have turned a gun on himself, he climbed five steps and pressed his finger to the bell.

"Somebody has to let him in," said Mme. Carette.

"Marie," said Berthe.

"It wouldn't seem right. She's never met him."

He stood quite near, where the top step broadened to a small platform level with the window. They could have leaned out, introduced him to Marie. Marie at this moment seemed to think he would do; at least, she showed no sign of distaste, such as pushing out her lower lip or crumpling her chin. Perhaps she had been getting ready to drop her Greek: Mme. Carette had warned her that she would have to be a servant to his mother, and eat peculiar food. "He's never asked me to," said Marie, and that was part of the trouble. He hadn't asked anything. For her twenty-first birthday he had given her a locket on a chain and a box from Maitland's, the West End confectioner, containing twenty-one chocolate mice. "He loves me," said Marie. She kept counting the mice and would not let anyone eat them.

In the end it was Berthe who admitted Louis, accepted the gift of chocolates on behalf of Marie, showed him where to leave his hat and coat. She approved of the clean white shirt, the jacket of a tweed similar to the coat but lighter in weight, the tie with a pattern of storm-tossed sailboats. Before shaking hands he removed his glasses, which had misted over, and wiped them dry. His eyes meeting the bright evening at the window (Marie was still there, but with her back to the street) flashed ultramarine. Mme. Carette hoped Marie's children would inherit that color.

He took Marie's yielding hand and let it drop. Freed of the introduction, she pried open the lid of the candy box and said, distinctly, "No mice." He seemed not to hear, or may have thought she was pleased to see he had not played a practical joke. Berthe showed him to the plush armchair, directly underneath a chandelier studded with light bulbs. From this chair Uncle Gildas had explained the whims of God; against its linen antimacassar the Greek had recently rested his head.

Around Louis's crêpe soles pools of snow water formed. Berthe glanced at her mother, meaning that she was not to mind; but Mme. Carette was trying to remember where Berthe had said that she and Marie were to sit. (On the sofa, facing Louis.) Berthe chose a gilt upright chair, from which she could rise easily to pass refreshments. These were laid out on a marble-topped console: vanilla wafers, iced sultana cake, maple fudge, marshmallow biscuits, soft drinks. Behind the sofa a large pier glass reflected Louis in the armchair and the top of Mme. Carette's head. Berthe could tell from her mother's posture, head tilted, hands clasped, that she was silently asking Louis to trust her. She leaned forward and asked him if he was an only child. Berthe closed her eyes. When she opened them, nothing had changed except that Marie was eating chocolates. Louis seemed to be reflecting on his status.

He was the oldest of seven, he finally said. The others were Joseph, Raymond, Vincent, Francis, Rose, and Claire. French was their first language, in a way. But, then, so was English. A certain Louis Joseph Raymond Driscoll, Irish, veteran of Waterloo on the decent side, proscribed in England and Ireland as a result, had come out to Canada and grafted on pure French stock a number of noble traits: bright, wavy hair, a talent for public speaking, another for social aplomb. In every generation of Driscolls, there had to be a Louis, a Joseph, a Raymond. (Berthe and her mother exchanged a look. He wanted three sons.)

His French was slow and muffled, as though strained through wool. He used English words, or French words in an English way. Mme. Carette lifted her shoulders and parted her clasped hands as if to say, Never mind, English is better than Greek. At least they could be certain that the Driscolls were Catholic. In August his father and mother were making the Holy Year pilgrimage to Rome.

Rome was beyond their imagining, though all three Carettes had been to Maine and Old Orchard Beach. Louis hoped to spend a vacation in Old Orchard (in response to an ardent question from Mme. Carette), but he had more feeling for Quebec City. His father's people had entered Canada by way of Quebec.

"The French part of the family?" said Mme. Carette.

"Yes, yes," said Berthe, touching her mother's arm.

Berthe had been to Quebec City, said Mme. Carette. She was brilliant, reliable, fully bilingual. Her office promoted her every January. They were always sending her away on company business. She knew Plattsburgh, Saranac Lake. In Quebec City, at lunch at the Château Frontenac, she had seen well-known politicians stuffing down oysters and fresh lobster, at taxpayers' expense.

Louis's glance tried to cross Berthe's, as he might have sought out and welcomed a second man in the room. Berthe reached past Mme. Carette to take the candy box away from Marie. She nudged her mother with her elbow.

"The first time I ever saw Old Orchard," Mme. Carette resumed, smoothing the bodice of her dress, "I was sorry I had not gone there on my honeymoon." She paused, watching Louis accept a chocolate. "My husband and I went to Fall River. He had a brother in the lumber business."

At the mention of lumber, Louis took on a set, bulldog look. Berthe wondered if the pulp-and-paper firm had gone bankrupt. Her thoughts rushed to Uncle Gildas — how she would have it out with him, not leave it to her mother, if he had failed to examine Louis's prospects. But then Louis began to cough and had to cover his mouth. He was in trouble with a caramel. The Carettes looked away, so that he could strangle unobserved. "How dark it is," said Berthe, to let him think he could not be seen. Marie got up, with a hiss and rustle of taffeta skirt, and switched on the twin floor lamps with their cerise silk shades.

There, she seemed to be saying to Berthe. Have I done the right thing? Is this what you wanted?

Louis still coughed, but weakly. He moved his fingers, like a child made to wave goodbye. Mme. Carette wondered how many contagious children's diseases he had survived; in a large family everything made the rounds. His eyes, perhaps seeking shade, moved across the brown wallpaper flecked with gold and stopped at the only familiar sight in the room — his reflection in the pier glass. He sat up straighter and quite definitely swallowed. He took a long drink of ginger ale. "When Irish eyes are smiling," he said, in English, as if to himself. "When Irish eyes are smiling. There's a lot to be said for that. A lot to be said."

Of course he was at a loss, astray in an armchair, with the Carettes watching like friendly judges. When he reached for another chocolate, they looked to see if his nails were clean. When he crossed his legs, they examined his socks. They were fixing their first impression of the stranger who might take Marie away, give her a modern kitchen, children to bring up, a muskrat coat, a charge account at Dupuis Frères department store, a holiday in Maine. Louis continued to examine his bright Driscoll hair, the small nose along which his glasses slid. Holding the glasses in place with a finger, he answered Mme. Carette: His father was a dental surgeon, with a degree from Pennsylvania. It was the only degree worth mentioning. Before settling into a dentist's chair the patient should always read the writing on the wall. His mother was born Lucarne, a big name in Moncton. She could still get into her wedding dress. Everything was so conveniently arranged at home — cavernous washing machine, giant vacuum cleaner — that she seldom went out. When she did, she wore a two-strand cultured-pearl necklace and a coat and hat of Persian lamb.

The Carettes could not match this, though they were related to families for whom bridges were named. Mme. Carette sat on the edge of the sofa, ankles together. Gentility was the brace that kept her upright. She had once been a young widow, hard pressed, had needed to sew for money. Berthe recalled a stricter, an unsmiling mother, straining over pleats and tucks for clients who reneged on pennies. She wore the neutral shades of half-mourning, the whitish grays of Rue St. Hubert, as though everything had to be used up — even remnants of grief.

Mme. Carette tried to imagine Louis's mother. She might one day have to sell the pearls; even a dentist trained in Pennsylvania could leave behind disorder and debts. Whatever happened, she said to Louis, she would remain in this flat. Even after the girls were married. She would rather beg on the steps of the parish church than intrude upon a young marriage. When her last, dreadful illness made itself known, she would creep away to the Hôtel Dieu and die without a murmur. On the other hand, the street seemed to be filling up with foreigners. She might have to move.

Berthe and Marie were dressed alike, as if to confound Louis, force him to choose the true princess. Leaving the sight of his face in the mirror, puzzled by death and old age, he took notice of the two moiré skirts, organdie blouses, patent-leather belts. "I can't get over those twins of yours," he said to Mme. Carette. "I just can't get over them."

Once, Berthe had tried Marie in her own office — easy work, taking messages when the switchboard was closed. She knew just enough English for that. After two weeks the office manager, Mr. Macfarlane, had said to Berthe, "Your sister is an angel, but angels aren't in demand at Prestige Central Burners."

It was the combination of fair hair and dark eyes, the enchanting misalliance, that gave Marie the look of an angel. She played with the locket the Greek had given her, twisting and unwinding the chain. What did she owe her Greek? Fidelity? An explanation? He was punctual and polite, had never laid a hand on her, in temper or eagerness, had travelled a long way by streetcar to bring back the mice. True, said Berthe, reviewing his good points, while Louis ate the last of the fudge. It was true about the mice, but he should have become more than "Marie's Greek." In the life of a penniless unmarried young woman, there was no room for a man merely in love. He ought to have presented himself as *something*: Marie's future.

In May true spring came, moist and hot. Berthe brought home new dress patterns and yards of flowered rayon and piqué. Louis called three evenings a week, at seven o'clock, after the supper dishes were cleared away. They played hearts in the dining room, drank Salada tea, brewed black, with plenty of sugar and cream, ate éclairs and mille-feuilles from Celentano, the bakery on Avenue Mont Royal. (Celentano had been called something else for years now, but Mme. Carette did not take notice of change of that kind, and did not care to have it pointed out.) Louis, eating coffee éclairs one after the other, told stories set in Moncton that showed off his family. Marie wore a blue dress with a red collar, once Berthe's, and a red barrette in her hair. Berthe, a master player, held back to let Louis win. Mme. Carette listened to Louis, kept some of his stories, discarded others, garnering information useful to Marie. Marie picked up cards at random, disrupting the game. Louis's French was not as woolly as before, but he had somewhere acquired a common Montreal accent. Mme. Carette wondered who his friends were and how Marie's children would sound.

They began to invite him to meals. He arrived at half past five, straight from work, and was served at once. Mme. Carette told Berthe that she hoped he washed his hands at the office, because he never did here. They used the blue-willow-pattern china that would go to Marie. One evening, when the tablecloth had been folded and put away, and the teacups and cards distributed, he mentioned marriage — not his own, or to anyone in particular, but as a way of life. Mme. Carette broke in to say that she had been widowed at Louis's age. She recalled what it had been like to have a husband she could consult and admire. "Marriage means children," she said, looking fondly at her own. She would not be alone during her long, final illness. The girls would take her in. She would not be a burden; a couch would do for a bed.

Louis said he was tired of the game. He dropped his hand and spread the cards in an arc.

"So many hearts," said Mme. Carette, admiringly.

"Let me see." Marie had to stand: there was a large teapot in the way. "Ace, queen, ten, eight, five . . . a wedding." Before Berthe's foot reached her ankle, she managed to ask, sincerely, if anyone close to him was getting married this year.

Mme. Carette considered Marie as good as engaged. She bought a quantity of embroidery floss and began the ornamentation of guest towels and tea towels, placemats and pillow slips. Marie ran her finger over the pretty monogram with its intricate frill of vine leaves. Her mind, which had sunk into hibernation when she accepted Louis and forgot her Greek, awoke and plagued her with a nightmare. "I became a nun" was all she told her mother. Mme. Carette wished it were true. Actually, the dream had stopped short of vows. Barefoot, naked under a robe of coarse brown wool, she moved along an aisle in and out of squares of sunlight. At the altar they were waiting to shear her hair. A strange man — not Uncle Gildas, not Louis, not the Greek — got up out of a pew and stood barring her way. The rough gown turned out to be frail protection. All that kept the dream from sliding into blasphemy and abomination was Marie's entire unacquaintance, awake or asleep, with what could happen next.

Because Marie did not like to be alone in the dark, she and Berthe still shared a room. Their childhood bed had been taken away and supplanted by twin beds with quilted satin headboards. Berthe had to sleep on three pillows, because the aluminum hair curlers she wore ground into her scalp. First thing every morning, she clipped on her pearl earrings, sat up, and unwound the curlers, which she handed one by one to Marie. Marie put her own hair up and kept it that way until suppertime.

In the dark, her face turned to the heap of pillows dimly seen, Marie told Berthe about the incident in the chapel. If dreams are life's opposite, what did it mean? Berthe saw that there was more to it than Marie was able to say. Speaking softly, so that their mother would not hear, she tried to tell Marie about men — what they were like and what they wanted. Marie suggested that she and Berthe enter a cloistered convent together, now, while there was still time. Berthe supposed that she had in mind the famous Martin sisters of Lisieux, in France, most of them Carmelites and one a saint. She touched her own temple, meaning that Marie had gone soft in the brain. Marie did not see; if she had, she would have thought that Berthe was easing a curler. Berthe reminded Marie that she was marked out not for sainthood in France but for marriage in Montreal. Berthe had a salary and occasional travel. Mme. Carette had her Fall River bounty. Marie, if she put her mind to it, could have a lifetime of love.

"Is Louis love?" said Marie.

There were girls ready to line up in the rain for Louis, said Berthe.

"What girls?" said Marie, perplexed rather than disbelieving.

"Montreal girls," said Berthe. "The girls who cry with envy when you and Louis walk down the street."

"We have never walked down a street," said Marie.

The third of June was Louis's birthday. He arrived wearing a new seersucker suit. The Carettes offered three monogrammed hemstitched handkerchiefs — he was always polishing his glasses or mopping his face. Mme. Carette had prepared a meal he particularly favored — roast pork and coconut layer cake. The sun was still high. His birthday unwound in a steady, blazing afternoon. He suddenly put his knife and fork down and said that if he ever decided to get married he would need more than his annual bonus to pay for the honeymoon. He would have to buy carpets, lamps, a refrigerator. People talked lightly of marriage without considering the cost for the groom. Priests urged the married condition on bachelors — priests, who did not know the price of eight ounces of tea.

"Some brides bring lamps and lampshades," said Mme. Carette. "A glass-front bookcase. Even the books to put in it." Her husband had owned a furniture shop on Rue St. Denis. Household goods earmarked for Berthe and Marie had been stored with relatives for some twenty years, waxed and polished and free of dust. "An oak table that seats fourteen," she said, and stopped with that.

Berthe had forbidden her to draw up an inventory. They were not bartering Marie.

"Some girls have money," said Marie. Her savings — eighteen dollars — were in a drawer of her mother's old treadle sewing machine.

A spasm crossed Louis's face; he often choked on his food. Berthe knew more about men than Marie — more than her mother, who knew only how children come about. Mr. Ryder, of Berthe's office, would stand in the corridor, letting elevators go by, waiting for a chance to squeeze in next to Berthe. Mr. Sexton had offered her money, a regular allowance, if she would go out with him every Friday, the night of his Legion meeting. Mr. Macfarlane had left a lewd poem on her desk, then a note of apology, then a poem even worse than the first. Mr. Wright-Ashburton had offered to leave his wife — for, of course, they had wives, Mr. Ryder, Mr. Sexton, Mr. Macfarlane, none of whom she had ever encouraged, and Mr. Wright-Ashburton, with whom she had been to Plattsburgh and Saranac Lake, and whose private behavior she had described, kneeling, in remote parishes, where the confessor could not have known her by voice.

When Berthe accepted Mr. Wright-Ashburton's raving proposal to leave his wife, saying that Irene probably knew about them anyway, would be thankful to have it in the clear, his face had wavered with fright, like a face seen underwater — rippling, uncontrolled. Berthe had to tell him she hadn't meant it. She could not marry a divorced man. On Louis's face she saw that same quivering dismay. He was afraid of Marie, of her docility, her monogrammed towels, her dependence, her glass-front bookcase. Having seen this, Berthe was not surprised when he gave no further sign of life until the twenty-fifth of June.

During his absence the guilt and darkness of rejection filled every corner of the flat. There was not a room that did not speak of humiliation — oh, not because Louis had dropped Marie but because the Carettes had honored and welcomed a clodhopper, a cheapjack, a ginger-haired nobody. Mme. Carette and Marie made many telephone calls to his office, with a variety of names and voices, to be told every time he was not at his desk. One morning Berthe, on her way to work, saw someone very like him hurrying into Windsor Station. By the time she had strug-

gled out of her crowded streetcar, he was gone. She followed him into the great concourse and looked at the
times of the different trains and saw where they were
going. A trapped sparrow fluttered under the glass roof.
She recalled an expression of Louis's, uneasy and roguish,
when he had told Berthe that Marie did not understand
the facts of life. (This is in English, over the table, as if
Mme. Carette and Marie could not follow.) When Berthe
asked what these facts might be, he had tried to cross her
glance, as on that first evening, one man to another. She
was not a man; she had looked away.

Mme. Carette went on embroidering baskets of flowers,
ivy leaves, hunched over her work, head down. Marie
decided to find a job as a receptionist in a beauty salon. It
would be pleasant work in clean surroundings. A girl she
had talked to on the bus earned fourteen dollars a week.
Marie would give her mother eight and keep six. She did
not need Louis, she said, and she was sure she could
never love him.

"No one expected you to love him," said her mother,
without looking up.

On the morning of the twenty-fifth of June he rang
the front doorbell. Marie was eating breakfast in the
kitchen, wearing Berthe's aluminum curlers under a
mauve chiffon scarf, and Berthe's mauve-and-black
kimono. He stood in the middle of the room, refusing
offers of tea, and said that the whole world was engulfed
in war. Marie looked out the kitchen window, at bare
yards and storage sheds.

"Not there," said Louis. "In Korea."

Marie and her mother had never heard of the place.
Mme. Carette took it for granted that the British had
started something again. She said, "They can't take you,
Louis, because of your eyesight." Louis replied that this
time they would take everybody, bachelors first. A few
married men might be allowed to make themselves useful
at home. Mme. Carette put her arms around him. "You
are my son now," she said. "I'll never let them ship you to
England. You can hide in our coal shed." Marie had not
understood that the mention of war was a marriage proposal, but her mother had grasped it at once. She wanted
to call Berthe and tell her to come home immediately, but

Louis was in a hurry to publish the banns. Marie retired to the bedroom and changed into Berthe's white sharkskin sundress and jacket and toeless white suède shoes. She smoothed Berthe's suntan makeup on her legs, hoping that her mother would not see she was not wearing stockings. She combed out her hair, put on lipstick and earrings, and butterfly sunglasses belonging to Berthe. Then, for the first time, she and Louis together walked down the front steps to the street.

At Marie's parish church they found other couples standing about, waiting for advice. They had heard the news and decided to get married at once. Marie and Louis held hands, as though they had been engaged for a long time. She hoped no one would notice that she had no engagement ring. Unfortunately, their banns could not be posted until July, or the marriage take place until August. His parents would not be present to bless them: at the very day and hour of the ceremony they would be on their way to Rome.

The next day, Louis went to a jeweller on Rue St. Denis, recommended by Mme. Carette, but he was out of engagement rings. He had sold every last one that day. Louis did not look anywhere else; Mme. Carette had said he was the only man she trusted. Louis's mother sent rings by registered mail. They had been taken from the hand of her dead sister, who had wanted them passed on to her son, but the son had vanished into Springfield and no longer sent Christmas cards. Mme. Carette shook her own wedding dress out of tissue paper and made a few adjustments so that it would fit Marie. Since the war it had become impossible to find silk of that quality.

Waiting for August, Louis called on Marie every day. They rode the streetcar up to Avenue Mont Royal to eat barbecued chicken. (One evening Marie let her engagement ring fall into a crack of the corrugated floor of the tram, and a number of strangers told her to be careful, or she would lose her man, too.) The chicken arrived on a bed of chips, in a wicker basket. Louis showed Marie how to eat barbecue without a knife and fork. Fortunately, Mme. Carette was not there to watch Marie gnawing on a bone. She was sewing the rest of the trousseau and had no time to act as chaperon.

Berthe's office sent her to Buffalo for a long weekend. She brought back match folders from Polish and German restaurants, an ashtray on which was written "Buffalo Hofbrau," and a number of articles that were much cheaper down there, such as nylon stockings. Marie asked if they still ate with knives and forks in Buffalo, or if they had caught up to Montreal. Alone together, Mme. Carette and Berthe sat in the kitchen and gossiped about Louis. The white summer curtains were up; the coal-and-wood range was covered with clean white oilcloth. Berthe had a new kimono — white, with red pagodas on the sleeves. She propped her new red mules on the oven door. She smoked now, and carried everywhere the Buffalo Hofbrau ashtray. Mme. Carette made Berthe promise not to smoke in front of Uncle Gildas, or in the street, or at Marie's wedding reception, or in the front parlor, where the smell might get into the curtains. Sometimes they had just tea and toast and Celentano pastry for supper. When Berthe ate a coffee éclair, she said, "Here's one Louis won't get."

The bright evenings of suppers and card games slid into the past, and by August seemed long ago. Louis said to Marie, "We knew how to have a good time. People don't enjoy themselves any more." He believed that the other customers in the barbecue restaurant had secret, nagging troubles. Waiting for the wicker basket of chicken, he held Marie's hand and stared at men who might be Greeks. He tried to tell her what had been on his mind between the third and twenty-fifth of June, but Marie did not care, and he gave up. They came to their first important agreement: neither of them wanted the blue-willow-pattern plates. Louis said he would ask his parents to start them off with six place settings of English Rose. She seemed still to be listening, and so he told her that the name of her parish church, St. Louis de France, had always seemed to him to be a personal sign of some kind: an obscure force must have guided him to Rue St. Hubert and Marie. Her soft brown eyes never wavered. They forgot about Uncle Gildas, and whatever it was Uncle Gildas had said to frighten them.

Louis and Marie were married on the third Saturday of August, with flowers from an earlier wedding banked along the altar rail, and two other wedding parties waiting at the back of the church. Berthe supposed that Marie, by accepting the ring of a dead woman and wearing the gown of another woman widowed at twenty-six, was calling down the blackest kind of misfortune. She remembered her innocent nakedness under the robe of frieze. Marie had no debts. She owed Louis nothing. She had saved him from a long journey to a foreign place, perhaps even from dying. As he placed the unlucky ring on her finger, Berthe wept. She knew that some of the people looking on — Uncle Gildas, or Joseph and Raymond Driscoll, amazing in their ginger likeness — were mistaking her for a jealous older sister, longing to be in Marie's place.

Marie, now Mme. Driscoll, turned to Berthe and smiled, as she used to when they were children. Once again, the smile said, Have I done the right thing? Is this what you wanted? Yes, yes, said Berthe silently, but she went on crying. Marie had always turned to Berthe; she had started to walk because she wanted to be with Berthe. She had been standing, holding on to a kitchen chair, and she suddenly smiled and let go. Later, when Marie was three, and in the habit of taking her clothes off and showing what must never be seen, Mme. Carette locked her into the storage shed behind the kitchen. Berthe knelt on her side of the door, sobbing, calling, "Don't be afraid, Marie. Berthe is here." Mme. Carette relented and unlocked the door, and there was Marie, wearing just her undershirt, smiling for Berthe.

Leading her mother, Berthe approached the altar rail. Marie seemed contented; for Berthe, that was good enough. She kissed her sister, and kissed the chosen husband. He had not separated them but would be a long incident in their lives. Among the pictures that were taken on the church steps, there is one of Louis with an arm around each sister and the sisters trying to clasp hands behind his back.

The wedding party walked in a procession down the steps and around the corner: another impression in black-and-white. The August pavement burned under the women's thin soles. Their fine clothes were too hot. Children playing in the road broke into applause when they saw Marie. She waved her left hand, showing the ring. The children were still French-Canadian; so were the neighbors, out on their balconies to look at Marie. Three yellow leaves fell — white, in a photograph. One of the Driscoll boys raced ahead and brought the party to a stop. There is Marie, who does not yet understand that she is leaving home, and confident Louis, so soon to have knowledge of her bewildering ignorance.

Berthe saw the street as if she were bent over the box camera, trying to keep the frame straight. It was an important picture, like a precise instrument of measurement: so much duty, so much love, so much reckless safety — the distance between last April and now. She thought, It had to be done. They began to walk again. Mme. Carette realized for the first time what she and Uncle Gildas and Berthe had brought about: the unredeemable loss of Marie. She said to Berthe, "Wait until I am dead before you get married. You can marry a widower. They make good husbands." Berthe was nearly twenty-four, just at the limit. She had turned away so many attractive prospects, with no explanation, and had frightened so many others with her skill at cards and her quick blue eyes that word had spread, and she was not solicited as before.

Berthe and Marie slipped away from the reception — moved, that is, from the parlor to the bedroom — so that Berthe could help her sister pack. It turned out that Mme. Carette had done the packing. Marie had never had to fill a suitcase, and would not have known what to put in first. For a time, they sat on the edge of a bed, talking in whispers. Berthe smoked, holding the Buffalo Hofbrau ashtray. She showed Marie a black lacquer cigarette lighter she had not shown her mother. Marie had started to change her clothes; she was just in her slip. She looked at the lighter on all sides and handed it back. Louis was taking her to the Château Frontenac, in Quebec City, for three nights — the equivalent of ten days in Old Orchard, he had said. After that, they would go straight to the duplex property, quite far north on Boulevard Pie IX, that his father was helping him buy. "I'll call you tomorrow morning," said Marie, for whom tomorrow was still the same thing as today. If Uncle Gildas had been at Berthe's mercy, she would have held his head underwater. Then she thought, Why blame him? She and Marie were Montreal girls, not trained to accompany heroes, or to hold out for dreams, but just to be patient.

LEAVING THE PARTY
✤

BY MAVIS GALLANT

Monsieur Fernand Blotte is leaving the Party. It was on the news tonight, just after the avalanche and before the weather report. There was a worrying image — a million tons of snow making for a herd of cows at seven knots. The avalanche music, the Berlioz "Requiem," sowed anxiety and apprehension. All at once, the music stopped, and there, instead of the peak of an Alp, was Fernand Blotte.

He wore a cable-stitch sweater in an attractive shade of gray. His makeup was yellowish along the hairline, with a touch of mauve on cheek and chin. They had propped him against a wall-to-wall bookcase, with his arms crossed on his chest — the leaving-the-Party stance. A thimble-size microphone hung round his neck like an amulet. He opened and closed his mouth without saying a word: perhaps it is his usual way of breathing. Once or twice, he bared his lower teeth — a symptom of political stress.

They were playing a leaving-the-Party waltz, a wistful air in a minor key, more suitable as background for a royal divorce or a thoroughly wet summer. Someone in the studio may have been rubbing it in.

On Blotte's head was a moderate amount of clean, short, serviceable hair — Party hair. A small comb in a plastic case could be seen lying on one of the bookshelves. The ready-for-use pocket comb is a Party sign — yes, even among the intelligentsia. It's too bad, but it's so.

When Germain Chaudfroid left the Party, about a year and a half ago, he wore a green turtleneck pullover. His hairdo was rather like Blotte's, but with a bit more bristle to it. A few months later Chaudfroid was interviewed again (his leaving-the-Party memoirs had been rushed into print), and this time the camera discovered a richer crop of hair, with a deep, strong, unequivocal part. Nothing straggling, nothing bushy, no random locks: just calm, glossy, abundant hair, tapered quietly to the nape of the neck — ex-Party hair.

Blotte's bookshelves, filled with thin, tired volumes in dull beiges and tans, offered nothing in the way of artistic ornamentation, nothing to appease the eye. Where were the strings of amber, the unframed graphics, the little squares of handweaving embroidered with pigs, pansies, watering cans?

Chaudfroid, at the time of *his* first interview, still had such artifacts on his shelves. In the old days, when Blotte and Chaudfroid led delegations of authors and thinkers Eastward, they would be met by similar delegations travelling very slightly Westward, and the East-to-slightly-West delegates would cover them with People's presents. (The West-to-East delegates offered subtle advice and praise.) But during his second interview it would be seen that Chaudfroid had replaced his People's presents with glass paperweights.

For the moment, Blotte had just the comb.

Blotte. Fernand Blotte. Isn't he the one who wrote the ground-breaking essay about paper knives? About the mutually supportive relationship that develops between reader and literature, provided that reader can learn to slice swiftly and coolly, leaving no ragged edges? Reader owes literature trust and fidelity, Blotte declared, and literature owes reader protection. The trouble was that by the time Blotte published his essay, ready-to-read literature had been on the market for some years and paper knives had become obsolete. His explanation was taken to be metaphor, and while it brought him acclaim on the one hand, it got him in trouble on the other. Blotte tried it again, apologizing for the mistake: it was reader that was supposed to offer literature protection, while literature stayed home and minded the children.

No, wait; that was Chaudfroid. Blotte's the fellow who turned up for his cell meeting, right as rain, happy as a lark, and suddenly they all started clapping and chanting, "Blotte, out! Blotte, out!" They took a vote, hands raised, and next thing Blotte knew he had been ejected into the dark street.

Actually, that sounds more like Chaudfroid. It's in

the third volume of his memoirs. Chaudfroid was attached to a working-class cell, a collar-and-tie cell. Most of
his comrades and acquaintances were in intellectual cells,
some wearing Shetland sweaters, some crewneck with
vertical ribbed effect, some peon-styled loose-sleeved
pullovers with woolly waist fringe, some two per cent
mixed-mohair. His comrades told Chaudfroid he was
lucky to be in a working-class cell. Chaudfroid thought so,
too. Then — boom! — the workers were clapping and
chanting, "Chaudfroid, Chaudfroid, out, out, out!," and
when they took the vote he saw he hadn't a friend in the
room. He felt lonely, of course, but, as he said in the
second interview, his arms folded over a black Italian cash-
mere T-shirt, "I knew I would never have to wear a tie
again."

(Soon after that, Louis [Loulou] Soupape, a worker,
left the Party. He tore up his card, sent the pieces to head-
quarters by registered mail, and stopped paying his dues.
His wife bought him a pale-blue shirt, because blue shows
up better than white on television, and did his hair with
the hand dryer in order to give it media volume and con-
sistency. Nobody ever came to interview him; nobody
hung a microphone round his neck, or littered the floor
with wires and cables, or blew all the lights out by plug-
ging them into the wrong place. He tried to issue a statement and was fined for pasting it on a wall. He went on a
hunger strike but eventually gave it up and turned to
poultry farming. Recently, Soupape told a visitor he
believed he had been ignored because there was no perceived cultural symbol in his surroundings. He had
thought of renting about twelve feet of an assembly line,
so that he could stand with his back to it, arms crossed
over the pale-blue shirt, but the place was too small; once
he had the assembly line in place, there was no room left
for a camera. His memoirs are on tape; he is still seeking a
publisher.)

The leaving-the-Party waltz had been playing for
about twenty seconds, with Blotte still silently breathing
through his mouth, when his voice came in, above the
music. It sounded oddly like Chaudfroid's. He was in the
middle of telling about a delegation and a journey by
helicopter over a spruce forest. Down in a clearing there
was a moral-rehabilitation center, where volunteers had

gathered and were making electric fans. You see, the economy was in such a shaky condition (mark you, they weren't too proud to say so, either) that there was no other way of getting electric fans to the— Unfortunately, the voice faded and Blotte began his wordless breathing again. The music changed to a sprightly passage from "Coppélia."

Presently Blotte recovered his own voice, just to say that the West had been beaten out on the electric-fan question. He could speak from a position of strength now, without being accused of special pleading: he was leaving the Party.

Was Blotte merry or regretful? Did he miss the little squares of embroidered handwoven material? Does it mean he will never say another word about paper knives? These are questions he will probably answer in his book.

Meanwhile, there was the weatherman, wearing hair of a neutral color, decently cut, texture perhaps a little dry. He could do with a fresh herbal soft-soap treatment — say, twice a week. He was showing the impressive satellite photo, with all those wisps of cloud. There was rain in all the major cities, and it was foggy, foggy everywhere. The weather music was good, though: a brass band to set your feet tapping, with the odd clash of cymbals to keep you from dozing off.

A RIGMAROLE

Memoirs of a Mud-Wrestler

ଌ

By John Mills

I

I t's not often I read critical commentary on my own writing, partly because there isn't much of it around, but mostly because once I've written something and let it loose upon the world my interest turns to what comes next. Recently, however, a friend pointed me to an article in *Books in Canada*, a sort of brochure published in Toronto, in which a reviewer had written that "John Mills is to the field of literary criticism what a mud-wrestler is to athletics." I am quoting from memory and may not have got the exact wording, but that was the gist of it and, judging by the context, it was not intended as a compliment. Nevertheless I was delighted with the remark — I know intuitively what it means and I am inclined to agree with it. Mud-wrestlers are coarse-fibred souls who embark on the crushing of a novel or a poem with a kind of fat and clumsy brute force. Their idea of finesse is the hundred-weight sack of cornmeal poised on a half-open door, and their chosen weapons are the bludgeon, the sap, the quarterstaff. I can offer from my own experience the example of a mud-wrestler named Robert Nye who, in the pages of the British newspaper *The Guardian*, called my first novel, *The Land of Is*, a "ghastly mish-mash of modernism," then quoted my publisher's ill-judged comment on the dust jacket that I had once earned my living as a gandy-dancer in order to say, "there's a great future for Mills as a gandy-dancer, whatever that means." Nye was wrong about *The Land of Is* (as was another Englishman, Maurice Wiggin, who, in

John Mills was born in 1930. He teaches English at Simon Fraser University. He has written three novels, *The Land of Is*, *The October Men*, and *Skevington's Daughter*, and a volume of essays and memoirs, *Lizard in the Grass*.

the pages of *The Observer* that same week, described it as "an august and noble work of art"), but his comment illustrates a chief mud-wrestling feature — extravagance, hyperbole, and carelessness in the service of either praise or denunciation. In contrast to Nye, myself, or even Wiggin, there is the more judicious, cooler, rope-dancing sort of critic — undeterred by abstract ideas, playful among philosophers and historians, filled with wisdom, culture, and creativity — who can approach a literary work with the delicacy and daring of a surgeon cutting into a living body, and in whom, even at moments of solemn pronouncement, there gleams a kind of mad gaiety, a wild *sprezzatura*, and whose tools are the scalpel and the poignard. Examples? Well, C. S. Lewis, for one — never mind his children's books, or his Christian apologetics (though these are useful if you haven't the time to read Hans Küng), look up *Allegory of Love*, or the work on sixteenth-century literature. Lionel Trilling — what about him? Eliot, Susan Sontag, Matthew Arnold, Edmund Wilson, Sir Philip Sidney. I admire these people but could no more aspire to their level of achievement than could my anonymous *Books in Canada* reviewer. My aspirations, my sympathies, are with another group altogether — the great mud-wrestlers, the put-down men and women of our literary history: Mencken, James Agate, Nathan Cohen, Thomas Nashe, Robert Graves, Ezra Pound. Perhaps even poor Lawrence, who wrestled Franklin and Whitman so deeply into the mud that their reputations have never fully crept out of it. These, if I had any culture heroes, would be mine — and I hasten to add that I don't regard myself, *qua* mud-wrestler, as fit to change their ribbons or sharpen their quills.

These two lists cannot, of course, be mutually exclusive: there is more than a touch of the mud-wrestler in Wilson, a very strong streak of the rope-dancer in Robert Graves. But in general they represent the two categories of critic before the rise of the new technologies and the Sahalization of literary criticism into semiotics, hermeneutics, language theory, grand theory, structuralism, Frankfurt School Obscurantics, phenomenology, post-structuralism, and so on, creating vast deserts over which many a poor graduate student, many a twitching Assistant Professor (as well as many a charlatan, many a band-wagonist), wander black of tongue and parched of throat in search of a T.A.ship, a merit increment, or a tenure-track appointment.

So, O most affable reader, what are you, rope-dancer or mud-wrestler? There will be an element of each in you, of course, but genes, temperament, training, and the accidents of your life will incline you towards one pole or the other. I knew, very early on in my career, that I was a mud-wrestler, and it was to those depths I bent my will. My own mother was a mud-wrestler to be reckoned with, and my propensities were encouraged by early years in Europe, and the friendship, in early-middle manhood, of some of the finest exponents of the art in our time: Bryan McCarthy, the poet and critic; John Richmond, the teacher, journalist, and con-man; and Irving Layton, poet and professional extrovert. What follows is a stretch of autobiography involving these people, an account of my apprenticeship under their mud-wrestling direction, and I shall call it a "Rigmarole" for reasons that will become clear as we proceed.

2

In January 1959 I re-entered Montreal permanently after spending eighteen months in and around the Arctic as a technician on the DEW Line, a system of radar stations obsolete even when it was being built. There was a certain futility about such work, but I left the north with some regrets and considerable anxiety. There was enough to worry about; first and most pressing on me was the problem of how to make a living. I had saved about ten thousand dollars, but this would vanish without trace or savouring under pressure of need, like *premier cru* wine at a hippie banquet, leaving me as broke as I was before. No investment could give me a decent wage, nor could I see any business enterprise in which I might willingly involve myself. Northern wisdom nagged at me: old hands used to say *never spend your capital* . . . spend other people's . . . work if you have to . . . get a job. There was a respectful, even melancholy, silence after these words, for men used to their freedom and the slow, easy rhythms of the outback do not speak glibly of getting jobs. Well, unless something turned up I would, to prevent my bank account bleeding itself white, have to look for one.

Furthermore I was returning to a situation of some complexity. A couple of years before, my sister Jill had become, long before it was fashionable, a single parent. She had escaped England and moved into my apartment in Ridgewood Avenue, a line of red-brick apartment houses which snakes up the hill from Côte des Neiges to St. Joseph's Oratory. A good friend of ours named Jerome, who had chosen to become a student at McGill, joined us, and when it became clear that I was to spend most of my time in the north I sent for my mother, who, Jill told me, had become a reformed character. There were a number of advantages in this scheme, or so it seemed to me: the apartment was certainly big enough to contain the three of them — celibate adults — and a baby; my mother had, though one might not think so to look at her offspring, some skill with small children, and in any case, in her early sixties, she needed a serious interest in life. Jerome would enjoy cheap board and lodging and supply a much-needed male presence. It wasn't long, though, before my mail was containing the most desperate cries for help. As far as my mother was concerned, Jerome had become an unmitigated force for evil, part of the Devil's brood. No redeeming social content . . . never mind that she'd been taken in by him at first meeting . . . that just showed the bestial cunning behind the smooth façade . . . a viper, that's what he was, and what's more important he was keeping potential suitors from Jill's door . . . and the first step we had to take, the most important thing in all our lives at the moment . . . was to get her *married off* . . . understand? *Married off*! And what's more, this creature's pretending to be a student . . . at his age! When most self-respecting men had embarked on their careers! Getting married to suitable girls! Not being a trial to their families! Friends! Respectable people around them! It was abnormal, that's what it was, and the sooner I got down from the Arctic and sorted things out, the better.

I would read these pages of invective in dim light as befitted them at a table illuminated only by the yellow vectors sweeping out circles on the radar screens. The Russians could've flown by in droves, squadrons, flotillas, for all I cared — let them pulverize all those little beasts pledging every morning allegiance to the American flag, all those apple pies cooling on the window sills. This crepuscular peace, this low and soothing hum of electric fans cooling the triodes, pentodes, magnetrons, and klystrons around me, was too valuable to waste on surveillance. Like my colleagues, I would use the time to write letters, novels, essays, and to read fiction, textbooks, manuals, and dreadful letters of the kind my poor sister was sending me. How the hell was she coping? Not very well, evidently, judging by her comments that she was slowly but surely being driven insane "by this mad woman, our mother," and that I had "better get down here quick and deal with this raging harpy, this demon, this poisonous and demented witch." These struck me as expressions of considerable pain, of genuine *angst*. But I was not going to leave this Arctic womb before I was ready to, before my contract was up. And I didn't look forward to adjudicating between the needs of three people all with legitimate and conflicting claims on my loyalty. Why, I even got a plaintive letter from Jerome, that soul of acceptance, advising me that life on Ridgewood had become problematic — an almost constant screaming match — and he wasn't sure how much longer he could stand it. He looked forward very much to my return.

When it came time to leave and I found myself in Edmonton, the first port of civilization and outpost of the American military empire, I very nearly stayed there. Let them get on with it, I thought. My God, they're all adults. Why should I become their arbiter? I paid the rent, made easy living possible for them; let them learn to live in harmony. As for me, I shall go to the South of France . . . sunshine . . . culture . . . love. I would wait here, in Edmonton, for my final cheque to come through, and not go home at all. But in two days the horrors of that town, its emptiness and banality, drove me to Montreal.

I lumbered up the stairs hefting my kitbag and a suitcase and rang the bell. My mother opened the door cautiously, then swung it wide and almost leaped on me.

O my God, you're back . . . I almost gave up . . . it's been utterly intolerable here . . . that man . . . you've no idea what I've been through trying to keep that man at bay . . . and your poor nephew . . . poor little David . . . that man's been turning him into a nervous wreck . . . and your sister . . . I've never seen her look so pale, so overwrought . . . not her fault if she's turning into a shouting, screaming minx . . . that man's done it . . . it would all be all right here if only he were to get out . . . so thank God you've come . . . he wouldn't budge for me . . . idle, scrounging, good-for-nothing . . . asleep all day . . . on the sofa, if you please . . . large as life . . . if you can call it life . . . broad daylight and the blinds drawn . . . no food in the refrigerator . . . you can't keep anything in it with that man around . . . and me coming in from shopping with an armful of bags and parcels . . . coming up those stairs . . . and him asleep on his back with the blinds drawn . . . two o'clock in the afternoon . . . I shook him . . . kicked him, more like it: I wouldn't touch that slimy creature with my bare hands . . . up! I said. Up you get, you guzzling, swilling, idle heap of muck. Up! before I throw cold water over you . . . and you know what that filthy, impudent snake in the grass had the gall to say to me? You sick, noisy old bag! That's right! Calling me names! Your own mother! Names! I rushed into the kitchen for a saucepan of water but by the time I got back with it he'd given me the slip . . . just as well . . . I wouldn't have thought twice about it . . . soaked him, that's what I was prepared to do, soak him from head to foot

. . . and then I told your sister about it and you know what she said to me? *I wish I was dead,* she said to me. *Wished she were dead.* That's gratitude for you . . . after all I've done for her . . . after I'd got rid of him, mostly on her behalf . . . because let me tell you this, my dear, she's better off without him . . . in more ways than one . . .

Just a minute, I said, just a damned minute. I've only just got in the door. I've had a hard trip . . . let me get this straight . . . where's Jerome now?

As if I cared where he's gone . . . all I know is that he'll be back . . . his filthy stuff is here . . . that's where you come in . . . getting rid of him for good . . . he's not wanted here . . . a bad influence . . . he bounces that little child on his knees and God only knows what's going on in his filthy, disgusting mind . . . it's frightening to think of . . . the papers in England are full of that kind of thing . . . pervert, that's what he is . . . he ought to be locked up . . . in jail . . . in the police station . . .

Are you telling me, I started to shout, that you think Jerome's a homosexual? Are you insinuating . . .

Insinuating! Don't use big words with me, my dear . . . and mind your tone . . . I'm your mother . . . you young people have no respect . . . you, your sister . . . that vixen downstairs . . . don't be so *rude.* There he is and there's your sister, and he hasn't looked at her that way once since I've been here . . . any normal man would've made a grab at her, walking around all day in her dressing-gown like the slut she is and men being the disgusting creatures *they* are, just wanting a woman for her body, that's all, just for her body, and he hasn't made a move, not one, in her direction, not when I've been in the building, and I've got a sharp nose for that kind of thing, though God knows what they get up to when I'm out . . . but it's little David I'm worried about . . . you've no idea what being fondled like that by men of his kind can do in later life . . . my God, it's criminal . . . we have to put a stop to it . . . you must get rid of him . . . throw his things out on the stairs . . . homosexual, did you say? Yes, and a sewer-rat as well . . . *a homosexual sewer-rat.*

Speak to me like that about my friend, I screamed, my sister? Your brain's diseased! You're sick!

Sheer malice made me add: And I can't kick him out . . . they're engaged! Engaged to be married!

My mother gasped as though I'd just hauled off and kicked her in the stomach.

Married? Married? What's this? Did you say they were

engaged to be married? This . . . this is news to me . . . this is the first time I . . . well, if that's true that puts a whole new light on the subject . . . it's . . . John! Where is he? Where's he gone? You must know where to find him! We've got to get him back!

That's right! I shouted, maddened by not being greeted, furious at being dumped on the moment I stepped in the door by a woman I'd last clapped eyes on eight years before and these were her first words. You want me to get him back, I said. You don't care who he is so long as Jill marries him . . . he could be a gangster, a dope addict, a homosexual sewer-rat . . . it's all the same to you. Well, I'm getting out.

Wait a minute . . . wait a minute . . . John, where are you going? Sit down . . . take your things off . . . let's discuss this calmly . . . an offer, you said . . . she's had an offer . . . John . . . don't go . . . don't go.

But I had dumped my bags on the floor and turned on my heel. I fled down the stairs and, *en passant*, rang the downstairs apartment bell. There was always a warm welcome there. But the vixen herself was not at home. I strode instead up the hill towards the Oratory to the apartment inhabited by another single parent and *her* brother, a man named Graham, where I could be pretty certain of meeting my old and valued friend Bryan McCarthy.

3

Between McCarthy, Graham, and me there was much in common. Struggling to become writers, we were each of us aware of having started rather late, moving towards our thirties, nothing done yet, nothing published, the world too much with us, no contacts in the literary world to speak of except with other would-be writers — Milton Acorn, for instance . . . Al Purdy . . . Leonard Cohen . . . none of whom had at that time achieved any recognition . . . and Irving Layton. He was the only one amongst us who had at least broken into the small magazines, had had books published by arty presses with eccentric names. Irving was then at the height of his drive to power; he would recite his poems anywhere — in a classroom, in a salon, on a bus to perfect strangers. His efforts were beginning to pay off. He lived in a small house on Côte St. Luc and it was there, whenever I was in town, that I would read my feeble writings to him. I was attempting to create short stories, even though (since each seemed to contain within itself the seeds of its own growth, like a grain of yeast) I was uneasy with the form. My first was about a young, intense student in North Wales out rock-climbing with a fellow mountaineer towards whom he feels great envy. There is a girl with them whom the hero covets, though she herself seems to covet the rival. This rival is struck by a falling rock during the ascent of some dank gully, an accident which, though badly hurt, he survives. During the rescue operation and while the rival is carried off on a stretcher the hero declares himself to the girl. She admits to being pregnant by the rival. It was a melancholy, self-pitying tale based on my own experience. The tense, jealous working-class boy was me, the rival a rich public-school man named Roy Evans who later in "real life" was killed in the Alps. Sad though it was, I was pleased with it, and the night I finished it I took it round and read it to Irving.

All right, I suppose, he said. But it's not a short story.

What do you mean, it's not a short story? You think it's a play? A villanelle, for Christ's sake?

It's not a short story, the Master replied patiently, because it contains none of the ingredients of a short story . . . no surprise . . . no epiphany . . . no sense of the intractable core of the bizarre in human affairs. You don't read, my friend, that's your problem. When did you read Faulkner . . . *last*? Hemingway . . . *last*? Conrad . . . Mansfield . . . James . . . Lawrence . . . when did you read any of them? . . . *last*? It's got no tension, no shape . . . it's too obvious . . . too *sculpted* whilst being at the same time formless.

You may be a poet, Irving, I said, though there are some, including myself, who might have trouble describing you as such, but you're a tyro when it comes to prose.

The Master sat back and smiled in a maddeningly superior way. There, my friend, you would be wrong. I know a lot about prose. And don't be so touchy. I didn't say you had no talent. You've a good eye for landscape . . . your descriptions have a certain lush, perfervid power. But as a short story your piece is a crock of shit. Go away and work on it.

I took off from there fuming with anger. That this cheap-jack, poetasting, gallowsglass should have the nerve to criticize a work of mine! It wasn't until I got home and reread it that I saw he was quite possibly right. Epiphany . . . intractable core of the bizarre . . . carefully, slowly, I began to tinker with it.

At any rate, the day I got home I was half expected at the Seals'. I received a warm greeting and a tumbler of Queberac, the remains of a gallon of which stood on the floor central to the three large sofas facing inward. Graham lay on one, McCarthy on the second, and I on the third. It was as though I had taken up my life again exactly where I had left off — before my Arctic travels — the three of us drinking white wine and discussing, much to the despair of our womenfolk, ways of avoiding work. McCarthy smiled crookedly.

Glad you're back, he said. We seem to be running out of booze.

I've got a bit of money, I said.

We know that, Graham said. We thought you probably had just under ten grand.

It should last us a year, McCarthy speculated, provided we don't overspend.

People around here, I commented, will have to get through life without the use of my bank account. As for me, I have to get a job.

There was a stunned silence.

A job? McCarthy said eventually. You're dreaming, old boy. There aren't any jobs. Not of the kind you could take . . . nobody would have you, in any case. You've been out of the work force too long . . . they don't like that. You've been a free man . . . they don't like that either.

They'll want to punish you, Graham said. I should lie very low if I were you.

We drank for a while in silence. I told them about my mother and the violent passions unleashed in the apartment block down the road. They were inclined to discount them. Jill, my mother, everybody in Montreal that was enslaved by money or the need to go to work each day, was in the winter doldrums. Post-Christmas blues . . . a new year dawning and nothing achieved . . . the mixture as before . . . no ecstatic vision, no promises of transcendence . . . nothing but eat, sleep, drink. Work. Look after babies and struggle to pay the rent, the mortgage. Where's the joy in that? And is that what human life is all about? No wonder they're a bit touchy . . . everybody is.

I denied this detached, sub-Kierkegaardian point of view and suggested demonic possession. They scoffed at this hypothesis and Graham went so far as to tell me he thought my mother rather a nice old lady.

But where am I to stay? I said. With a girlfriend, they said.

Naturally I had given this some thought. I had left town on good terms with a number of young women, but what they had done in my absence was problematical. Aviva had become more and more tied to Irving Layton, Edith and I had fought bitterly by mail, Lucille was amiable but private and rather weird. There were two others, but both had got married in my absence. I was not going back to that apartment, certainly not that night, and in any case I wanted to find Jerome.

You should meet John, McCarthy said. John Richmond. He'll find Jerome for you . . . and a place to live. He knows everything.

Doctor Richmond?

The Herr Doktor. I've just found out he lives down the street, here on Ridgewood. I told him you were due back. He's keen to meet you.

Why?

Matters of mutual interest, old boy.

The locution of this statement, coupled with the "old boys" my friend had started to throw around, seemed uncharacteristic, and I later discovered that McCarthy had consciously or unconsciously adopted a Richmond mannerism. McCarthy had met him at a Jewish private school called the Herzliah where they were both part-time teachers. And so, oddly enough, was Irving, whom they had both started calling "the Gaffer." McCarthy had written to me about this new star in our rather limited firmament in terms of delight and approval — it made me jealous and intensely suspicious. I doubted that Richmond was a genuine Ph.D. What would a man with such qualifications be doing, in those days, outside a university? Much later Jerome, who hated him, went to great lengths to discover if Richmond had indeed earned a doctorate from St. John's College, Cambridge, as he claimed, and drew a blank. Nevertheless the Rabbis who ran the Herzliah were impressed with him, as were the parents of the school's frenetic teen-agers (whose vast energies were focussed on minor gangsterism, cheating, establishing and defending territory, rape, destruction, and the consumption of massive quantities of junk food). McCarthy used to say it was very nearly impossible to keep order in such a place, a maelstrom, at the best of times, of screaming and violence, and a common sight there was a gentle rabbi, his head pressed to the wall, shuddering as though afflicted with the bleakest of agues. But Richmond evidently *could* keep order, and when I met him later that night I could understand why. He was half a generation older than us, in his early forties, short, frowning, and stubbily built. His forehead was high and made higher by a receding hair-line. Thick spectacles made his prominent, mad eyes swim out at you like a brace of barracuda in a bullet-proof tank. The secret of his success as a disciplinarian, McCarthy said, was his ability to fly in an instant into psychotic rages, feigned or otherwise, which would amuse the children as well as cowing them and which featured hysterical screaming accompanied by wild swings of a stout walking-stick or knob-kerrie, an implement he was never without. He answered his door and spoke, his voice deep and patrician.

Come in, old boy, he said to me. By Jove, I *am* glad to meet you . . . by Jove . . . come on in for *God's* sake . . . in from the icy fang and churlish chiding of the winter's wind.

Piss on this, I thought. The Montreal winter was indeed at its bitter peak but we were standing in the hallway of an apartment block kept, as is the Eastern custom, at eighty degrees or more. Inside his apartment, however, there was greater comfort, for Richmond had opened a window half an inch. Deep armchairs and large bookcases produced an effect of wealth and seclusion, though Richmond could not, at that time, have been particularly well off. An attractive blonde woman in early middle age, rather subdued and verging on the timid, was introduced to us as his wife, Nina. This household also contained, though not the first night I was there, a child named Christie, a plump, demanding adolescent destined to blossom later into a very beautiful young woman indeed.

Scotch? Richmond boomed. McCarthy and I nodded eagerly. Richmond clapped his hands briskly. Nina disappeared into the kitchen and came back with a tray on which stood a decanter and three glasses. Richmond nodded, and Nina vanished into another room.

Burra peg, old boy? Richmond asked. Or chota peg?

I selected the former. He poured the whisky neat. In this house, he said, Scotch is not served with water.

Isn't Nina drinking with us? I asked.

She's Greek, you know, Richmond said, dropping his voice into confidentiality. They know their place, old boy.

I nodded wisely. Here was a man, I thought, clearly engaged in the practice of curmudgeonmanship. This is as effective a way of confronting the world as any other, though it isn't for every-body. You need a strong and commanding personality, at the back of which is a violent streak, visibly repressed. You need to intimi-date rather than befriend, and you must seek victims rather than equals. You need a brass neck and little in the way of a conscience. And you have to be solemn about it: any hint that you were not to be taken too seriously, and you were done for. There are excel-lent models: Samuel Johnson; Evelyn Waugh, of course. Alexan-der Woollcott. That ghastly Sitwell parent, Lord Whatshisname. The trick is to surround yourself with natural vassals. Here, I think, I did Nina an injustice. Her own very quiet sense of humour allowed her to acquiesce publicly in Richmond's game, but she wasn't exactly the doormat she appeared. I discovered in her a strong compassion and general sweetness of disposition. I think she pitied her husband and nursed him in his insecurities like a parent does a child. I was very fond of her, and many years later when I heard she had died I grieved for her a long time.

Richmond handed us the Scotch. We sipped it and it was good. I said something polite about his books. He began to explain some of the intricacies of his library. He'd begun his collection of Loeb classics while he was in the fifth form of some minor public school and extended it while an undergraduate, though his interests had switched to literature. The man's a fake, I immediately assumed. I was wrong. Even Jerome, who fought with him violently over some technicality in the use of the aorist tense, acknowledged, though grudgingly, Richmond's command of classical Greek, while Richmond could do something Jerome could not — speak fluent, demotic Greek to his wife, her family, and an admiring crowd of Athenians, Spartans, Corinthians, Cretans, and Macedonians at the Elnikon Taverna on Pine Avenue where we were all of us wont to hang out. Richmond pointed to a shelf of Penguin books beautifully bound in board and cloth.

Look at these, old boy. Little man in Alexandria did them for me. A bob apiece! Imagine it! A bob!

I uttered a phrase in my British army Arabic which means, roughly, *wow!*

Richmond, delighted, addressed me in a sudden stream of liquids, gutturals, alveolar fricatives, and glottals until I had to beg him to stop.

I only learned a few words, I confessed.

Then I'll teach you the rest of them, he offered. And Greek too, if you like.

Suddenly he burst into a muezzinesque wail: yah tah bee-bee, tirallah, yuhumnick shirallah yahummnick, ya ah ah ta bin . . . and repeated it until the three of us were singing it loudly and with the strength of three or four excellent Scotches behind us. Some twenty-five or so years after the events recorded in this Rigma-role I happened to sing Richmond's song to a Lebanese graduate student of mine. She joined in and sang the whole thing from start to finish. Richmond had only taught us the chorus. But it was genuine, that was the point, and I had supposed he was inventing mock Arabic to entertain us and himself.

Who was Richmond? What was he? To this day I couldn't say. I never heard him utter a word that wasn't carefully constructed to impress, disguise, bamboozle. Nothing of him that was genuine ever came through to me, though evidently it did to McCarthy, who soon became a close friend, and, to a lesser extent, to Graham. His languages were genuine enough and, in an Anglo-Saxon culture where facility even with beginner's French is regarded as a sinister affront to respectability in the order of flashing, say, or child abuse, enabled him to be not only one up on his environment but satisfactorily at odds with it. Apart from his Greek, his Arabic, I'd heard him converse with sailors off the *Aleksandr Pushkin*, aboard which vessel he was greeted with roars of joy and approval, with editors of *La Presse* and *Le Devoir* in fluent and witty French with now and again a trace of Joual to show he was one of the boys, in German with waiters in the Schnitzelhaus and Hungarian in the coffee bars along Stanley Street. It was all part of his effort to assert himself against the *pax Americana*. So one might observe him, strutting across Mount Royal, into the busy intersections of the city, head erect, stick swinging, a heavy, disapproving frown on his face, uttering loud abuse at the swishing, maniacal Montreal traffic, and he would step off the sidewalk with his cane held firmly and horizontally like a matador's killing sword as though challenging the city's demented, homicidal drivers to mow him down. Brandishing his stick he would get to the other side of the street unscathed, something that could not happen to ordinary mortals. I often wondered how it was he had escaped being broken up, flattened, and pulped by the malevolent traffic he teased and thwarted, and concluded that the drivers, in their primitive consciousnesses, must have taken him for a Divine Idiot, a holy man on whom God had laid his hand, and that he was taboo. Or perhaps he touched some residual compassion in them — a man the Almighty had so drastically afflicted must surely deserve a tincture of grace.

That night I spoke of the tearing passions of Upper Ridgewood and my own dilemmas about money. It amused Richmond to listen to me carefully whilst wearing on his face an expression suitable to a whisky priest hearing confession from the sleaziest, most deadbeat of sinners. Every now and again he would wipe a handkerchief across his brow and examine it as though for stains. At lugubrious points in my narrative he registered mournfulness and nodded compassionately. Suddenly he burst into a series of noisy, face-splitting, multiple yawns.

I'm boring you, old boy, I said. I'm sorry.

No, no, old bean . . . no, no . . .

He allowed his eyes to glaze over and his head to move from side to side as though seeking ways of escape.

You think I should go ahead and bugger off to the South of France?

No, no, old boy, definitely not. Suddenly a look of enormous *gravitas* composed itself on his face. *Hell is portable*, he said. This was an expression I was to hear him use on many occasions. Suddenly he pretended to cheer up in the manner of one perceiving the solution to a difficult problem in ontology.

When in doubt, old boy, teach.

Teach? I'm not a teacher.

Nonsense. Anybody can teach.

Teach what, my dear fellow?

Teach what? Why, teach anything.

Arabic, old cheese?

Why not? Get a book. Stay one page ahead of the student. Teach, old fruit, that's the ticket.

At the Herzliah?

Oh, no, no, no, no, no, no . . . definitely not. Not the Herzliah. Stay clear of the Rabbis. (He chuckled at some private joke.)

And the Gaffer, McCarthy said. His eyes had furred over noticeably, his voice was not what it was an hour before, and his nose seemed to have reddened and become bulbous.

Particularly the Gaffer, Richmond affirmed.

The Gaffer hath the falling sickness, I said in revenge for the quotation with which we'd been greeted at the door.

Ah, Richmond said, as though he'd caught me out. The Gaffer hath it not, but you and I, and honest Bryan here, we have the falling sickness.

By now it was late. I'd had enough for one day. McCarthy was flopping down on one of the Seal sofas. I decided to sleep on the other. Together we staggered up Ridgewood, the night cold, but clear and hopeful, and showered with a million stars.

4

I'd always thought of Jerome as sad and self-imprisoned, yet there were unexpected riches to his personality. His voice was one of the slowest, deepest, and most beautifully articulated I have ever heard. He acquired it partly from his school, partly from his habit of phoning people he admired to ask them how they'd achieved their personas. He would phone dukes, actors, financiers — you couldn't be in London five minutes without Jerome getting on the blower to ask for the address of your tailor, your elocutionist, your shirt-maker. He modelled himself on one of his victims, George Sanders, particularly as that actor had played Sir Henry Wotton, Dorian Grey's mentor, and carefully studied the gracious-living magazines together with *The Tailor and Cutter*. This immaculate being would emerge on week-ends from his working-class dwelling in Pimlico (he'd been a scholarship boy) to confront the world as a suave, intimidating English gentleman. He fleshed out the physical side of his personality with body-building and jiu-jitsu — the martial art in fashion before the days of karate. Thus one might observe the contradiction between the sophisticated lounge-lizard manner and the tough, heavily delted, triked, and latted physique. Later, in Canada, he developed karate, shaved his skull, and force-fed himself almost to obesity on scrounged pro-tein — festoons of steak, cod, spareribs, haddock. Thus Jerome trundling down the street towards you was a figure to be reck-oned with — huge gut and shoulders, shaven skull, bespoke suit, gentle expression, and, by Canadian perceptions, poofter's voice, moving with the nautical role he'd cultivated at an earlier stage in his life.

When Jerome lived with you there were only three disad-vantages: he was more often than not low in funds and would feel forced to raid your refrigerator, emptying it, such was the vast-ness of his appetite, his sheer need for protein, at a swoop. Sometimes he would work for a living, though with understand-able reluctance, as night porter, watchman, night clerk . . . jobs that suited his nocturnal habits. Thus the second disadvantage was that during the day your house would be cast in shadow, for the curtains would be drawn and Jerome, who detested beds, flat out on your sofa, mouth puffing in a series of faint snores. No remon-stration would do any good. He would apologize, sleep in a spare bedroom for a day or two, then revert to the sofa. It was like trying to train a bat, or a three-toed sloth. The third was this, that he was a lover of classical music, a mine of information on the subject, and a man of eclectic tastes. When awake he might enter your home, frisk your record collection, switch on your stereo, and start to play his selection. He'd crank up the volume and settle down . . . Bach . . . Villa-Lobos, Janacek, Dukas . . . it was all the same to him. One day he invaded the downstairs apartment I have previously mentioned. It was occupied by Aviva Cantor and its rent was paid by the ubiquitous Irving Layton. Jerome found a recording of *Lohengrin*, stuck it on the machine, and turned it up full blast. Within seconds this howling, demonic music smashed through the air. Irving and Aviva were in the bedroom, enjoying a quiet siesta, when this violent noise shook the entire building. What? Irving shouted. What's this? He leaped out of bed, CanLit's performing flea, *What in the name of Christ's going on?* It's all right, Jerome assured him. Don't you worry about me . . . you go back to bed . . . I'll just make myself a piece of toast . . . cup of tea . . . don't happen to have a couple of eggs, do you? . . . piece of haddock? . . . Never mind . . . toast and a cup of tea will keep me going. . . . That was his attitude. What with unpredictability and contrasts, his apparent somnambulism, and the darkened, sepulchral room, he was perhaps more than most people could take, let alone an English working-class mother with petit-bourgeois aspirations, anxious for her daughter's matrimonial advancement, and a concern for the good opinion of neighbours.

Where was he, that was the point. Jill, half out of her mind with desperation, couldn't even guess. I had phoned her at work — she was at that time a clerk in the accounts department of a big store and had that very day mislaid, on paper, some hundred and seventy thousand dollars and was facing the prospect of dismissal with less equanimity than most of us would have felt. It seemed to me that the South of France was even further in the future. I put the phone down with an oath. What in hell was the matter with all these people? I slipped down Ridgewood towards my own apartment block, dashed in through the door, and rang Aviva's bell, keeping a weather eye out for the Mother on the Stair. By the Grace of God, though, Aviva was in. I crept inside the door, closed it, she shouted a delighted greeting, and we stood for the next few minutes locked in one another's arms.

Where's the Gaffer? I asked eventually.

Gaffer?

The Poet.

She howled with laughter and delight. Irving was a constant source of joy to her, half of it directed against him. Jerome had been in love with her, and she felt close to Jerome. I reminded her of his invasion that day of the Wagner and asked her if she knew where he was. She shook her head and then played a variation of a scene that was to become commonplace in the future, particularly after I had bought a car.

Johnno, she said, her voice bantering, high-pitched, and with an edge of wheedle. Oh Johnno!

She had retained the Australianism of adding this open vowel to first names. I wasn't sure whether I liked it or not.

Cup of coffee, Johnno?

Yes, yes.

And then we go to Steinberg's, eh loved one? In a nice taxi, eh heartsease?

Nope.

Oh, Johnno!!!

Not unless you pay.

Are you doing that tough, working-class London male again?

My mother says you're a vixen.

Oh Johnno she *didn't* . . . she *didn't* . . . a vixen . . . how did she say it? I have to know how she said it . . . *vixen* . . . does she know it's a German word for wank? I bet her eyes flashed and her teeth glittered . . . like gravestones in the moonlight . . . Steinberg's, my dove?

Nope.

Coffee first, my darling, then we'll go shopping. Get a nice, nice cab and go to Steinberg's.

I'm starving, Aviva. What's in the fridge?

Just a little cheese, my lovely. A little slice of Oka . . . until we go shopping . . . it's Irving's favourite . . . you can't have it . . . Johnno! No! I said you couldn't have it! You're so transparent! You can't have Irving's woman, so you steal his cheese. . . .

Vixen, I said, my mouth full of Oka. And for her benefit and of course my own I role-played my mother saying *vixen* . . . a performance that seemed to satisfy her only at the twentieth repetition. A percolator came to orgasm over the stove. Slices of toast popped forth warmly, then grew soft and limp under the ministration of butter. Cheese vanished. I sighed with pleasure. This little apartment had always seemed a haven, a warm and frolicsome refuge where I could always recapture, presuming I'd mislaid it, my *alegria* — that birthright of us all, the basic, unutterable joy a child takes in its own creation, its vitality. And as for Aviva, she was fresh, joyous, and completely uninhibited. I had loved her when I first knew her, before Irving had gaffed her, then lost touch with her after I started working in the North. Irving had set her up in this apartment while he was in the long and painful process of separating from his wife. She used to crow about being a kept woman, the kind of entity her mother, back in Australia, frequently anathematized, and a factor strongly in the consciousness of my own mother, whose opinions in such matters were rigid to the point of judgementalism.

Irving himself seemed to approve of the word "kept" in

relation to Aviva. He would answer the door, call her to him, then, his arms about her, would say: *How about this, then, hey? How do you like my pussy-cat, eh my friend? What do you think of this pussy-cat of mine?*

Very nice.

Oh, *Irving* . . . Aviva would squirm in embarrassment, trying to escape his iron grip.

A struggling, sensuous pussy-cat . . . how do you like her, hey? Soft, furry body . . . ha! and little claws too . . . look at them!

Very nice indeed. . . .

I used to see her as a glorified playmate, then as a serious contender for some sort of quasi-monogamous relationship. But I began to recognize that I existed only on the periphery of her sexual life, usually, as happened frequently enough, when she fought with Irving, grew disgusted with his slowness in leaving his wife, or nauseated with his possessiveness or solipsistic self-approval. So, as a sort of defence, I had chosen to discount her, even though she made most of the other women in my life seem leaden, shallow, and vacuous.

I explained that I didn't think *vixen* was a German word, though it sounded very much like their expression for masturbate. But as I spoke I sounded pedantic and heavy — she had the capacity sometimes to make me feel as though I had a grand piano tied to my arse. I found myself staring at her with mouth agape in the throes of what Irving, following James Joyce, would have called an epiphany — a showing forth of the true nature of things. And the epiphany was this: *there is no reason why you should play second fiddle to Irving Layton.* His woman ought to be mine, in so far as one person can be said to belong to another. To hell with Jerome . . . my mother . . . sister . . . I deserved Aviva. I would take her with me to the South of France. Get her to slough the Poet. And then . . . Nice . . . Cannes . . . St. Trop' . . . Porquerolles. It was purely a question of tactics. I had good reason to believe I was not unattractive to her. But soft! I knew too much to broach this serious matter in the present atmosphere — dropping the Gaffer would mean a major shift in her life's priorities. Even I, euphoric with renewed love, could see that. But I wanted her and was going to have her. Gaffer or no Gaffer.

My mood grew lighter, more and more frolicsome. We washed cups . . . wrestled . . . rolled about on the floor . . . took the telephone off the hook . . . deadbolted the front entrance . . . got a taxi . . . visited Steinberg's . . . and in all these actions my soul was as light as gossamer: the resolution underlying it as hard as steel.

5

Ah, but how to proceed, that was the point. One of the things I thought I knew about women was the more you pursue them, the more they will evade you. I must remain stand-offish . . . detached . . . then, when the opportunity was ripe — the moment of sexual *kairos* — I would strike. But what of Irving? I had been reading Machiavelli's *The Prince* for practical advice, and what I found there was disconcerting:

> . . . *[The Prince] should pick the fox and the lion, because the lion does not defend itself from snares, and the fox does not defend itself from wolves. So one needs to be a fox to recognize snares and a lion to frighten wolves.*

This seemed very sound to me, though difficult to translate from metaphor to action. Much trickier was the advice on fortune:

> . . . *it is better to be impetuous than cautious, because fortune is a woman . . . and one sees that she lets herself be won more by the impetuous than by those who proceed coldly. And so, like a woman, she is the friend of the young, because they are less cautious, more ferocious, and command her with more audacity.*

Irving was more than a snare and a wolf: he was an opponent with all the advantages except youth; and Machiavelli was wrong about fortune — I was as impetuous and as foolhardy as anybody I'd ever met, and fortune had eluded me. I vowed this time to "proceed coldly." Meanwhile, other matters called on my attention.

I found a bed-sitting room not far from McGill where I could write and be at peace. I acquired a used Morris Minor, and my friends took this as a sign that their days of riding buses and hiring cabs were over, and they made my new telephone loud with requests for rides. My complaints did me no good: if it wasn't you, McCarthy told me in a variation of the argument used by munitions-makers against pacifists, it would have to be somebody else. I needed that car badly, however, to race around the city — job interviews, assignations, the search for Jerome. A good friend who worked for the National Film Board set me up for a meeting with a producer who outstared me and demanded to know what these short stories were like that he'd heard so much about. I said I'd send him some, and went home to make clean copies of "Dinas

Cromlech'' (named after the Welsh cliff where the action was located), one about reporting sick in the British army and dying of meningitis (a true story, except for its ending), another about a Salvation Army hostel in Hull. All were based on personal experience and each was about as joyous and life-affirming as the corpse of a red snapper lying fly-blown on a polluted beach. The producer sent them back with a note to say they were of little interest. I gritted my teeth and tinkered with these stories again. I wrote one about the mad pursuit of a beautiful girl by an impoverished student newly flunked out of college (myself). She encourages him to join her at a resort hotel in Cornwall. He camps outside, on the beach, and observes her making love to a toff in the back seat of a Bentley. I was quite pleased with it and read it to the Gaffer.

The beach scenes are okay, he said. I don't even mind that crap about how phosphorescent the sea is at night. But it's not a short story.

Fuck it, Irving, I shouted. I've just about had all of you I can take. You're perverse, sanctimonious, envious, and dishonest. You haven't the faintest clue as to what you are talking about . . . you're an oaf, an ignoramus. An illiterate, crass, and insensitive lout.

You prick! Aviva screamed, for she too, squirming on a pouf, had listened to my recital with mounting irritation. You're just not a writer! You're a nothing! A man without art! Give it up! Get a job! Go back to that stupid Arctic of yours and make some money. . . .

You wheedling, treacherous bitch . . . I began.

Hah! the Gaffer shouted. You snivelling little half-arsed punk, you think I haven't better things to do than to listen to your pathetic, castrated drivel? You English fart, weeping snot through keyholes, haven't you heard the good news? Where's your joy? Your life? Your energy? Your *élan vital*? You whimpering half-man, you give me the creeps . . . take that idiot piece of prose out of here and go and put some guts into it. . . . Get your nasty, self-abusing hero murdering the man in the Bentley. Have him do the girl in for good measure . . . she deserves it . . . then end it with the murderer crowing in triumph, striding into his new destiny. Now get out of here.

Furiously I snatched the story from his grasp and strode home. I reread it. It was more than possible he was right. The logic of the story demanded such an ending. It enraged and humiliated me to discover he was right again. I tried to rewrite it, but couldn't. *Things in real life just hadn't happened that way.* I hadn't even fought with the girl. Freda, her name was. Freda Webb. I'd just megrimed off, bemoaning the class system and my inability to compete with rich young men with good accents and access to power.

Hoping for a more encouraging response, I showed my "Dinas Cromlech" to Graham and McCarthy the next day. But, as fellow Europeans, they too had been brought up where writers publish or read their works aloud at owner's risk. Graham's response was normally to mock, to imitate, to reduce to absurdity any foolishness latent in work, while McCarthy would fall into a daze broken sometimes with a sharp and adverse comment.

Is this your personal experience? he said.

Yes.

Then why is your narrator a Welsh quarryman? You ever work in a slate quarry?

You know I didn't.

No, and that's obvious from the story. The consciousness, the tone of voice, is Lavender Hill, or the East India Dock Road.

Why not make him a Lascar, Graham said. Straight out of a ship's hold. Then, of course, he'd get the girl, and where would you go for your self-pity?

He'd find plenty more where that came from, McCarthy said. But seriously, if you're going to write about you, make him *you*.

At home again, I thought about it. I wanted when I began the story to make the class distinction sharper by injecting a racial, cultural difference. But I could see where this sounded fake. What if I took it out of the first-person mode altogether? I'd lose immediacy, the reader's attention. But it looked as though I hadn't got it anyway. What had I to lose? Cautiously, hesitantly, I took the first step in the story-teller's art: I imagined the action as though it took place before me on a stage. I tried to describe the events as though I were an invisible observer. What this forced me to do, of course, was to cut out my sullen hero's inner processes, his unverbalized feelings, and replace them with signs — the whitened knuckle, the sudden grating in the voice, the sharp, unnecessary movement. I began to see him from the perspective of the girl, the viewpoint of the rival. As I warmed to this exercise, against the grain though it seemed at first, I found it exciting and delightful. My hero even began to seem faintly comic.

Meanwhile my advertisement had gone into the *Montreal Star*: Tutor available, maths and physics. B.Sc. (Wales), M.Sc. (London). My invention was stronger on creating degrees for myself than it was on developing an omniscient narrator for "Dinas Cromlech." I stopped short of following Richmond's example and calling myself "Doctor." Even so, I was surprised to find that very quickly I had accumulated a small but loyal clientele and was making enough to pay for my room, meals, and car expenses such as gasoline, constant repair bills, and the cascade of parking tickets that deluged me whenever I ventured outside.

6

It wasn't very long before John Richmond became a frequent visitor to Upper Ridgewood. From the Seals' window he could be observed striding up the hill — bouncing, military gait — through the snow, walking stick at the high port. *Here comes Uncle Mad*, we'd say, or, more concisely, *Here's Mad*. He had indeed presented himself to us in an avuncular role, not only because of the two small children connected to us, but because he was conscious of our youth — he considered himself wiser and more experienced. His natural portliness in both waist and manner gave conviction to this pose and we ourselves were comfortable enough with it.

Let us go, Mad would say. Let us go to and fro on the earth and walk up and down on it.

And we'd dress up in our Arctic clothes — overshoes, parkas, mukluks, relics of our different adventures in wilder parts — and stride with him — duffle coat, cap, pipe, stick —up through the Côte des Neiges cemetery, over the mountain, into the chalet for a warm-up, down the steps to Peel Street, then to the pubs and bars along Ste. Catherine Street speaking of a thousand things — money, investments, the sacraments, the South of France, what we were to do next, each of us, in our lives. We followed Richmond across intersections, plunging into the shrieking, rabid traffic which would squeal and blast to sudden halts as Mad, chin up, stick out, scowling ferociously, strode across without fear. We stayed close to him, delighted observers, as he went about his business.

Our first day out with him was typical. I remember Mad stalking into the CBC offices on Dorchester Street and demanding, in the most peremptory of tones, to "speak to somebody responsible." The cowed receptionist brought down a fluttering producer who listened to a long, pompous, and irate lecture on how the word *hamartía* had been mistranslated, on some radio talk on tragedy, as "tragic flaw," when every schoolboy knew, provided he'd been to a half-decent school, that it meant "mistake.'' Tragedy is about a good man making a mistake, old boy, never forget it. After this we moved on to a peculiar Gothic building on Guy Street into which Mad, excusing himself, suddenly popped, emerging five minutes later with fruity apologies and a secret smile. It was only later that we understood the significance of this building in Richmond's strange career: for the moment he invented a convenient story about visiting an old student of his. We nodded and followed him into the bar of the Ritz. The barman looked at our outer clothing with dismay, but was mollified, or at least intimidated, by Mad's ultra-respectability and drill-master's frown.

It was on this occasion that we began to fence with one another concerning our futures as pedagogues. I was doing fairly well with my tutoring, but the next step for me was problematic. The job interviews, the dreary encounters with personnel managers, pension-plan apparatchiks, sceptical plant managers and engineers in charge had depressed me, and I knew that my days of working for a living were over. From their point of view I was unreliable, and indeed was unreliable from my own. From now until the day I die, I thought, it'll be a question of nip and tuck.

I'm grateful to you, I said. Without your encouragement I'd've been working for a living by now.

No, no, no, old boy. You are too kind. I think you would have succeeded in not working for a living well enough without me.

When in doubt, says you, teach. How right you are.

Ex cathedra, old boy, but not cast in stone. Let us not monumentalize our utterances, for *God's* sake.

But I would like to take it a step further, I said. When in doubt . . . *start a school*.

He stared at me with a sort of disgust as though my face had suddenly blossomed forth in a lethal midline granuloma.

I've been thinking that myself, he said.

There was an uneasy pause.

You are perfectly right, he said. The next logical step for us all would be to start a school.

Consider it, I said. I'm doing one pupil a time for four dollars. Why not two in an hour for eight? Three for twelve? And so on.

Exactly, old boy. Thirty students an hour at four dollars an hour each for three hours a day, five days a week, gives us eighteen hundred, times four, less rental of a building, chairs, and desks, would give us about six thousand a month profit. Split four ways and we each have a living wage for one hour's work a day. The bread and butter, old boy — the jam we'll have ample leisure to pursue.

I can do maths, I said. Physics and maths. So can McCarthy here. You could do English and languages. Graham could do philosophy.

Count me out, Graham said.

Let's get started on it, old boy. I could do with the challenge. In any case, the Rabbis and I are coming to a parting of the ways.

So it is, McCarthy said, with Irving.

That is what is being said, Richmond agreed. So it is with the Gaffer.

The rumour that Irving was to leave the Herzliah turned very soon into hard news. Aviva and I pondered its implications.

It may shake him out of his stupid rut, she said. A cataclysm in one area of his life may provoke it in another.

He may get the guts to leave his wife?

Oh Johnno, what else could I mean? But it isn't that he hasn't the guts — it's mostly that he's holding back, waiting for other things to develop.

What others?

McClelland and Stewart may be publishing his collected poems.

That's quite a coup.

But Johnno . . . listen . . . you mustn't tell anyone else but . . . *he's been nominated for the Nobel prize.*

I could do nothing here but nod wisely. Apart from the prize, I said, for which he's an obvious shoo-in, what's happening at the school?

She told me that Irving's cultivation of the mass media, his growing reputation — quite undeserved and based so far as I could see on the reiteration of certain words then taboo, at least in print, but secretly hankered after by the suburban housewives he excited and tantalized — as a pornographer and corrupter of children, his frequent assertions, reprehensible to the more orthodox of the Rabbis, that he was the Messiah, and his general uninhibited behaviour, particularly in the sexual jungle, had prompted the Board of Governors to ask for his resignation.

But you know Irving, she said. He's not the kind of person to eat shit, rabbinical or otherwise. Come and look.

She took me over to his desk and broached a file. There, in orderly fashion, were copies of the Gaffer's correspondence, all of it denunciatory in content and scabrous in tone. One was a bold statement of his Messianic claims: tradition, he said, predicted that the Messiah would be born without a foreskin: he was born without a foreskin. Therefore he was the Messiah. Even I, with my tendency towards making wild and unsupportable statements, could see that the Gaffer's conclusion did not follow from the premise. But the letter went on to suggest penalties adumbrated by various Old Testament prophets for failure to recognize the King, descendant of David, and these, most of them blood-drenched and bowel-bespattered, would be visited on the Rabbis. There were several addressed to a publisher who had turned down a manuscript. "You could have achieved honour and fame in your lifetime and immortality beyond it as the first to recognize the greatest poet of the age. You have missed your chance, my friend." Another, in similar vein, was sent to a producer who had rejected a radio play of his.

Sad stuff, I commented.

Megalomania, she agreed. Sometimes I think he's a great genius, at others that he's off his head.

This led her to speak of the Gaffer's selfishness, insensitivity, what we would now call male chauvinism, and acts of what seemed deliberate cruelty. She followed up with descriptions of the kind of things she had to endure and grew emotional, vengeful. I hugged her while she sobbed out grievances and disillusions. Things are going very well, I thought: this was the first time I'd heard her denounce her lover. I considered pressing home my proposal — that she should dump this zany and elope with me to the Mediterranean littoral. But I decided to let these insights into Irving's character mature, and the impulse to elope come from her. One should approach a seduction, as Lao-tze must have put it, as one prepares a little fish for the table.

Jerome, whom we'd given up, reappeared quite suddenly. He phoned Aviva, explained he'd been lying low owing as much to pressure of work as to my mother's animosity, but knew I must by now be in town and would like to see me. As for him, he was quite comfortable in his new lodgings: a friend of a friend had found him a bed in a basement curtained off from the furnace on one side, and by boxes of old newspapers, telephone directories, and *National Geographics* on the other. There were no windows and not much air, which suited him, but no means of consoling himself with music. He arranged to meet me in the Kiltie Lounge of the Laurentien Hotel.

This was a bleak and darkened bar, almost always empty, hung with fake tartans and plastic claymores. It was as close to being inside a catafalque as one could get without closing the lid. It suited Jerome, of course, for with his etiolated appearance and sunken eyes he never seemed much further than a hand's clutch from the charnel-house.

I wanted to lie quite low, he explained. You must understand that my life in the Ridgewood apartment was growing steadily more insupportable.

I can see that, Jerome. You took a lot of abuse.

Yes, I did, and I would've walked out before had I not felt guilty about leaving Jill to face that termagant alone. I say, I'm most awfully sorry.

About what?

Calling your mother a termagant.

It's the least of her problems.

A sick old woman, in my opinion. But of course one ought not to judge.

She had plenty of names for you.

I know.

Vicious, lazy sponger.

I know.

A fat slug.

Yes.

A homosexual sewer-rat.

I hadn't heard that one. What a warped mind she has!

She thinks your presence in that house has probably screwed up David's future sexuality.

It's a wonder to me, given what must have been your upbringing, that you're not a homosexual sewer-rat yourself.

I explained that his absence had not improved matters with regard to the relationship between the two women in the house; they spent their time together in mutual recriminations, going over old wounds, insults, failures of loyalty, etc., and Jill was almost totally worn down by it. Then I took a rash step, one that was to have the direst consequences.

Jerome, I said. Would you consider going back to Ridgewood?

My dear fellow, your mother has made that quite impossible, surely you must see that.

I shall ask her to leave.

You can't do that.

Kick her out.

She's your mother.

And Jill's my sister. And they're driving one another mad. One of them has to go.

How will you kick her out?

Find her a place near by. She can have my room, in fact. Down by McGill. It's begun to give me the creeps.

I don't know, my dear fellow, I don't know.

My nephew needs you there. I shan't be there. I'm heading off to the South of France very soon.

Lucky you.

I have a couple of irons in the fire, I said, deliberately not mentioning Aviva. But it'll be the situation as before . . . back to the days before my mother arrived.

We ordered more drinks from the mute and pallid waiter, and I left him to deal with events transpiring at Richmond Academy.

We had placed a carefully worded advertisement in the *Star*, and it wasn't more than an hour after that paper came out that calls started to flood in and the first appointments were made. I sat with Richmond and McCarthy, all of us dressed to the nines, in Richmond's book-lined study. The bell rang, we smiled grimly at one another. Richmond ushered in a couple (Westmount, middle-class, I would've said) and a tall, bespectacled male teen-ager of unprepossessing complexion, lank hair, and dangling hands.

Not doing very well at school, Mad said after the preliminaries. What do your parents mean, you're not doing very well at school?

The boy shrugged.

Mad's voice suddenly took on a kind of thunderous growl.

Are you failing examinations? he asked.

Shrug.

Are you failing, yes or no? Richmond suddenly screamed. His face had swollen in a trice, turned red, apoplectic veins knotted on his forehead, tendons bulged and quivered in his throat, his stick, in his hand, began to vibrate. Yes or no! Richmond shrieked, and if you shrug at me again, sir, I shall crack your skull! Yes sir, crack your skull! With this stick! *I shall crack your skull!*

Christ, I thought, this evil bugger's headed for the bin.

Yes, the boy muttered. I can't seem to concentrate.

Concentrate! Richmond bellowed. Well, you'll concentrate in *my* school if we decide to admit you. Yes, we'll teach you how to concentrate, don't have any illusions on that score. He's not as stupid as he makes out, Mad said, turning to the parents, just idle, pampered, and over-indulged. We can knock that out of him. Give me your phone number and I'll call you when we've made our decision.

With a good imitation of badly concealed contempt for the three of them, he showed them out.

Damn it, I said as the door closed behind them. Is there a sense in which we might possibly have overdone it?

No, no, old boy. They'll be on the blower again. Within twenty minutes. You'll see.

And indeed he was right. McCarthy took the call in the next room as Richmond, shrieking with demonic frenzy, threatened the next candidate, a plump and sullen girl, with twisted arms and shattered teeth.

7

It seemed to us that Richmond's exit from the Herzliah, timed so precisely with Irving's, was too fortuitous to be ignored. We ought, McCarthy pointed out, to include the Gaffer in Richmond's Academy. Accordingly, he got on the phone and was greeted by the most enthusiastic reception he had experienced from the Poet in a very long time. They set up a meeting of the four principals for the following evening.

We gathered, then, chez Seal, on what might be termed neutral ground. Mad entered first — short, stern, batrachoid as to mouth — then Layton — white sports shirt open at neck, black chest hair, hairy forearms — slightly out of his element here; at home, in Côte St. Luc, he could stand close to a bust of Beethoven, an artist to whom he felt a great affinity, and defy the elements and human animosity to do their worst. Here, on Upper Ridgewood, he was among people as lunatic, and therefore as unpredictable, as himself. Perhaps that is why he had brought Aviva — light, frolicsome, dressed in a low-cut blouse and dark-blue pants that hugged her halfway up her calves. Graham had declined to join us. Bryan McCarthy was there already — red of beard, blear of eye, but at this stage of the proceedings, clear-headed and acute. Then there was myself, slightly above middle height, long of hair, shifty in expression, and twitching with needless jokes and smiles. McCarthy took the chair.

We are here, he said, to discuss ways in which we may pool our expertise. Each of us is an experienced teacher; each of us is dissatisfied with the present school system. We are therefore to discuss possibilities of creating some form of educative alternative. For my own part I have to tell you that I am in it for the money.

After this unwontedly long but characteristically honest speech, McCarthy helped himself to a tumbler of Queberac, a gallon of which stood on the coffee table, and as the session wore on retreated into silence.

And I am not in it for the money, Irving declared boldly. I am in it for my principles. I have taught in the school system and found it destructive of body, soul, and spirit. It crushes creativity and celebrates mediocrity. It erases courage, individualism, and ambition, and affirms servility, incuriosity, and the mentality of the herd. The public school system is an abomination and a disease; the private schools, at least the Herzliah, are chaotic, undirected, and controlled by eunuchs and poltroons. I want to set fire to the imagination of the people of this country, to inspire them with a love of life, a delight in art and poetry; I want to prepare them to recognize the Master Spirit. . . .

By whom you mean yourself? Richmond could not resist saying.

By whom he most certainly means himself, Aviva said loudly, have you any objections?

I do *not* mean myself, wench, Irving said. I am a prophet, a *vates*. I prepare the way, the path, the wide road along which Dionysus shall one day stride.

But I've heard you claim to be the Messiah, Mad said. And now you also want to be John the Baptist. Come, come, old boy, you cannot strive to be both.

McCarthy grunted, either to conceal a belch or to express approval at this rather cheap quip.

Well, let's hear from you, John Richmond . . . *Doctor* Richmond . . . let's hear the word from the Groves of Academe. Let's have the moderate, detached, judicious, and unexcited point of view. You think what I've said Utopian?

Oh utterly, old boy, utterly.

Then tell us, you pompous bullfrog, Aviva screamed. Tell us before I piss my pants in anticipation.

I am finding it very difficult to make my point. And will you not, Layton, endeavour to control that vile trollop of yours.

Just talk, old boy, McCarthy said. Never mind the noises off.

Under normal conditions, said Uncle Mad, I would support

the idea of a school where a core curriculum had been re-established. And by this I mean a suitably supervised study of the classics — particularly Greek. Never mind the cant about the will of the child — that is so-much liberal wish-wash. Greek is all a man needs to get him through life. Is he unhappy? Let him learn Greek. Unfulfilled? Let him learn Greek. Does he question Providence? The problem of evil? Greek. His own purpose in life? Greek. Make him learn Greek, sir, do you follow me? Greek. Greek. Greek.

Are you saying, Aviva said through clenched teeth, leaning well forward, that you want the little buggers to learn Greek?

He's being idiotic, Irving said. Take no notice.

But conditions are not normal, Richmond continued. What we have in this country is a lack of cultural base. We have the melancholy spectacle of parents afraid of their own children, writhing in a constant state of guilt as to whether they are bringing them up correctly according to current liberal notions. With the result that discipline has gone out of the window and they are unable to get their children to learn the simplest things like the alphabet, or the eight times table. Unable to stop them haunting the streets, fighting in gangs, mugging pedestrians, falling into the hands of the policeman, the magistrate, the probation officer. They want their children taken in hand, force-fed, caned if neces-sary, so long as they don't have to do it themselves. They want to relinquish to stern and capable hands their own parental responsi-bilities which they no longer have the courage to administer. That's it, old boy, in a nutshell. They want a return to the days of spare the rod and spoil the child. And for this they are willing to pay good money. I propose to set up a school where we can give them what they want, educate their brats, their cretins, their morons, to pass these really very simple government exams, and relieve them of their disposable income.

Caned, you say, Irving muttered.

Yes indeed, old boy. Caning if necessary, but not necessarily with the cane.

I see it all now, the Gaffer said. I've often wondered about you. You're a simple sadist, that's what you are, a man who disguises his sexual inadequacies under a guise of moral rectitude, love of discipline, order, and reason. What's the matter, Rich-mond, can't you get it up? Is that what your walking-stick means? Is it a substitute penis? Is that why you thrust it at the traffic? What's a car to you, a ravenous, insatiable female equipped with *vagina dentata*? You're a coward, Richmond, afraid of a mere automobile — a cheap thing of plastic and tin.

Try putting your cock in splints, Aviva yelled. Tie it between a brace of chopsticks. . . .

Sir, Richmond roared, you are a mountebank with the mentality of a street urchin.

And you, sir, with your deformation of the sexual impulse have the sort of mentality that leads to war, genocide, the rape of the environment.

Shut up the pair of you! I screamed, unable to contain myself any longer. You couple of glib and paltry maniacs. I came here to discuss turning an honest dollar, not for facile cultural analysis.

There was a silence that rather shocked me. I was unused to being listened to. Perhaps I was learning what the others knew by instinct — that a forceful and brazen manner will, regardless of content, secure attention.

What you are observing, old boy, said Mad, turning to me, is the locking of horns of two impotent bulls of Bashan. . . .

This was a shrewd stroke. Irving's method of attacking people who disagreed with him was to accuse them of being undersexed. Richmond, though a mud-wrestler, was — unlike the rest of us — no guttersnipe. He could manage the well-turned phrase, but his notion of abuse was of the sir-your-wife-under-the-pretence-of-keeping-a-bawdy-house-is-a-receiver-of-stolen-goods variety. Thus he was too literary for this rough-and-tumble city: phrases like *cockatrice* or *bolting-hutch* hurled at taxi-drivers, etc., seldom produced a reaction. Yet, oddly enough, the simple device of turning the charge of sexual inadequacy against its originator was enough to trigger a quite violent response. Fuming and bubbling with rage, foaming at the mouth and punching the air before him like a brain-damaged ex-pug, Irving shouted, Impotent! Speak for yourself, you over-bred, ineffectual bully-boy from the rabbit-chinned, asinine, and twittering class of petit bourgeois, counter-jumpers, vestrymen, and lounge lizards. Where was your power when my people were rounded up and gassed? Where were you when the Warsaw ghetto was pulverized by the Nazis and betrayed by Stalinist thugs? Where were you when Hitler strutted into the Rhineland and began the massacre of the Jews? Busy sucking the arse of the likes of Neville Chamberlain when you weren't masturbating, or stealing the straw from your mother's kennel.

The conversation had taken what to me was a quite unexpected turn. It was a sign of Irving's discomposure that he had resorted to the oldest stand-by in the book — the charge of anti-Semitism.

Irving! Aviva pitched in loudly. He called you a mountebank. You know why? Because you mount banks! You take sides! You don't sit with your arse safely tucked across a fence, facing both ways. . . .

I was deprived of all those delights you mention, Mad replied acerbically. I was neither at the hot gates nor at the Iron Gate; I was neither in Warsaw nor in the Rhineland. I did not have the pleasure of putting your family to death.

Putz! Aviva bellowed, turning on the Poet. How much longer are you going to tolerate these worthless and preposterous squares? When are you . . .

Irving, too far gone to hear her, was beginning another tirade with the words You Nazi, Jew-burning, culture-hating psychopath when an extraordinary thing happened. Richmond started, quite literally, to bark. The noise was sharp, loud, and a cross between the yelpings of a seal and a dog.

Ha'karf, he barked, standing up. H'ruff! . . . k'chah! . . . h'roof! . . . kah! . . . k'chah! He reached for his cap . . . kaff! . . . his stick . . . h'roof! woof*kaff!* . . . and he was out of the door.

He left the rest of us in a stunned silence. For a moment I wondered if, in the give and take of argument and persuasion, one of us had gone too far. Then I thought of the frogs in Aristophanes . . . kr, kr, kr, kr . . . koax, koax . . . and said so. McCarthy smiled amiably. The Gaffer and Aviva, good humour restored, were chuckling and feeling one another up. McCarthy said he didn't think Richmond's feelings were discomposed, but that he had better traipse down to Lower Ridgewood and find out. He poured us all a *deoch an doris* from the fast-failing Queberac bottle and we all parted with many expressions of mutual regard.

Two days after this encounter, Irving astonished us by leaving on a jet plane for Paris. He had left the Herzliah, his wife, their house on Côte St. Luc, and a letter for Aviva, slipped under his other door on Ridgewood.

Well, Pussy Cat [he wrote]. *By the time you read this I shall be in Europe. Paris! Then on to Rome! Athens! Florence! Venice! What names these are for my imagination to conjure with! I have taken out my small savings, sold a bond or two, screwed the school for severance pay, and got an advance from McClelland*

and Stewart. And that's the most exciting thing of all! My first book with a commercial publisher! An epoch making event, the beginning of a new age in literature. At any rate, do not worry that I will not have enough money. I have more than enough for my modest needs. I shall send you postcards with exotic stamps.

Aviva phoned me in a state of great turmoil. That this utter bastard should take off to Europe, finally leaving his wife, and she worth not much more than a postcard. The thought of these legendary places, though she had in her time seen them all, drove her mad, for one of her fantasies was of steering her lover around Europe . . . hand in hand along the quais . . . gondola to Torcello, snuggled on cushions . . . roistering with Cretans to bazouki music . . . making slow and tender love under the cypresses of Capri. Treachery! She embarked on a description of the Gaffer's character which, even divided by four, seemed utterly damning. I put my arms about her and kissed her gently. I've finished with him, she said. She kissed me back. Forever and forever, she said. She sobbed bitterly. Johnno, she whispered. Are you still going to France? And do you want me to come with you?

I paused for reflection — the game had gone entirely my way without any effort on my part. The enemy, as Machiavelli pointed out, may in his confidence overreach himself, bringing about his own downfall. I did not fully believe that this could be Aviva's last word — no attachment as strong as hers and Irving's could be dissolved by a mere oath. And if we went away together, all kinds of exciting, but also terrifying, possibilities opened up. My pause lasted a full second and a half.

Not France, I said. We're too likely to run into the Gaffer. It's a big place.

Mexico! I said. Let's go to Mexico! We'll leave Europe to the Gaffer! Vera Cruz! Oaxaca! Yucatan!

With delighted cries we got out maps and atlases and made plans with energy that took us far into the night.

We couldn't, of course, go immediately. There was much to be done . . . much unfinished business. I began winding up my Montreal affairs. A morning's work and "Dinas Cromlech" lay on my desk — finished. I read it over to McCarthy and Graham a couple of hours later. I was greatly moved by it — the young man's longing, his bitterness, came over as strongly as it had before, but the omniscient narration made clear the *inevitability* of the situation: much as the woman in the story might have liked or admired the hero, she was pregnant by his rival. I uttered the last word with a sigh. Then I looked up at my friends. Graham giggled slightly, then fell silent. McCarthy stared at me with a kind of stony severity, as though my upper lip and cheek bore traces of a carelessly wiped nose.

Why is he telling all this? McCarthy said.

What?

Why's he going to the trouble of telling us this story? What's its point? Why should I be interested?

And I for one, Graham said. Am not. What's the subject?

Are you kidding? Do I have to read it over again? It's about a young man in love with a woman who turns to somebody weaker, more effete, than himself. It's about class antagonism . . . it's about . . .

God help us all, McCarthy said.

Amen, said Graham.

Your plot and your characters are trivial, McCarthy said. Everybody knows that there are class antagonisms. Everybody in Montreal knows that if two men compete for the same woman she will gravitate to the materially better advantaged of the two. Everybody on this street knows that the loser will be upset. What's the matter with you?

Graham said: What you really want to write about is North Wales — its steely grey cliffs, dark skies, and deep, mysterious mountain tarns. Take the people out, and you may have something. Or even better — put in another person, the narrator. Put it back into the first person, but a person acting as a minor character in the action.

I swore at them both and stalked out. On the way down to Côte des Neiges I dropped in on my mother and told her, as gently as I could, that I was coming back into the apartment, and so was Jerome. There wouldn't be room, I said, for all three of us. It seemed also that she and Jill were not hitting it off. There is no need to describe this interview in any detail: suffice it to say it was long, painful, and acrimonious, but in some ways unnecessary. My mother had already decided to leave, and had found a room for herself on Bishop Street. I left her feeling exhausted and at a loss. Further down Ridgewood I called on Uncle Mad to inform him that, since I was about to leave for Mexico, I would no longer be associated with Richmond Academy. He accepted my resignation with fake sorrow — he knew I would have been a source of dissension. We parted with expressions of mutual good-will.

I got back to my room and began packing my few belongings into my Morris Minor. Some I would take to Ridgewood and store there, and the rest to Mexico.

The phone rang.

Johnno! Aviva said, her voice breathless and delighted. You'll never guess what's happened! He *phoned*! . . . Irving phoned! He's sent for me! He wired me the fare! Oh Johnno, I'm so happy . . . so delighted . . . he's left her! Given up the house! . . . Johnno, come over and help me celebrate!

I raced over. She was already packing . . . stuffing books into cardboard boxes from the basement . . . dismantling shelves . . . wrapping pieces of china in newspapers . . . hanging clothes in garment bags for storage . . . a whirlwind, a flurry.

Christ! I screamed, *What about Mexico?*

Johnno . . . Johnno . . . don't you understand? I got a call from Irving! He's sent for me!

With growing desparation I pointed out that the previous night she had cursed him roundly, up and down, sideways and across, to the effect that she never wanted to see him again, that her most fervent wish was that he would come down with typhoid fever, or botulism, or salmonella, or die of the bloody flux in Venice, unnoticed and unmourned. And I reminded her how we had spent the previous night, working out the best route to Oaxaca, a place sacred to her through its Lawrentian connections. She looked at me as though I were a moron.

Johnno, she said, *he sent for me.*

It's not good enough, I said. What about me? Self? *Ich?*

Suddenly it was as though a wave of comprehension washed over her; as though, yes, she had remembered some vague commitment to elope with me. Let's sit down, she said.

We stared at one another; the expression in her eyes resembled that of a doctor who tells you in one breath that you are terminally ill, in the next that he is conducting a rollicking affair with his receptionist.

Johnno, she said, you're a man. It's a very good thing to be a man. But Irving's a God. Do you see now? When he calls me, it is as though I were being invited to dance — by Dionysus. You must see that. You're a man . . . but Irving's a God.

I thought about this. How wrong they were, McCarthy and Graham. The woman did not gravitate to the better off of two suitors. She went straight for the Godhead. There was nothing to be done here but declare myself *hors de combat.* I stood — an unaccommodated mortal: we said good-bye. I wished her, in all sincerity, the joy of Irving and her journey to Europe in his company, but I left the champagne she had bought for us deliberately untasted in the glass. Thus we parted — with many expressions of mutual regard.

8

That night I left for Mexico on my own. When I returned, some months later, it was fall. My mother had left for England; I saw her there, some six years later, when she was dying of cancer. There is an account of this in my *Symbols at Your Door*.

I began teaching at a crammer's school run by a man named Ross and, with a friend from the DEW Line, invested in a laundry on Burnside Street which cost about six thousand dollars and was eventually sold for one — whereof quit.

Before he retreated into silence, Bryan McCarthy published a fine book of poetry, *Smoking the City*, and opened a café on Stanley Street called The Place. It was a run-down building awaiting the wrecker's ball which the landlord allowed him to use for the remainder of its limited time. For a while, and despite the impoverishing bribes paid to fire marshals, cops, tax-men, bailiffs, etc., it thrived . . . one of the first "alternative life style" places in the city — late Beat and early Hipster. There of an evening one might observe assorted literati: Leonard Cohen, then going through an Oscar Wilde phase — trilby hat, tweed suit, nosegay carried and ostentatiously sniffed; Milton Acorn presenting a picture, on the whole deceptive, of a solid working-class poet who had got himself together; Al Purdy, a lurching, unpredictable presence who never seemed to me wholly sober, never wholly drunk. One day Richmond and I stopped off at The Place on some errand or other. We checked my laundry, strode along the busy street in the direction of Park Avenue. Without thinking about it, Mad raised his cane to the horizontal and, still speaking to me with great animation, stepped off the sidewalk.

There was the customary squealing of brakes. Then another. A car swerved to avoid him, squealing, almost sideswiping a panel truck trying to overtake on the inside. We were almost across, but I could sense trouble. A car had moved forward quickly to cut us off from the far curb. I saw the driver's face — it was frozen into a diabolical expression of hatred and ferocity. He moved his vehicle forward very slowly, then swung it at Richmond's legs. Scowling savagely, Richmond brought his heavy stick down on the car's hood as though firmly rapping its knuckles. The driver jammed on the brakes, flung open the door. He began to scream, rounding the hood with clenched fists. There was no mistaking his intention — it was to beat Mad to a pulp with his bare hands, dig his steely fingers into his stomach, rip him open from crotch to sternum, then stuff liver and lights down his tormentor's gullet. Richmond fled. He dropped the stick and scuttled for the nearest doorway; it was a pharmacy. The insane driver, business suit, tie, but big and clearly rendered psychotic from a day spent in an office, went after him like a stoat after a shrew. Richmond yelped, ran the length of the store, and literally dived behind the pharmacist's counter. A man in a white coat held off the gibbering pursuer, police were called, traffic was tied up for several miles, the demented driver hauled away, Richmond questioned and pushed around a little by the police. I took him off, clearly shaken to his deep heart's core, to irrigate him with whisky at a convenient bar.

A few years later Nina, presumably unprotected by the magic stick, and after a married lifetime of being metaphorically crushed by her husband, stepped off the sidewalk of Côte des Neiges and was flattened by one of those speeding cars Mad had so tormented over the years.

Perhaps half a decade on, Richmond himself died. He had left the teaching profession and, in that little office along Guy Street, had set himself up as a marriage counsellor. He became a hot-line broadcaster, then wound up as the literary editor of the *Montreal Star*, where he exercised, though personally grown more mellow, his own dark power. He choked on a morsel of food in a restaurant and died of a heart attack.

Fallings from us, vanishings.

After many stormy and bitter years, Irving and Aviva separated. I have, I regret to say, totally lost touch with her. I encounter the Gaffer once in a while. A year or two ago a rather unreliable biography of him was published in which my own role in his life was mentioned, quite inaccurately, and where it is stated that I "hated" the poet. My attitude towards him was not simple, as I hope I have shown in this memoir, but hatred was certainly never a part of it. I did not show him my final version of "Dinas Cromlech" because I failed to complete it — the narrator became, following Graham's suggestion, a minor character in the action. He so interested me that I could see no alternative to writing a novel about him — a novel I have never yet attempted. Irving would in any case have reiterated his unanswerable comment that "it wasn't a short story." I knew now that his concept of the form was derived from Henry James and from Poe's theory of "the Single Emotional Effect." Accordingly I wrote a piece called "Joust in Eight Rounds" in a new and totally artificial form I called Rigmarole. It consists of a number of narrative threads, all of them autobiographical, drawn together and interwoven, then divided, quite arbitrarily, into eight parts. "Joust" dealt with the Ross School, the end-game with my old flame Edith, and that truly dreadful laundry on Burnside Street.

It's good, Irving admitted, in parts. But it isn't a short story.

You maladroit bumbler, I shouted triumphantly. Of course it's not a short story . . . it's a Rigmarole!

It took the wind out of his sails, I could tell that. But I think he saw the point of it. Rigmarole is designed to reflect a vision of life as constant peripeteia, change of fortune, as the source of what he called "the intractable core of the bizarre in human affairs," together with my growing conviction that we are caught up in a universe essentially playful — *Deo ludens*. I wrote two Rigmaroles and they were published in a little magazine called *Evidence*. At about this time I had the pleasure of reviewing for another journal Leonard Cohen's *Beautiful Losers*. Thus I embarked on my career as a mud-wrestler.

Canadian Literature can be said to have entered the modern world with Layton's *The Swinging Flesh* and Leonard Cohen's novel. Prior to those events, fiction in this country was disguised journalism with Victorian overtones, poetry milk-and-water imitations of Wordsworth, Edward Thomas, or Coventry Patmore. Literature and criticism of literature were hamstrung and thwarted by a cult of politeness, of coy and smiling self-ingratiation. Cohen is not a mud-wrestler, but he wrote a mud-wrestler's novel. Layton was and, praise the Lord, still *is* a mud-wrestler — for this Canadian Literature owes him a debt, as Gulley Jimson says, that can only be paid in cash, and it is to him this Rigmarole is dedicated.

Canadian Writing 1987:

A Review 🌸 By *Michael Darling*

"It is my pet conceit . . . that prose in Canada is sadly undistinguished."
— B. W. Powe

Let us begin with an appropriate example of the Canadian book in the post-literate age: *The Solitary Outlaw*, by B. W. Powe. This is a work that has been called "dazzling," whose pages are said to "crackle with anger, brilliance, energy, authority, and a sweeping range of vision," and which is confidently proclaimed "the most important [book] of the year." Of course, all this puffery did appear in *Books in Canada*, but it is disturbing none the less to find a book as egregiously bad as this one being praised in such hyperbolic terms. Only in Canada, you say? Pity.

Powe's book consists of five essays on twentieth-century intellectuals who might also be considered "solitary outlaws": Wyndham Lewis, Marshall McLuhan, Pierre Elliott Trudeau, Glenn Gould, and Elias Canetti. The idea of Trudeau as an intellectual is, as his ex-wife might put it, beyond reason, but let that pass for the moment. The main problem with the book is that its form and content are irrevocably opposed. Powe deplores post-literate culture but reflects it in every paragraph of his writing. His style is a bizarre mixture of the ponderous and the elliptical, and can best be described as "*Chatelaine* edited by Margaret Atwood." One-word paragraphs shout "Significant Word Here!" Sentence fragments replace inde-

Michael Darling teaches English at the University of Western Ontario. His most recent book is *Perspectives on Mordecai Richler*.

pendent clauses in order to show *emphasis*. The colon is used interminably. It says: I am now going to say something important. There is much use of blank space, different typefaces, bold type, quotation, epigraphs, and so on. The long shadow of McLuhan falls heavily across the page. Indeed, the whole book might more accurately be titled *A McLuhanite Discovers His Master's Voice in Unexpected Places*. But I must not digress. Here is a random sampling of the sins of Powe:

Or: if you are conscious and intelligent, you are outside the mainstream.
Picture: a World War I battlefield.
We add: the origin of the tragic may be in a person trying to become a machine.
The effect: of a mind thinking, not a unified theory.
The reaction: bewildered.

Particularly offensive is his repeated use of "Note" followed by a colon, as in "Note: the word 'zero' is repeated with ominous regularity in his last books." Powe has evidently learned the use of the colon from high school mathematics textbooks.

When he is not being self-consciously clever (Powe has all the right qualities to review books for *The Journal*), he descends into the flatlands of cliché: "go with the flow," "Lest we forget," "the media's darling," "*Caveat lector*," "political chameleon." But the banal journalist-Powe is a great deal easier to take than the social philosopher-Powe who is capable of producing nonsense like the following:

The average novelist-poet-critic (each vocation distinct from the other; you must accept your box in the Great White North) stumbling in from the nineteenth-century bush, taught to detest North American society, having received the blessings of the Two Essential Grants (George and the Canada Council), after ripping out in record time (ten years) yet another work on the True Themes (bestiality and the Small Town) — well, you wouldn't expect those who claim that they don't do research to see that electric politics determine most of our social-cultural environment.

Does this make any sense at all? Is this supposed to pass for wit, for insight, for informed reflection on the state of Canadian writing? Of course, this *is* only one paragraph, and as Powe succinctly reminds us, "with certain writers you have to read a lot of their work before you can approach what they say."

The book is replete with quotations set off by their own bold-type headlines. Alas, few of these quotations are even vaguely related to the subject under discussion. They intrude into the text with all the pertinence of a sanitary-napkin commercial during the broadcast of a football game. What follows, though regrettably unaccented by the three different typefaces of the original version, is vintage Powe:

Concentration is constantly shattered; the word is processed; and ours may already be the anti-book world that Lewis antici-pated.

SOLITARY OUTWIT

You can't expect people to pay you for enjoying yourself!
Pound to Lewis

Yet when I return to Lewis's writings, I find pleasure in his outmoded demand for truth. . . .

Powe evidently subscribes to the Maidenform-bra theory of quotation, hoping that other people's words will lift and separate his own flaccid prose into something shapely and aesthetically pleasing. Unfortunately, the attempt sags noticeably.

I give *The Solitary Outlaw* pride of place in this review because it is the very best example of that "sadly undistinguished" prose that B. W. Powe has discovered in Canada. I warn of its baneful existence because Norman Snider, writing in the *Globe and Mail*, calls it "endlessly provocative, mandatory reading for anybody in this country who still cares about reading, writing or ideas." I lament — in bold type — its publication because it panders to the debased literary values of the Norman Sniders who form the tastes of Canadian readers. I predict that *The Solitary Outlaw* will win the Governor General's Award for Non-Fiction. It is that bad.

Three books of short stories were included among the mass of fiction sent me for review. Two are part of the Penguin Short Fiction series — Eric McCormack's *Inspecting the Vaults* and Rohinton Mistry's *Tales from Firozsha Baag* — and the other is published by Collins — W. P. Kinsella's *Red Wolf, Red Wolf*. Readers who have enjoyed Kinsella's Indian stories will probably like this latest collection, though nothing in it is particularly distinguished. These are clever and pleasant little stories, the kind you like to find in the guest bedroom at somebody's cottage, providing a welcome relief from the Baby Boomer edition of Trivial Pursuit. In the title story, a character created by Flannery O'Connor comes to live with her; in "Elvis Bound," a man whose wife is obsessed with Elvis Presley improves his sex life by tying up the poster of Elvis that hangs over their bed; and in "Billy in Trinidad," a friend of Billy the Kid describes some of the more appealing aspects of Billy's character, including his doctoring of a fawn with a broken leg. The problem with these stories is that they amount to no more than clever ideas for stories; nothing in Kinsella's style redeems them from triviality or the sentimental banality into which so many of them eventually lapse. His characters are almost uniformly flat, subordinated to the demands of overly contrived plots. There is humour, to be sure, and pathos, and an overall feeling of warmth that one associates with small furry animals and Norman Rockwell illustrations, but there is nothing very challenging, either intellectually or morally. Beside Kinsella, Leacock is a deep thinker.

Kinsella's sins, however, are mere peccadilloes in comparison with those of Eric McCormack in *Inspecting the Vaults*. This is a book heavily and clumsily indebted to Borges, with none of his wit and delicacy, but a great deal of his heavy-handed narrative manipulation. McCormack offers up horror stories pretentiously framed in a post-modern context of narrative instability. In "Sad Stories in Patagonia," for instance, a group of men searching for a rare prehistoric creature tell "sad stories" of human barbarity and then comment on the stories, with the ship's cook (since Chaucer's time the epitome of mindless sensuality) presenting the most sophisticated "literary" analysis:

The cook rarely liked the chief's stories. He could hardly wait, his scraggy beard bristling, to denounce this one as "another rather boring instance of the metaphysical/erotic struggle for authenticity and freedom in daily life, and of the problems of coping with the dichotomy of the Word/word, its abstract and concrete dimensions in experience and language."

No one seemed enthusiastic about pursuing this particular line of analysis.

The narrator's comment is nicely ironic; one can't help being attracted to the authorial point of view that informs it. Yet what sticks in the mind after a reading of this story, and indeed of every other story in the book, is not narrative playfulness but the images of degrading violence and depravity on which McCormack dwells with seemingly perverse pleasure.

The villagers often hear howls of anguish from the apprentice

Guardian in the middle of the night. This is caused by the operations the witch-doctors perform upon him at each full moon to give him the walk of a spider, in the image of the god. They have a method of grafting four thick membranes of human flesh (no one dares ask where they find the material) onto his arms and legs. The membranes form a webbing at the angles of his knees and armpits, so that he cannot ever straighten out his limbs. He is forced to crouch, on all fours, like a monstrous spider, with his genitalia exposed to the skies, his chest and haunted face to the ground.

The lid squealed ajar. The cardinal and his team moved closer to have a good look at the disinterred saint. "Oh Christ!" shouted the cardinal, cowering back at what he saw inside that half-open coffin.

He saw that the interior of the lid of the coffin was grooved with deep scratches. That Thomas à Kempis's dead face was indeed perfectly preserved, but his eyes were bulged open. That his fingers were curled like the claws of a vulture and his finger-nails were all broken with wooden splinters to the quick. That his winding sheet was stained around his middle with urine and excrement.

"The resident then cut the sutures and lifted them away. He slid his fingers into the wound and groped around. He said he could feel a lump of some sort. He managed to grip part of it with his calipers, and carefully fished it out, holding it up in the air.

"All of those assembled round that table saw something they would never forget. The resident had snared in the calipers a severed human hand, dripping blood and pus. He was holding it by its thumb, and they could all see, quite clearly, the gold wedding ring on its middle finger, and the scarlet polish on the long fingernails."

No one stirred around that camp-fire in Patagonia. The night had turned chilly, the members of the expedition crouched nearer to the fire's heat. The chief engineer continued:

"That was how they found out that the new doctor had killed his wife. He had cut off parts of her and buried them inside the children. Each of the four children contained a foot or a hand. . . ."

The foregoing quotations are all from "Sad Stories in Patagonia," but they might be from any of the stories in Inspecting the

Vaults. I quote so extensively because it is impossible to convey the full effect of this sort of thing through paraphrase. This is truly pornographic writing: obscene, vulgar, exploitative, without moral value. Moreover, McCormack's writing skills bear as much resemblance to craftsmanship as spot-welding does to sculpture. There isn't a single well-turned phrase in all that I have quoted. Instead, we are treated to the portentous commentary characteristic of the second-rate horror story: "no one dares ask where they find the material," or "All of those assembled . . . saw something they would never forget." Equally repulsive is the blatant attempt to titillate by the use of gratuitous images of grotesquerie and violence: "his genitalia exposed to the skies," "his fingers . . . curled like the claws of a vulture," "a severed human hand, dripping blood and pus." Throughout the book there are similarly gross images of castration, ritual dismemberment, blood spurting, bones protruding from the skin, limbs crushed to a gelid pulp, and, of course, lots of lurid and ridiculous sex scenes. In "A Train of Gardens," there is an account of native sexual practices which would have delighted Frank Harris ("Soon I was kissing her magnificant *zumbas*, noting all the time the coloration and texture of the upright *atitas*"). Frankly, I would rather have my children read *Hustler* than this collection of formulaic stomach-turners.

And yet — and yet — this is a book that has been widely praised by reviewers. *Books in Canada* suggested that the stories were "characterized by an astonishing creativity, a clear, confident style and a courageous imagination." The *Globe and Mail* praised them as "vigorously imaginative and technically adventurous." But is it really "technically adventurous" in 1987 to use the story-within-a-story structure employed by thousands of writers in this century? Is it "vigorously imaginative" to fill out such a structure with the kind of horror story a hundred times more skilfully rendered by M. R. James, L. P. Hartley, and H. P. Lovecraft? And is it "a clear, confident style" that produces sentences like the following: "That part of the training takes another three years: no outsider may witness it and live"? Call me Bwana.

The praise for McCormack arises out of the mistaken assumption that sex and violence graphically depicted are somehow "literary," as if the aesthetic sensibility needed an electric shock to activate it. But any real understanding of what constitutes good prose is sadly lacking in McCormack and his admirers. If they have read O'Connor or Gallant or Porter or Munro, they have not understood why these are among the finest short-story writers of our time, writers who know what paragraphs are for, know how sentences sound, and can make language dance. These are writers who possess an imagination that encompasses, indeed ennobles, their readers. To dignify the snickering prurience of a McCormack with the term "imagination" is akin to viewing the spray-painted four-letter words in a subway station as "art." I'm appalled that a book like this could garner such fawning reviews. But then Susan Musgrave's *The Charcoal Burners* was short-listed for the Governor General's Award. In Canada, at least, wonders never cease.

Rohinton Mistry's *Tales from Firozsha Baag* is quite a different thing. Although the writing is frequently clumsy, there is far more understanding of the human situation in these stories than in any of McCormack's. Mistry is not deceived that story-writing is an academic game of narrative hide-and-seek; he has a moral vision and a desire to impart it through carefully structured language. The fact that the language often fails him does not negate the sincerity of the attempt.

The tales focus on the inhabitants of Firozsha Baag, an apartment complex in Bombay: a lawyer, a veterinarian, students, old women, children, the whole panoply of middle-class Indian life. The stories are linked by setting and characterization, and are arranged chronologically so that characters who are young children in the early stories have grown to maturity by the end of the book. One gains from the stories a vivid sense of the emotional life of the apartment dwellers, their individual longings and frustrations. The best stories, such as "The Paying Guests" or "The Collectors," possess a finely developed sense of timing. Mistry allows his plots to evolve slowly and inevitably from conflicts between characters who act on the basis of comprehensible motivations. In "The Paying Guests," a young couple decide to supplement their income by dividing their apartment and taking in an old couple as lodgers. When the wife gets pregnant, they decide they need the extra space and try unsuccessfully to evict the paying guests. Throughout her life, Khorshedbai, the old woman, has dreamed of a flock of crows pecking at a dead animal, and she has decided that she will not allow herself to be pecked without fighting back. She therefore embarks on a campaign of revenge, littering their common veranda with garbage and dog feces, playing her gramophone long into the night, and burning foul-smelling incense that permeates her landlord's side of the apartment. The story reaches its climax with the disappearance of the young couple's baby. The baby is discovered in the old woman's parrot cage, while she re-enacts a sequence from a dream in which she had offered green peppers to the bird.

Ardesar sat on a chair with his face hidden in his hands. He was shaking visible. The baby, liberated from the swaddling clothes, was inside the cage. Intermittent whistling came from Khorshed-bai, mixed with soft kissing sounds or a series of rapid little clicks with tongue against palate. From her fingers she teasingly dangled two green peppers, long and thin, over the baby's face.

Now this scene has its element of horror, but it is not gratuitous horror of the kind that permeates McCormack's book. There is a reason for the old woman's behaviour, a believable motivation for her action. No severed hands or spurting blood assault the reader.

Mistry's weakness is his diction, which occasionally seems to evoke the legacy of the Raj: phrases like "high dudgeon," "unbeknownst to," and "cherubic features" don't really fit the contexts into which they're placed. Also, the Indian words are often strung together in what seems like an unnecessary striving for "local colour": "*Bawaji* got *paan pichkari* right on his white *dugli.* . . ." A little of this goes a long way, which Mistry seems to be aware of, as by the end of the book the non-English words are few and far between.

Of the six novels I received for review, none is an unqualified triumph. Three are fairly good, and three are quite dreadful. Let's deal with the latter first.

Brian Moore's *The Color of Blood* is a thriller set in an eastern European country under Communist rule. The protagonist, Cardinal Bem, is the object of an assassination attempt by right-wing extremists, and is taken into protective custody by the Security Police. He escapes and goes underground, surfacing at the end of the novel to deliver a statement which, we are led to believe, will determine the political destiny of his country. And then he is shot. As a thriller, *The Color of Blood* is less than gripping. As a novel of character, it is a bust. Presumably we are meant to be caught up in the Cardinal's struggle to understand the relationship between his political role and his spiritual duty, but the book is so lacking in psychological insight that we are never really moved to sympathy or judgment. The bad guys are colourless (not even particularly bloody), and the good guys equally so. This is a shallow, tedious novel.

Moore's prose has never been triter. Waitresses are said to have "undulating hips," children are "wraithlike figures," and church attendance is described as "a spiritual weather vane." The Security Major smokes a long Russian cigarette, "smiling behind it as though it were a mask." And the following sample of the Cardinal's insight is as deep as thoughts ever get in *The Color of Blood*: "He had accepted this young man's story, yet it could be a trap. Suddenly, he did not feel like talking anymore. This, he thought, is what life must be like for those who no longer trust each other." This, I thought, is what passes for profundity among those who write with the sole purpose of selling the film rights.

Writing a comic novel is a little like seducing a squad of cheerleaders: it's easy to start, but after a while you begin to wonder if you can keep it up. Susan Musgrave's *The Dancing Chicken* doesn't quite make it through to the end. She eventually runs out of one-liners, and since her characters never commanded much sympathy to begin with, it's not easy to stay interested in their fates. This is not a *compelling* novel — it lacks cohesion, explores no significant themes, confronts no moral dilemmas. It offers no more than entertainment, and, after the first hundred pages or so, not much of that.

There's little reason to explain the plot of this novel. A plot, after all, is a series of episodes connected by cause and effect. Since the world Musgrave describes seems to be based on the absence of cause and effect or rational motivation, there's no real attempt made to create a plot. We're dealing not so much with a novel here as with theatre of the absurd. This is a world where cutting down a Christmas tree is a capital offence, where people who have been dead for years come back to life, where you put quarters into a peep-show viewer in order to watch chickens dance. And, as might be expected from the author of *The Charcoal Burners*, the absurd goes hand-in-hand with the repulsive:

The [tea] leaves on the bottom had left an image of a young girl being sexually assaulted with a pair of garden shears.

Six months ago Ursula had arrived on his office doorstep having fled her husband, a fast food operator who liked to dress in women's clothes and be taken, rectally, with the leg of a chair. Ursula had been looking for her spiritual equal.

The office was being refurbished by his partners. Personally Cod thought they'd carried refurbishing too far, with a signed print of

Warhol's Electric Chair *hanging in reception. Most of their clientele were criminals and wouldn't appreciate what the picture was worth.*

This is wit, to be sure, but the humour is not maintained, and the characters never come alive to compensate for the lapses in tone when they do occur. There is nothing human about this novel: the narrator is cold, clinical, detached, and without any moral vision.

Katherine Govier's *Between Men* has been widely praised, in terms almost as lavish as those accorded McCormack's *Inspecting the Vaults*. It's not surprising, then, given the standards of Canadian reviewing, that Govier's book is equally bad, though in a different way. The novel's protagonist is Suzanne Vail, a history professor in Calgary. She finds herself between men — her husband, whom she is divorcing, and an older man with whom she is carrying on an affair. She is researching the murder of an Indian woman in 1889, retelling the story through the medium of a journalist named Murphy. But this is not an historical novel. It is, alas, a novel of Contemporary Women's Problems:

Jennifer became a driven woman, getting up at four in the morning and working until eight at night to make things better in the world. Gemma, despite her practical skills, failed to find a way to change her name from Miss Starchuk to Mrs. Anything. Suzanne's search for true love and freedom too led her down the rabbit hole of history.

The historical "research" is merely an attempt to give "literary" significance to what is no more than a Harlequin Romance: a woman's "search for true love and freedom" when she finds herself torn "between men."

Govier's attempts to explore Suzanne's psyche reveal the limitations of her skills as a novelist. Her prose style lacks sensitivity; it is blunt, fumbling, lacking any feel for the language, and often unintentionally hilarious:

And what was she longing for? Some release that did not come from orgasm. Something further. Suzanne was confused.

She, Suzanne, was a childless mother. She must have a child to be complete. She sat in the dark, and looked inside herself.

Likewise, Ace's crystal eyes were outlets for the power of the mechanism. He tried to melt her in place with them, to weld her attention exclusively to him.

People who write like this can make a pretty good living churning out five or six novels a year. But they have the sense not to pretend to be producing anything other than light entertainment. By grafting her re-invention of the Canadian West onto the obligatory stuff of romance fiction — the affairs, the agonizing about the affairs, women talking about men, women talking about other women, women feeling "unfulfilled" — Govier aspires to a much higher place in the CanLit world than her work can possibly give her. But there is a large audience for this sort of thing, and *Between Men*, when reprinted in paperback, will sit happily on the supermarket shelf with the *National Enquirer* and the monthly horoscope, and go home in the same bag with the Lite Delight weight-watcher dinners and the colour-coordinated panty liners.

So much for the disasters. We come now to the successes, modest but none the less real. Carol Shields' *Swann* is subtitled *A Mystery*, and though I don't propose to reveal the solution, it's fair to say that *as* a mystery the book is a disappointment. The dénouement is unconvincing, and readers who are expecting something Agatha Christie-ish will be left wondering what the point was. But this is really a novel of character and only incidentally a mystery story. It deals with four people — two professors, a librarian, and a retired newspaper editor — united in their obsession with Mary Swann, an uneducated farmer's wife who published one small pamphlet of poems that has brought her posthumous fame. The poems are actually quite insipid — undergraduate Emily Dickinson — and part of the novel's attraction is its satire of the academic tendency, especially in Canada, to apotheosize everyone who ever wrote a line. Swann's idolaters are Sarah Maloney, a 28-year-old feminist from Chicago whose dissertation, *The Female Prism*, has become a bestseller; Morton Jimroy, biographer of Ezra Pound *and* Mary Swann (the idea is not quite so ridiculous as it sounds: Leon Edel once intended to be the biographer of A. J. M. Smith); Rose Hindmarch, 50-year-old spinster and self-proclaimed friend of the famous poet; and octogenarian Frederic Cruzzi, Swann's publisher and, we find, more than editor.

There are five sections to the book, one devoted to each character, and a coda dealing with The Swann Symposium, written as a drama complete with stage directions. This last part, containing the solution to the mystery of who has been stealing everything related to Mary Swann, is badly bungled, as Carol Shields seems to believe all the clichés about academic conferences. Even if the whole section is meant to be taken ironically, it is really not very funny. A short sample of conference chatter:

> . . . *personally, I see Swann as being blinded by innocence, and by that I mean —*
> . . . *no use pretending the woman's a feminist when she makes it perfectly clear she's accepted the values of —*
> . . . *well, when you consider that Nadeau, Ontario, is not exactly the centre of the world —*
> . . . *remarkable, yes, remarkable. I agree, yes, remarkable!*
> . . . *Emily Dickinson never . . .*
> *It's the love poems I'm waiting for.*
> . . . *now this is only a suggestion, but if you look at what Swann does with the stanza and think of it as the microcosm . . .*
> . . . *time for another edition. Past time, if you ask me.*
> . . . *is it true old Cruzzi's here? My God, the man must be a hundred years old.*
> . . . *It's a pleasure, an honour, as I was saying to Mick here —*
> *And this, ahem, is Frederic Cruzzi.*

This sounds to me like a journalist's idea of how academics talk at conferences. In fact, no self-respecting English professor would ever be caught dead using the phrase "blinded by innocence" — except, of course, in a published paper, where such mawkish phrases are occasionally admitted if they can be shown to be translations from the French or the German.

Of all Shields' characters, Sarah Maloney, whose story is told in the first person, is the hardest to like. She is given to statements such as "a lightweight can be good company at times" and "Among my friends I'm known as the Queen of Correspondence." But the more we learn about her, the more vulnerable and sympathetic she seems, and that is a tribute to Shields' skill as a novelist of character. She never allows her people to lapse into the trite formulaic thinking of Govier's yuppies.

The male characters compel our interest in the same way, but the real triumph of this novel is Rose Hindmarch. We see her agonizing about her one "sexual" encounter — sleeping, but no more than sleeping, with another woman. We laugh as she nervously wonders how to explain to the pompously pedantic Jimroy that the poem he is interpreting as an allegory of holy communion is really about menstruation. Shields' narrative technique, especially her use of the present tense, is ideally suited to the exploration of Rose's tortuous moral universe:

As always Rose leaves her eyes half open and directs her prayers toward the railing that encloses the pulpit, a railing composed of four pine panels topped with a pretty moulding of carved leaves. The prettiness of the carving, which by rights ought to be neutral, seriously challenges the few moral choices made by Rose Hindmarch in her life. From where she sits, row six this morning, she can see light shining between the leaves, and it is to these lighted spaces that she addresses her prayers, or rather her questions. Why? is what she usually asks, the whys coming like a bombardment of electrons — why, for instance, is she thinking about Mary Swann this morning instead of Bishop Tutu and Nelson Mandela?

Rose feels the moral slackness of the pretty carving and therefore addresses her questions to the light, presumably a morally superior receptacle. Although she clearly feels that Mary Swann is an inappropriate subject for thought during a church service, we realize that her feelings for Mary are likely of far more moral significance than those of any conventional church-goer for Bishop Tutu. The light touch of irony here is another sign of Shields' control of voice and tone. Rose's relationship to Mary, like all of her relationships, is very much the product of her imagination, yet only Rose comes anywhere near the reality of Swann. Perhaps Shields is suggesting that the humanity of those we mythologize can be understood only by those who knew them as people rather than as cult figures.

Few devoted readers of Canadian fiction would fail to recognize the source of the following quotation:

When the girl from the Peruvian freighter walked for the first time through Port Annie, on the twenty-second day of constant rain, it's true old Magnus Dexter collapsed in front of his daughter's house, but who could blame him?

This is, of course, the first sentence of Jack Hodgins' *The Resurrection of Joseph Bourne*. Hodgins' style and his subject matter are instantly recognizable. Take, for another example, this excerpt from his first and best novel, *The Invention of the World*:

She'd been bush herself once, and there were people who said Maggie Kyle had the smell of pitch and the mountains on her yet for all her moving down to civilization, to the coast. . . .

One of Hodgins' constant themes is the uneasy relationship between nature and "civilization," and he is particularly adept at conveying the essence of characters and communities on the edge of both. In his latest novel, however, the characters — with one exception — don't "smell of pitch and the mountains"; in fact, they don't smell of anything at all. They are, for the most part, bland and boring.

The protagonist is Jeffrey Crane, a 66-year-old retired professor of art history, living in Zürich, who has been invited to return to his home town to be "Honorary Patron" of the Pacific Coast Festival of the Arts. We learn that Crane's title subtly conveys the lack of real commitment he is making to the remaining years of his life: he is no more than "an honorary human being." Returning to his home town, then, at the request of an old girlfriend who is organizing the festival, is a search for his past and the seeds of what he has become. Unfortunately, what Crane has become is a bloodless old bore, and nothing in the narration succeeds in making his story come alive.

By contrast, the one character in the novel who really steps off the page is a fabulously wealthy, foul-mouthed old reprobate called Blackie Blackstone, Crane's former enemy and now, in old age, a would-be friend. He plays Boy Staunton to Crane's Dunstan Ramsay, and does it with the flair and bravado we expect of Hodgins' characters. But the old girlfriend is no Maggie Kyle, and the young girl Crane takes up with seems vapid and shallow.

This failure of characterization and the comparatively unexciting plot will make this novel a disappointment to Hodgins' readers who have been waiting for the invention of another world. But, despite the limitations cited above, the book still has enough sheer good writing in it to carry it beyond the achievement of most recent Canadian novels. Let me quote just a couple of sentences as proof:

Damp wood, placed on blazing fireplace kindling, hissed its displeasure at first but soon settled into the sort of contented crooning heard amongst happy laying hens on a warm summer afternoon. And windows, though tattooed with tiny spots of dried sea, arranged for all the rays of the falling sun to perform gradually ascending light-and-shadow shows against the cedar walls.

There is a lovely play of assonance and alliteration in this passage. Particularly striking is the modulation of vowel sounds in "arranged for all the rays" and the mimetic rhythm of "gradually ascending light-and-shadow shows." This is excellent prose, and there's absolutely no question of Hodgins' capabilities as a writer. He is head and shoulders above the Goviers and McCormacks. But *The Honorary Patron* does not do what Hodgins does best — create characters who are larger than life, involve them in outlandish situations, and set them against a background of vividly realized time and space. Hodgins is a novelist of excess: he should stick with that.

Michael Ondaatje's *In the Skin of a Lion* is a long poem masquerading as a novel. It deals with life in Toronto in the 1920s and '30s, focussing specifically on the building of two grandiose projects: the Bloor Street Viaduct and the enormous water-filtration plant in the east end. Ondaatje is especially good at capturing the feelings of the workers who suffered and often died to build these monumental structures, and he does it primarily through the use of imagery. Motivations are obscure in this novel, even actions are obscure. Events are only tenuously related to each other, and dialogue floats on the page like thought balloons released from neighbouring cartoon strips. Yet all of this seeming chaos is held together by Ondaatje's poetic style. Here is an image from the protagonist's youth, the sight of ten men skating on a river while holding flaming bunches of cattails:

Patrick was transfixed. Skating the river at night, each of them moving like a wedge into the blackness magically revealing the grey bushes of the shore, his shore, his river. A tree branch reached out, its hand frozen in the ice, and one of them skated under it, crouching — cattails held behind him like a flaming rooster tail.

This is poetry without line divisions, but it is easy to see where they would go.

The early reviews of this novel have tended to see it as plotless, which is perhaps a fair criticism of it *as* a novel. However, if we think of it as a poem, held together by images of light and darkness, water and fire, creation and destruction, and men living their lives on the edge of the elements, between air and earth, earth and water, we get a quite different sense of Ondaatje's achievement. This is definitely not a novel to give your Aunt Mary for Christmas; it is, however, the one Canadian novel published this year that I will reread, if only for passages like this:

Patrick allows her to guide him back to the bench. They sit and she grips his hand, not letting go of him. He feels she receives all of his qualities, in this still garden, raucous with noise. The blue veins are narrow and clear in the tight skin of her hands. He is unable to talk, even if all he said would be hidden within her blindness. Alice Gull, he could say, who once pushed her hands up against the slope of a ceiling and spoke of a grand cause, who leapt like a live puppet into his arms, who died later on a bloody pavement, ruined in his arms.

It seems that the quality of Canadian poetry varies inversely with the number of poets being published. Where once there might have been ten books published in a year, of which five would contain some memorable poems, now there are dozens and dozens of books produced every year, and hardly a good poem to be found anywhere. W. W. E. Ross, one of the most original and interesting of Canadian poets, once wrote a series of pastiches of various poets, based on Coleridge's famous lines beginning "Water, water everywhere." The Canadian poets whose style he imitated (or, in some cases, parodied) were Patrick Anderson, P. K. Page, E. J. Pratt, Ralph Gustafson, Audrey Alexandra Brown, Raymond Souster, Earle Birney, A. M. Klein, Bliss Carman, F. R. Scott, A. J. M. Smith, W. W. E. Ross, and Charles G. D. Roberts. In a version published in *The Canadian Forum* in 1957, he added Louis Dudek, Irving Layton, and Anne Wilkinson. It cannot be said that Ross's pastiches are wholly successful: without the author's name appended, it would be difficult in some cases to know whose style Ross was imitating. But what would he have done with contemporary Canadian poets? How many styles are sufficiently individuated to enable a reader to recognize a specific poet's voice, as we surely can distinguish a Purdy, an Atwood, or a Souster?

Of the five poets reviewed here, all of whom have published at least four books, not one can be said to have an instantly recognizable voice, though all are reasonably well-known. The works under consideration are Milton Acorn's *The Uncollected Acorn*, Patrick Friesen's *Flicker and Hawk*, Patrick Lane's *Selected Poems*, Gwendolyn MacEwen's *Afterworlds*, and Don McKay's *Sanding Down This Rocking Chair on a Windy Night*. Let me quote a few lines from each, not in the order given above:

grandfather didn't want anyone to know he was going
he held the news sweetly and told his stories
who would have guessed he could leave just like that
giving up the way a man of humour will
the way a person faces what was dreamed long ago
who would have guessed it on a dreary afternoon
snow falling and curtains trifling with light

It's soaking winded cold up here, mother.
I've just perceived that the eye is a lake,
Reflected snowslides seeming to be clouds,
Which is best. I was afraid I hung down
Shivering, listening, frightened to break
From feet frozen in a melting picture.

Certainly the dead watch us, but not
as opera, nor as the Great Grey Owl
tunes in gophers underground.
We are their day-time television.
Sometimes, mid-line, you can
sense their presence like the
o in rôle beneath its roof, a lope
detached from body.

Syllable of stone, the lizard lies prone
under the bright dome of the moon.
His patience lasts forever.
I know I am almost old and my bed is made of sand
but even among stones love is possible.
The lizard waits forever in the ruins.
Come to me.
I will wait for you at least one more night.

You reach out your hand to touch it, and
This is the first time you have ever seen your hand, as it is also
The first time you have smelled the blue fire
Within a stone, or tasted blue air, or
Heard what the sea says when it talks in its sleep.

In the order of the quotations, the poets are Friesen, Acorn, McKay, Lane, MacEwen. But could you have guessed?

The test of good poetry is not just the deftness of its

rhythm, the precision of its diction, or the startling certitude of its figures of speech, but also the avoidance of unnecessary discords. A great poet, like Philip Larkin, hardly ever makes a mistake. There isn't a word in his verse that we feel is out of place, redundant, or inapt.

Now, of the poets under consideration, only MacEwen fulfils these requirements, though all are capable of writing well. Let's begin with the excerpt from Friesen's "ghost." The first line is too long and gets the poem off to a stumbling start, but the next two lines are much better: "sweetly" and "stories" balance each other nicely and the third line ends strongly with three emphatic stresses. The next two lines fall into a nearly regular rhythm, though the fifth line is spoiled somewhat by the collocation of stresses on "dreamed long," which tends to detract from the power of the line and mute its resonance. The stanza concludes strongly, however, with the bouncing rhythm of the penultimate line leading into the magnificently sonorous closure of "snow falling and curtains trifling with light." The last three words with their chiasmic pattern of assonance make a truly memorable word-image. But the poetic sensibility demonstrated here is too rarely visible in the rest of the poem, and Friesen's rhythms frequently lapse into the banality of the first and fifth lines quoted above.

Milton Acorn is a poet whose work has always cried out for a good editor. He is (I should say "was") capable of writing some very musical lines, but too often spoils the total effect of a poem by an unfortunate choice of words. This excerpt, the last six lines of "Sonnet Seeing with MacDonald," is no exception. The juxtaposition of "soaking" and "winded" is surprising, but not discordant. On the other hand, "perceived" is too formal a word here, and the phrase "that the eye" is ill suited to follow the iambic beat of the first words in the line. The third line recovers somewhat, but is brought up short by the peculiar phrase "Which is best." The poem recovers and closes strongly with a nice balance of fricatives and plosives in the last line and a half. But the whole effect is largely ruined by the one phrase, "Which is best," which seems to have no thematic relevance to mitigate its cacophony.

Don McKay is not as well-known as he should be. He is at least as good a poet as any of the others reviewed here (with the possible exception of MacEwen), and much better than the celebrated post-modernists Bowering, Davey, Kroetsch, bissett, and Dewdney. Yet, like them, he is frequently content to write poetry rather than poems, forgetting that a memorable work of art requires a sense of wholeness and undiluted harmony. The poem "Edge of Night" (with its soap-opera connotations very much in evidence in the part quoted here) starts strongly and builds to the end of the third line with a lovely sequence of modulated vowels: "The Great Grey Owl/tunes in gophers underground." We do not miss the hint of end-rhyme, or the subtle assonance in the last two words. But the next line is banal, and the word "television" drags down the poem. It has three syllables too many to have other than a deleterious effect. One might argue, of course, that this is intended, but how then to explain the skilful arrangement of the next four lines with their playful self-reflexivity? The poem breaks down completely after this ("Tell Brenda/ that you've had a sex change or that/Harold has run off with her Electrolux . . ."). Larkin focuses on the same banal images of bourgeois existence, but never makes the error of allowing the form of the poem to suffer at the hands of its content.

Patrick Lane is a poet whose work has never moved me. Like Eric McCormack, he seems to be a writer who believes that images of violence can do his work for him, and there is little in such poems that is worthy of being accorded permanence in verse. But there is also a curious streak of romantic slushiness in Lane, and the poem quoted in its entirety here, "Small Love Song," is a typical example of this side of him. The poem is very reminiscent of Leonard Cohen, but without Cohen's gift for metaphor that gives his work an attractiveness that it would not otherwise possess. The younger Cohen, I submit, would not have written a line like "but even among stones love is possible." The word "possible" destroys the rhythm of the line; its ugliness in this context works against the lilting quality of the rest of the poem. Even if that word were changed, the line would still fall flat. The poem turns on ideas of permanence and transience, which are effectively conveyed though the images of stone, lizard, moon, sand, and ruins. The idea of love's possibility is implicit in all that; it does not need to be stated. By declaiming in this way, Lane undoes all the good work of the surrounding lines. This failure to know what to prune mars a number of otherwise excellent new poems in Lane's selection, such as "And of Song, Its Terrible Order," "The Cheating Heart," "Dominion Day Dance," and "Night."

Finally there is Gwendolyn MacEwen, probably the finest pure poet writing in Canada today. The lines quoted from "The White Horse" are tangible evidence that she rarely misfires; there isn't a false note here, a syllable too many or too few. Those who have been to a MacEwen "reading" can understand why her verse possesses this rare quality of assurance. She does not read, she recites. Because the music is there to be felt, she can transmit it without the necessity of the written word before her. The only criticism I can offer of this book, and this would apply equally to the rest of her work, is that her poems leave little for the mind to work with. There are patterns of imagery that run thoughout her work which have enabled MacEwen's critics to write about her vision, her mythology, her symbolism, and her themes. But there have been few attempts to treat any one of her poems in depth, and this suggests to me that individual poems simply don't stand up to intellectual scrutiny. They communicate emotion, though, and for those readers who are content with emotion and rhythm, there can be few more powerful voices in Canadian poetry. Let me quote the concluding lines of "The White Horse":

Go and tell this: It is morning,
And this horse with a mane the colour of seafoam
Is the first horse that the world has ever seen,
The white horse which stands now watching you
Across this field of endless sunlight.

By way of conclusion, I would point out that my general impression of Canadian writing in 1987 is not so much that it is bad but that the worst of it has been grossly overpraised. There is a kind of fawning quality about the reviews in such organs as *Quill & Quire* and *Books in Canada*; they remind me of small-town newspaper articles headed "Local Boy Makes Good." It's as if publishing a work of poetry or fiction or criticism in Canada were such a rare occurrence that, to paraphrase Dr. Johnson, though it not be done well, you are surprised to find it done at all. Surely the time is past that we should feel it necessary to praise a work because it is about life in Calgary, or because it deals with our past, or because it is metafictional, or because its author was once nominated for a Governor General's Award. The only true test of a work is whether or not it is well-written, and by that test most of these works fail. It is no shame to fail by the highest standards, but no author should be content to succeed by the lowest.

THE EDITORS

JOHN METCALF

Sam Tatta

New Canadian Writing, 1969: Stories by John Metcalf, D. O. Spettigue and C. J. Newman. Toronto: Clarke, Irwin, 1969.

The Lady Who Sold Furniture. Toronto: Clarke, Irwin, 1970.

Going Down Slow. Toronto: McClelland and Stewart, 1972.

————. Don Mills, Ont.: PaperJacks, 1975.

The Teeth of My Father. Ottawa: Oberon, 1975.

Metcalf, John, and John Newlove. *Dreams Surround Us: Fiction and Poetry by John Metcalf and John Newlove.* Delta, Ont.: Bastard, 1977.

Girl in Gingham. Ottawa: Oberon, 1978.

Private Parts: A Memoir. Scarborough, Ont.: New American Library, 1980.

General Ludd. Downsview, Ont.: ECW, 1980.

————. Toronto: General, 1981.

Selected Stories. New Canadian Library, No. 168. Toronto: McClelland and Stewart, 1982.

Adult Entertainment. Toronto: Macmillan of Canada, 1986.

NON-FICTION

Kicking Against the Pricks. Downsview, Ont.: ECW, 1982.

LEON ROOKE

Sam Tata

Last One Home Sleeps in the Yellow Bed. Baton Rouge: University of Louisiana, 1968.

The Love Parlour. Ottawa: Oberon, 1977.

The Broad Back of the Angel. New York: The Fiction Collective, 1978.

Cry Evil. Ottawa: Oberon, 1980.

Fat Woman. Ottawa: Oberon, 1980.

Death Suite. Downsview, Ont.: ECW, 1981.

The Magician in Love. Toronto: Aya, 1981.

The Birth-Control King of the Upper Volta. Downsview, Ont.: ECW, 1982.

Shakespeare's Dog. Toronto: General, 1983.

Sing Me No Love Songs I'll Say You No Prayers. New York: Echo, 1984.

A Bolt of White Cloth. Toronto: General, 1984.

Submissions

Submissions for consideration for inclusion in next year's *Macmillan Anthology* may be sent to:

John Metcalf,
P.O. Box 2700,
Station "D",
Ottawa, Ont.
K1P 5W7

or

Leon Rooke,
1019 Terrace Avenue,
Victoria, B.C.
V8S 3V2

All material to be returned or answered must be accompanied by a stamped, self-addressed envelope. Cut-off date for submissions is October 1988.